KUNIYOSHI
The Warrior-Prints

But as they left the dark'ning heath,
More desperate grew the strife of death.
The English shafts in volleys hail'd,
In headlong charge their horse assail'd;
Front, flank, and rear, the squadrons sweep
To break the Scottish circle deep,
    That fought around their King.
But yet, though thick the shafts as snow,
Though charging knights like whirlwinds go,
Though bill-men ply the ghastly blow,
    Unbroken was the ring;
The stubborn spear-men still made good
Their dark impenetrable wood,
Each stepping where his comrade stood,
    The instant that he fell.
No thought was there of dastard flight;
Link'd in the serried phalanx tight,
Groom fought like noble, squire like knight,
    As fearlessly and well;
Till utter darkness closed her wing
O'er their thin host and wounded King.

Scott, *Marmion*, Can. VI, xxxiv.

Frontispiece: Higuchi Jirō struggling with a giant monkey.
c. 1825. Detail of S1a.14. (Reproduced by courtesy of Richard Illing.)

樋口治郎兼

KUNIYOSHI

The Warrior-Prints

B. W. ROBINSON

Cornell/Phaidon Books

CORNELL UNIVERSITY PRESS

Ithaca, New York

To Oriel

First published 1982 by Cornell University Press

International Standard Book Number 0–8014–1488–1
Library of Congress Catalog Card Number 81–70706

Printed in Great Britain

Author and publisher would like to thank the Trustees of the British Museum for their permission to reproduce the Catalogue illustration to S68, and the Museum of Fine Arts, Boston, for permission to reproduce Plate 31 and the Catalogue illustrations to S71, S72, and S91.

CONTENTS

Map of Japan   6
PREFACE   7

INTRODUCTION   9
  THE SUBJECTS   17
    I. Early History   17
      (a) PRINCE YAMATO-TAKE-NO-MIKOTO   17
      (b) THE EMPRESS JINGŌ   17
      (c) PRINCE SHŌTOKU TAISHI   17
    II. The Rebellion of Masakado   18
    III. Raikō and his Four Retainers   18
    IV. Kiyomori in Power   19
    V. Tametomo the Great Archer   19
    VI. Youthful Exploits of Yoshitsune and Benkei   20
    VII. Yorimasa and the Beginning of the Taira–Minamoto War   21
    VIII. The Career of Yoshinaka   21
    IX. The Destruction of the Taira   22
    X. Yoritomo in Power   23
      (a) THE PERSECUTION OF YOSHITSUNE   23
      (b) THE GREAT HUNTING-PARTY AND THE
        SOGA BROTHERS' REVENGE   25
      (c) ASAHINA SABURŌ THE STRONG MAN   26
    XI. The Tragedy of Kesa-gozen   26
    XII. The Wars of the Nitta and the Kusunoki   26
    XIII. The Sixteenth and Seventeenth Centuries   28
    XIV. *Chūshingura*, 'The Treasury of Loyal Retainers'   29
    XV. The *Hakkenden* and Other Popular Fiction   30

PLATES   31

CATALOGUE   97
  Part I: Single-Sheet Prints in Series   99
  Part II: Triptychs and Diptychs   169

SIGNATURES   185
GLOSSARY   186
BIBLIOGRAPHICAL REFERENCES   187
LIST OF ILLUSTRATIONS   189
INDEX of Characters Portrayed   192

Map of Japan

*(showing the provinces, towns, and other sites
most frequently mentioned in the text)*

N

MUTSU

DEWA

ECHIGO

SADO

Hiraidzumi

Hagui

Kanazawa

KAGA

Kurikaradani

Kawanakajima

KŌDZUKE

SHIMOTSUKE

OKI

SHINANO

KISOKAIDŌ ROAD

ECHIZEN

HIDA

KAI

Sumida river

SHIMOSA

MINO

Nagaragawa

Mount Fuji

Yedo

Anegawa

Shidzu-ga-mine (Shidzu-ga-take)

Ashigara mountains

Kamakura

TAMBA

Miidera

Lake Biwa

Fujikawa

SAGAMI

Tsuru-ga-ōka

SETTSU

Kuramayama

Kyoto

Awadzu

TŌKAIDŌ ROAD

Uchide-hama

Ōtsu

Ishibashiyama

TSUSHIMA

IDZUMO

Ichi-no-tani

Ujigawa

Shijō-nawate

ŌSHIMA

Hyōgo

Nara

ISE

Minatogawa

Miyajima (Itsukushima)

Daimotsu bay

Yoshino
mountains

Dan-no-ura

Yashima

IKI

SANUKI

Kumano

SHIKOKU

KYŪSHŪ

HIGO

Nagasaki

SATSUMA

0   250 km

0   250 miles

KIKAI-JIMA

PREFACE

This is an unfinished book; with an artist as prolific as Kuniyoshi it cannot be otherwise. His total output of prints during a working life of forty-six years is virtually impossible to compute, and almost every batch of fresh material examined produces hitherto unknown items. Thus unfamiliar triptychs and even new series continue to turn up, and I have little doubt that a number of readers will be able to add to the lists here given. If so, I should be grateful if they would let me know, c/o the Publishers, so that, in the event of a second edition being called for, such additional information can be included. But there comes a time when one tires of awaiting further material, and when it seems more useful and important to set down what is available at the time of writing, rather than to aspire to an unattainable perfection. The book is designed as a companion for collectors, dealers, and museum men, and I hope that the Catalogue, which forms the second and more important part, will provide a useful framework for the results of future research.

I have concentrated on one particular branch of Kuniyoshi's huge output, the warrior-prints (*musha-ye*), mainly, I must admit, because I have myself been enjoying them ever since I was bowled over by the 'Skeleton-Spectre' (T138) at the age of fourteen, in an exhibition at the British Museum, but also because it was with these prints that he made his name, and because they were undoubtedly the branch of his work in which he took most pride and pleasure. Interest in them among western collectors and dealers is increasing, and they provide a rich and fascinating panorama of Japanese history, legend, folklore, and drama.

In the present work, the term 'warrior-prints' has been interpreted in a wide sense; readers need not fear that they will be exposed to an uninterrupted succession of battles and bloodshed. It has been taken to include all subjects of a historical or legendary nature. Thus they will find here the 'Hundred Poets' (S19), in many of which are depicted peaceful scenes of court life in the Fujiwara period; the 'Chinese Paragons of Filial Piety' (S13, S60, S79) in which, in view of the foreign origin of the subject-matter, Kuniyoshi took the opportunity of experimenting with western ideas, and which include no scenes of military activity; several sets devoted to the women of Japanese history (S20, S21, S29, S30, S33), amongst whom only Tomoye-gozen and Hangaku seem to have donned armour; and a number of series from the middle 1840s in which scenes and characters from the popular theatre (*kabuki*) are included, and the features of well-known actors are sometimes recognizable (especially S36–S46). Comic and erotic prints, even those in which heroes and warriors appear, have been excluded; they cannot be classed as 'warrior-prints' by any stretch of the imagination. In borderline cases the selection has been, admittedly, subjective or instinctive, with a tendency to include rather than exclude. In all, 358 triptychs and 95 series, the latter comprising 1,520 single prints, are surveyed in this book.

The subject of Japanese names is a somewhat complicated one. For example, a Japanese thought nothing of assuming a succession of different names at various stages of his career, from the child-name, often ending in Maru, to the posthumous Buddhist name conferred after death. These difficulties are enlarged upon in the introductory paragraph to the Index (p. 192). In the transcription of Japanese names I have preferred the traditional forms (e.g. Kwannon, not Kannon; Idzumi, not Izumi) hallowed by *Koop*, for reasons which, already in print elsewhere, it seems unnecessary to reiterate. In this I crave the indulgence of the younger generation of collectors and connoisseurs, who have no doubt been brought up on the new (spoken language) system.

I have been fortunate in securing the periodical co-operation of Mrs Michiko MacIver, who has given largely of her time and knowledge, especially in the identification of the more obscure dramatic characters; I should like to express here my deep sense of obligation to her. I must also thank colleagues at the British Museum, the Victoria and Albert Museum, and the Royal Scottish Museum for giving me ready access to the collections under their charge, and, in the United States, to the Director of the Museum of Fine Arts, Springfield (Mass.), and, especially, to Mr Money Hickman of the Museum of Fine Arts, Boston, who, though in the throes of a departmental move, found time and took trouble to accommodate me and to place at my disposal the large and important range of Kuniyoshi's work held by that institution. I have had many profitable discussions and looked at many fine and sometimes unfamiliar prints in the company of my old friend Mr Merlin Dailey of Victor (NY), and for this, and for his hospitality on many occasions, I offer him my very warm thanks. My wife has been, as always, a constant source of support and encouragement, and has carried out the black-and-white photography for the book with her customary patience and skill; here again I put on record my consciousness of an inestimable debt of gratitude to her.

Finally, it is my hope that this book, the outcome of some years of collecting and looking at the works of Kuniyoshi, will prove of use to those with a similar interest, and may even serve to introduce the artist where his name has been hitherto unfamiliar. It is here dedicated as an affectionate, though unworthy, tribute to his memory.

London, July 1981   B. W. R.

INTRODUCTION

The Sword and the Fan, it has been remarked, aptly symbolize two of the main elements of the Japanese character. As a people they have always been (till recent times) warlike; the wearing, and use, of swords by the *samurai*—the Japanese gentleman—continued till 1877, and the military virtues were the ones most admired. On the other hand, they have always been a people of great aesthetic refinement. An elaborate system of etiquette was built up, and is still to some extent current; such activities as flower-arrangement, the tea ceremony, and extempore versifying provided outlets for this side of the national character, and it is noticeable that even their commonest household utensils are products of an exquisite taste. Aspects of these apparently contradictory but coexisting strains are illustrated in many of the prints covered by this book.

General histories, introductory volumes, and picture-books of Japanese prints have been available in considerable numbers for nearly a century. The path from Moronobu and Kwaigetsudō through Harunobu to Utamaro and Hiroshige has become familiar and well trodden; every art student knows Sharaku's actors and Hokusai's 'Wave'. But this is a book of a different kind, concentrating on the work of a single artist in a single field, and the prints it describes and illustrates are intended to appeal not only to the aesthetic sense, but to the fascination which most of us feel, to a greater or lesser degree, for old stories of history and romance, and to a natural love of the heroic, the marvellous, and the exotic. They are, quite unashamedly, 'pictures with a story'.

This is not the place for a detailed history of the Japanese wood-block print. Suffice it to say that it began with black-and-white book-illustration at the beginning of the seventeenth century; half a century later separate sheets were being published; a full range of colours was in use from the 1760s; and the form continued to develop, with a sometimes excessive richness of technique and colour scheme, well into the present century. The subjects at first consisted almost entirely of actors and women, but, by the beginning of the nineteenth century, landscapes, comic illustrations, and historical subjects were being added to the regular repertory. The Japanese print, it should be remembered, was at all times a product of team-work by artist, engraver, and printer, co-ordinated (and paid) by the publisher, and the social position of these craftsmen was a fairly humble one. It is indeed impossible not to admire their almost inspired co-operation as displayed in these sheets. When one looks at, say, 'Kintoki and the carp' (S1d.1) or 'The death of Masayasu' (S62.36), and tries to work out exactly how the effects of falling water in the one, and in the other the disintegration of a spearman in a volley of musketry, are produced, the technical mastery and inventiveness displayed by these simple craftsmen almost take one's breath away. How one would like to have overheard the discussions between them that must have preceded the production of such prints as these!

A large proportion of Kuniyoshi's warrior-prints are in the form of triptychs, that is to say, three sheets of standard size placed side by side (or, more rarely, one above the other, e.g. T253). The reason for this is that the size of paper sheets available for print-making was strictly regulated by law, with the result that if an artist wished to publish a large composition he necessarily had recourse to the diptych or triptych. Compositions of six or even more sheets are not unknown (e.g. T346/T347).

The leading facts of Kuniyoshi's life and career are by now well established, and only a brief summary is called for here. Born on 1 January 1798, the son of Yanagiya Kichiyemon, a silk-dyer, he entered the studio of Toyokuni I about 1810, and was trained in the Utagawa style of theatrical portraiture. At this time he associated with his senior fellow-pupil Kuninao, and studied the rapid brush-drawings of Masayoshi and, we may be sure, the colour-prints of Shuntei. His earliest known publication was *Gobuji Chūshingura*, an illustrated book published in 1814; his earliest prints are illustrations of current *kabuki* productions of the following year. His first heroic triptych (T1) appeared in 1818, and though it made a favourable impression he had a hard struggle for recognition, and even for a bare living, till 1827, when the first few prints of the *Suikoden* series (S2 Fig.1) brought him public acclaim. His theatrical work continued throughout his career, but, his reputation once gained, he was able to convert the public to his own tastes for legendary and historical subjects, and for various experiments with western methods (Fig.2). During the 1830s and later he contributed to every branch of the art—women, landscapes, comics, *surimono*, fan-prints, and book-illustrations—in addition to his theatrical and warrior-prints. His lifelong love of cats also began to show itself (e.g. S1e.3, S4b.2, S5.8, S20.31).

The Tempō Reforms of 1842, with their suppression of subjects connected with *kabuki* and the Yoshiwara (the licensed or brothel quarter of Yedo), undoubtedly contributed to the success of both Kuniyoshi's heroics and Hiroshige's landscapes. The former had two brushes with the authorities, in 1843 and 1855, owing to suspected political satire in his work, but apparently suffered no ill effects, and shared with Kunisada and Hiroshige (with both of whom he collaborated on a number of occasions) the highest position amongst his contemporaries. A certain decline in the quality of his work is noticeable from the early 1850s, probably due partly to over-production and partly to ill health, and he died from the effects of a stroke on 14 April 1861.

Fig.1. The Chinese hero Konseimaō Hanzui attacked by demons. *c*.1827–30. S2.36.

It is now just over twenty years since the centenary of the death of Kuniyoshi, and that period has seen a remarkable rehabilitation of the artist's reputation. The occasion was marked by memorial exhibitions at the Victoria and Albert Museum, at Düsseldorf, and at Memphis, Tennessee, the last two due to the enthusiasm of the late Herr Willibald Netto and Mr Merlin Dailey respectively. Although in Japan itself the event passed relatively unnoticed at the time, a delayed reaction has evidently since taken place, recent evidence for which is provided by exhibitions of Kuniyoshi's work at the Riccar Art Museum, Tokyo, in 1978 and 1979 and the authoritative and enthusiastic writings of Mr Suzuki Jūzō amongst others.

Certain of Kuniyoshi's prints, the landscapes and the Nichiren series (S6) in particular, have always been popular with even the most orthodox collectors; but it was probably the Victoria and Albert exhibition of 1961 that first brought a fully representative range of his work before the public, demonstrating how considerable a proportion of that work was devoted to the celebration of Japan's heroic past. It was, indeed, the warrior-prints which most impressed critics and public alike; they had never really had a full and fair showing before.

A good range of Kuniyoshi's warrior-prints is only to be found in a museum which has a very large and miscellaneous collection of Japanese prints. Many museum collections have been built up on the orthodox and highly selective lines laid down by Mr Davison Ficke (*Chats on Japanese Prints*, London, 1915) and other leading American and French collectors of two and three generations ago; anything produced after the death of Utamaro (exceptions always made, of

Fig.2. Prince Hansoku of India subduing a lion. *c*.1849–50. S66.2.

course, of Hokusai and Hiroshige) was looked upon askance. I have therefore concentrated my attention on collections of the former kind, of which, in this country, those of the Victoria and Albert Museum and the Royal Scottish Museum are outstanding examples. The bulk of these two collections was acquired in the 1880s, when an enormous cargo of albums, containing something like 20,000 prints, was purchased in one lot from a London general merchant, and divided between the two museums, then sister establishments under the benign aegis of the Board of Education. Naturally the vast majority of the prints in these albums date from the period 1820–70, and Kuniyoshi is very well represented.

The British Museum's is more of a 'collector's collection', but is large enough to include a good showing of Kuniyoshi's heroic triptychs. The late Sir Laurence Binyon, formerly Keeper of Oriental Prints and Drawings, was an enthusiastic admirer of them, and put on the exhibition in the summer of 1926 to which reference was made in the Preface. The Museum of Fine Arts, Boston, reputed to contain the largest collection of Japanese prints in the world, manages to combine these apparently contradictory qualities; not only has it some of the finest possible examples of the earlier masters, but it also possesses an enormous mass of later work, including that of Kuniyoshi, which made it an essential source for a book of this kind. The collection at the Museum of Fine Arts, Springfield (Mass.), is something quite apart. It was amassed by the late Mr Raymond Bidwell, a prominent citizen of Springfield, who conceived a passion for Kuniyoshi in the early years of this century, when his works were plentiful and cheap, and was thus able to form a collection that provides an absolutely unrivalled representation of the artist's achievement in every field, including, of course, the warrior-prints.

These, then, have been my main sources. Never having visited Japan, I must admit that I have not attempted to cover Japanese collections; that would in any case be far better done by a native scholar. But in the course of the past fifty years I have naturally seen a vast number of Kuniyoshi's prints in private collections, auction rooms, and dealers' stocks. These sources all come under the abbreviation PC in the Catalogue. Sometimes, alas, due to unfavourable conditions or lack of time, I noted them hurriedly or inadequately, perhaps twenty or more years ago, and have never seen them again; hence it will be found that a few of the Catalogue entries are very spare. If any reader is in a position to fill them out, I should be most grateful to receive the additional particulars.

Kuniyoshi's predilection for heroic subjects showed itself from the earliest period of his career. At that time Shuntei (d.1820) was virtually the only exponent of that type of work, and Kuniyoshi's warrior-prints at first follow his style fairly closely, as do a handful of similar prints produced at the same time by Hiroshige (*Strange*, Pl.XVI). Kuniyoshi's early warrior-prints consist of boldly designed single sheets, the forerunners of a long series of such compositions which he continued at intervals well into the 1840s (S1), and triptychs. A characteristic feature of them is the very effective use of masses of black. It soon became clear that the triptychs were to be Kuniyoshi's outstanding contribution to the art of his country. Apart from their obvious dramatic—sometimes melodramatic—qualities, they show a broad masterly appreciation of the possibilities of the triptych as a complete integrated composition, such as is rarely found amongst earlier examples of the same form. Separate sheets of triptychs by, for example, Utamaro or Toyokuni can usually be appreciated on their own, but in Kuniyoshi's best work the three sheets are inseparable if the impact of the composition is to be felt. He very soon developed the ability to stir our feelings and enlist our sympathy for his heroes. In 'Tadanobu's fight at Yoshino' (T2) for example we can almost hear the whistle and thud of the arrows, and in 'The ghost of Yoshihira' (T10) we sense the violence of the explosion as the avenging spirit springs in the air on a ball of fire to strike his killer dead.

Bakin's *Suikoden*, a translation or adaptation of the Chinese semi-historical romance *Shui-ho-ch'uan*, relating the exploits of a gang of desperadoes in the twelfth century, had begun publication in 1805, with illustrations by Hokusai, and had proved very popular. Kuniyoshi began his first series of these Chinese 'heroes' in 1827 (S2), and they give the impression of an almost superhuman release of energy; the contorted figures with their strange and terrible weapons seem to burst from the confines of the *ōban* sheet. It is no wonder that the public responded with enormous enthusiasm, urging the artist on till he had completed over seventy of these masterly designs. A parallel set of Japanese heroes (S4) in the same large and immensely vigorous style quickly followed, and was added to at intervals, like the original *Suikoden* set, during the following decade.

It was in the *Suikoden* that Kuniyoshi broke free from the influence of Shuntei, evolving a truly individual style, equally large and forceful, but much more lively than that of his predecessor. This can be seen in both single sheets (e.g. S1b, Fig. 3) and triptychs (T16–T22). By the later 1830s this ebullience had settled into what became Kuniyoshi's normal historical style (S8, S9): the scale of the figures is reduced, and the drawing, though still full of vigour, shows less variation in the strength of the brush-strokes. Triptychs of the same period display an increasing mastery of this impressive medium (see especially T30, T41, T47).

In the years about 1840, on the eve of the Tempō Reforms, Kuniyoshi's production was enormous, and he experimented with a number of different formats and styles. Several sets were issued in *chūban* (S15, S22–S26), *tanzaku* (S16, S17, S21, S28 Fig. 4), and *yokoye* (S13, S14) format, and there is even a triptych of three *chūban* sheets (T72). In the 'Hundred Poets' (S19) he adopted a restrained courtly style, more appropriate to the peaceful Fujiwara period in which many of the scenes are set; but even here his predilection for ghost-stories (S19.71, S19.77) and cats (S19.86, S19.97) occasionally breaks through. His experiments with western style can best be seen at this time in the Chinese 'Paragons' (S13).

It may be helpful at this point, about half-way through Kuniyoshi's career, to pause and consider his rate of production of warrior-prints, so far as it can be calculated. The following statistical table, constructed from the prints listed in the Catalogue, provides an approximate but broadly reliable picture (averages to the nearest whole number):

Fig. 3. Koshibe no Sugaru catching a thunder-beast. *c.*1834–5. S1c.2.

Fig. 4. Minamoto no Yoshi-iye at the Nakoso Barrier. *c.*1843. S28.16.

PERIOD	SINGLE PRINTS		TRIPTYCHS		TOTAL	
	Number	Annual average	Number	Annual average	Number	Annual average
1818–30	133	11	17	2	150	13
1831–5	47	9	12	3	59	12
1836	32	32	13	13	45	45
1837–42	156	26	40	7	196	33
1842–6	486	97	101	25	587	122
1847–52	322	54	91	15	413	69
1852 (¾ year)	85	113	14	19	99	131
1853	58		19		77	
1854	25		6		31	
1855	35		12		47	
1856	13		13		26	
1857	46		10		56	
1858	6		6		12	
1859	—		—		—	
1860	6		1		7	
1861 and later	3		3		6	

Fig.5. Hatsu-hana under the waterfall. *c*.1841–2. S20.7.

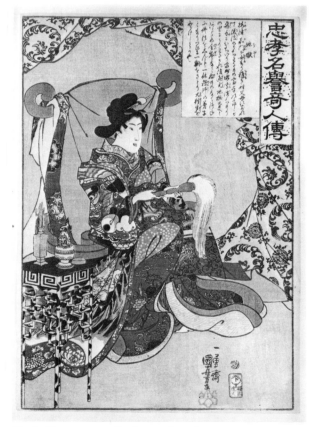

Fig.6. The courtesan Jigoku. *c*.1845. S35.3.

This table shows in general, as might be expected, a successive rise, peak, and decline, and the peak, in the earlier (one seal) censorship period, is a very high one. It is noticeable that his production falls sharply from 1858, and that 1859 (Goat year) is completely blank. This may be due to ill health—he is known to have suffered partial paralysis (*chūbū*) in 1858—but also, perhaps, to his preoccupation with the illustrations to *Toyotomi kunkōki* (see p.14). His period of greatest production was 1836–53, and nearly all his best work was produced in those years. It is possible to define certain prints within that period as having been published in the early months of 1849. A correlation of theatrical prints with the stage annals contained in *Kabuki nendaiki* shows us that the schedule of censors was changed at the beginning of 1849, and that one of the partnerships, Kinugasa–Yoshimura, only lasted a few months before Yoshimura dropped out, for what reason is not recorded, his place being taken by Watanabe. Looking at the triptychs with the Kinugasa–Yoshimura seals, we find three outstanding compositions: 'Kamei Rokurō and the bear' (T215), 'The rival generals at the Uji river crossing' (T217), and 'Asahina and the crocodiles' (T218)—an average of one fine triptych a month, which seems to have been Kuniyoshi's normal rate in these highly productive years.

The Tempō Reforms of July 1842 suppressed the production of prints of actors and courtesans, but they could not suppress the demand for them. Where there is a demand, especially in the East, means will be found to provide a supply, and so it was that in the period 1842–6 Kuniyoshi designed a number of series and triptychs which, whilst overtly illustrating history, legend, and popular romance, were in fact derived from current theatrical productions; such are S36–S46. A comparison of the prints with stage records (see, in particular, the Catalogue entries for S46) puts this beyond doubt. So far as the Yoshiwara is concerned, we may note during the same years the publication of several series devoted to women (S21, S25, S29, S30, S33), and we may suppose that, though the subjects were eminently respectable, the public's passion for prints of beautiful women (*bijin*) was thereby partially catered for (Figs.5, 6). By the beginning of 1847, it may be noted in passing, the restrictions seem to have been considerably eased (whether officially or otherwise is not clear), and direct illustrations of current stage productions became once more as frequent as they were before the Reforms. However, the letter of the law was still honoured by the omission of the actors' names. The style of most of these series may be described as semi-theatrical (Fig.7); the characters often assume theatrical postures (*miye*) and are sometimes shown with stage make-up. A number of contemporary triptychs are in the same style, and the grouping of the figures often suggests a theatrical performance; examples are T91, T95, T96, T98, T102, T107, T130, T131, T144, T155, T158, T164.

By this time Kuniyoshi was training a number of pupils, several of whom—Yoshitora, Yoshikazu, Yoshimori, for example—followed his historical style closely, and produced many triptychs not unworthy of their master. Others, such as Yoshiyuki and Yoshikuni, migrated to Osaka, bringing fresh ideas to the highly individual and almost exclusively theatrical stylistic tradition of that city.

Till the middle 1840s, Kuniyoshi's historical subjects were mainly drawn from Japanese history of the tenth to twelfth century, especially the wars of the Minamoto and Taira clans, and from the loyalist struggles of the Nitta and Kusunoki against the Ashikaga a century and a half later, with occasional excursions into popular historical drama, the Chinese histories of the Wars of the Three Kingdoms, and the *Suikoden*. But he now began to apply himself to the sixteenth century, and especially to the ten-year struggle between the war-lords Takeda Shingen and Uyesugi Kenshin on the narrow strip of land called Kawanakajima ('island between the rivers'), a sort of no man's land between their respective territories. During the 1840s and 1850s he poured forth a stream of illustrations of the Kawanakajima campaign and its protagonists, especially the redoubtable one-eyed general Yamamoto Kansuke, whose desperate last stand had a strong appeal for him (T190, T313), not only in many triptychs, but in series (S34 Fig.8, S63, S82, S83). One of his most popular sets, S62 (Fig.9), is devoted to the later sixteenth-century wars in which the leading figures were Nobunaga and Hideyoshi. Japanese convention decreed that this period was too recent for the real names of the participants to be used, and they appear in slightly altered forms, thus adding considerably to our problems of identification. This penchant for the sixteenth century seems to have culminated in the gigantic task undertaken by Kuniyoshi in 1855, and no doubt continued for several years, of preparing more than 600 double-page illustrations for *Toyotomi kunkōki*, a history of Hideyoshi's career running to some 7,000 pages, the publication of which was not completed till 1884. Mr W. M. Hawley's publication of the illustrations in *Pictorial Biography of Toyotomi Hideyoshi* is an invaluable source for the subject-matter of prints covering this period.

In about 1843–4, with the series *Meikō hyaku yū den* (S31 Fig.10), Kuniyoshi evolved a set form for his series of historical biographies which served him well for the next ten years. A full-length figure, generally in action, is placed on a plain background, with or without accessories, and with the upper part of the print occupied by a biographical or descriptive text. Another distinctive form is first found in S44, S45, and S46 of *c*.1845–8, but occurs again in S89 and S90 of 1856–7. In these series the upper third of the print is divided off, being occupied by the series title, text, and often an allusive design, with the main design below (Fig.11).

A characteristic of the late 1840s and early 1850s is the extraordinary proliferation of series on the *Chūshingura* theme (see p.29). *Seichū gishi den* (S54) seems to have been the first of these, and on one of the prints (S54.50) we are fortunately given the exact dates of the commencement and completion of the set, corresponding to August 1847 and 20 January 1848. This series proved immensely popular (many poor late reprints are encountered) and was followed almost immediately by several others devoted to the adventures of the Forty-Seven *Rōnin* outside the main plot of the *Chūshingura*, and to their relatives and friends who find a place in the story (S55–S59). Other sets of the *Rōnin* themselves came in 1851 (S71, S72), 1853 (S78, S80), and 1857 (S90), and the twelve acts of the drama were illustrated in 1854–5 in a fine series of *yokoye* format (S86). A considerable number of *Chūshingura* triptychs were also designed by Kuniyoshi during the same period (T186–T188, T209–T211, T249, T260, T272, T273, T276, T285). Perhaps a Japanese scholar will be able to explain this phenomenon.

But Kuniyoshi certainly had his own favourite subjects, to which he returned time and again; the battle of Yashima is illustrated in a dozen triptychs, as is the Soga brothers' revenge, and the night-attack in the *Chūshingura* rates eight. Several other incidents come close behind. It may be instructive to select one of these and to compare Kuniyoshi's treatment of it at different stages of his career, and for this purpose the best is probably that of the storm-tossed ship of Yoshitsune attacked by the Taira ghosts from the depths of the sea (see p.24), which provided the subject for four triptychs. The first, dating from 1818 (T1), is Kuniyoshi's earliest recorded heroic triptych. The figures are comparatively large, and very much in the style of Shuntei, but the ghost of Tomomori, which dominates the left-hand sheet, already shows something of the artist's individual style, as well as his affectionate admiration for the ill-starred Taira leader which is obvious from several of his later works (see especially S1f.7, T144). The next representation (T70) is about twenty years later, and shows a fully developed style and a much wider vision. Yoshitsune's vessel is here a full-sized sailing-ship; the one depicted in T1 is no more than a large boat. The Taira ghosts, led as usual by Tomomori, move through the waves in a baleful procession ac-

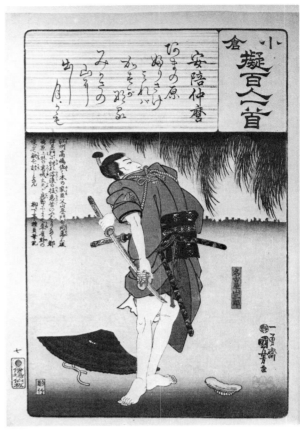

Fig.7. Nagoya Sanzaburō wiping his sword. *c*.1845–8. S46.7.

Fig.8. The one-eyed general Yamamoto Kansuke. *c*.1845. S34.4.

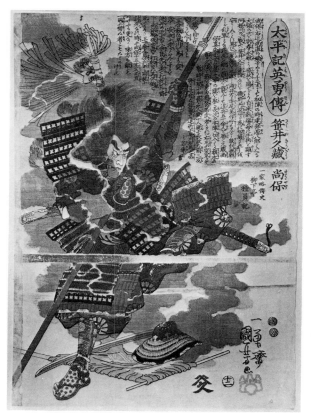

Fig. 9. Masayasu disintegrating before a volley of musketry. *c.*1848–9. S62.36.

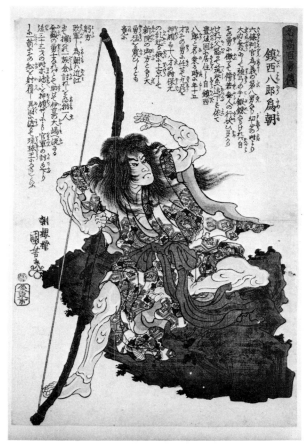

Fig. 10. Tametomo the great archer. *c.*1843–4. S31.19.

companied by flickering ghost-fires, and the wide sweep of the triptych is fully exploited. Six or seven years later comes another masterly triptych (T147 Fig. 12), perhaps even more impressive. Here the stricken vessel plunges and staggers through the rolling waves, while lightning plays over the water (the ship in T70 is sailing perhaps a trifle too serenely). The ghosts are poised above it in a menacing crescent on the crest of a rearing wave, and round the ship the foaming spray takes the form of skulls and clawing dead hands. The last one (T242), dating from about 1850, is thought by some critics to be the best of all. The mountainous blue wave and the sinister distorted silhouettes of the ghosts against the stormy sky are certainly impressive, but may perhaps seem a trifle forced, and the immediacy of the ghosts' attack, and the important circumstance of their rising from the sea are lost in a rather frantic striving after sensation and originality. These four triptychs thus provide an epitome of the development of Kuniyoshi's style. Beginning in 1818 in almost total dependence on Shuntei, though already showing promise of power and originality, it achieves independence and maturity by the late 1830s, rises to its peak by 1845, and soon after 1850 begins to show signs of strain and fatigue.

That is indeed the general trend. But right to the end of his life Kuniyoshi could still produce triptychs of enormous power and effectiveness: 'Asahina breaking down the gate' (T281 of 1852), 'Kanetaka at bay in the Yamaki palace' (T312 of 1854), 'Yoshitsune recovering his bow at Yashima' (T339 of 1857), and 'Raikō's retainers playing *go*' (T357 of 1861) in which, only two months before his death, he returns to the forceful drawing and large figures of the early 1830s (cf. T28)—these bear comparison with the works of his prime.

But it must be admitted that the decline of his later years is often apparent when he repeats a subject he had already treated in fine fashion in his peak period. A comparison of earlier and later versions of the battle of Fujiidera (T34 of 1836 and T333 of 1856), the Soga brothers' last fight (T159 of 1845 and T349 of 1858), and Asahina breaking down the gate (T281 of 1852 and T342 of 1857) makes this abundantly clear. It is also evident in some single-sheet prints, such as those portraying Yamato-take and the 'grass-mowing sword' (S4b.5 of 1835 and S88.27 of 1855). But considering Kuniyoshi's enormous output this is scarcely surprising. In assessing an artist's achievement it is more valid, as well as more charitable, to concentrate attention on his best work. Japanese colour-print artists, especially those of high reputation, were subject to enormous pressure to pour out designs to meet the public demand, and it is really not fair to judge them by their pot-boilers. If we adopt the more reasonable attitude, we shall find that Kuniyoshi maintained his mastery throughout his life, even towards the end, when he was in poor health. By the time of his death he had completely altered the balance of subject-matter in the popular prints. In his earliest years they were virtually monopolized by actors and courtesans; Shuntei was the only artist who specialized in warrior-prints, and he was not particularly popular or successful. But at his death Kuniyoshi left over forty-five pupils (whose names are engraved on his tombstone) the great majority of whom followed his style and taste. The warrior-print had achieved an almost excessive popularity.

The heroic triptych, indeed, enjoyed a splendid Indian summer during Japan's wars with China (1894–5) and Russia (1904–5) when many remarkably dramatic and imaginative illustrations of the fighting were published almost as soon as news of each incident reached the capital. Behind these undoubtedly stood Kuniyoshi's magnificent series of triptychs with which he had so often and so effectively quickened his countrymen's consciousness of their heroic past.

The prints treated of in this book are a true mirror of the spirit of pre-Meiji Japan, of which the best evocation in English is still Mitford's immortal *Tales of Old Japan*. The most admired manifestations of that spirit were unquestioning loyalty, fidelity in revenge, and pure cool courage, and we naturally find them

Fig.12. *Triptych:* The Taira ghosts attacking Yoshitsune's ship. *c.*1845. T147.

constantly emphasized in the prints of Kuniyoshi. Such qualities often combine and culminate in the theme of the desperate last stand against overwhelming odds, which runs through these prints like a sort of leitmotiv. Yorimasa at the Uji bridge, Tomomori at Dan-no-ura, the Soga brothers on Suso moor, the Kusunoki clan at Shijō-nawate, and Yamamoto Kansuke at Kawanakajima were heroes *in extremis* in whom Kuniyoshi found inspiration again and again. Heroism of this kind may be somewhat out of fashion nowadays, but it was not so very long ago (in Kuniyoshi's lifetime in fact) that the last stand of Harold at Hastings and of James IV at Flodden (who can ever forget that splendid passage in Scott's *Marmion?*), the 'thin red line', and the Charge of the Light Brigade provided equally potent inspiration to our own poets and painters. For them (and for Kuniyoshi) history was not the dreary succession of economic trends and working-class movements that it has become in this era of the Common Man; it was the gay glitter of heroism, romance, and chivalry on the one hand, and the darker hues of vice, treachery, and rebellion on the other. If we are to appreciate in any depth the art and culture of Old Japan, we must accept the aims and ideals of the Japanese artist in this context, and anybody who can recapture something of the spirit of his unsophisticated boyhood will not find it hard to do so.

With such thoughts in mind, then, let us enter Kuniyoshi's exotic yet somehow familiar world of warriors, monsters, and fair ladies, reminding ourselves, if we can, of the excitement of a first reading of the ballads of 'Sir Patrick Spens', or 'Kinmont Willie', or the 'Unquiet Grave'. These sprang from our own feudal soil—not, after all, so very different from that of Kyoto or Kamakura. There are as many heroic deeds and as much bloodshed at Dan-no-ura as at Chevy Chase; Yoshitsune is as irresistible (and sometimes as unscrupulous) as Lord Thomas; Shidzuka is as beautiful and as ill-starred as Fair Janet; and in robust fidelity and brute strength Benkei is by no means inferior to Friar Tuck.

Fig.11. The *rōnin* and the ghost of his murdered wife. *c.*1845–6. S44.26.

Fig. 13. Yamato-take-no-mikoto and his 'grass-mowing sword'. 1834–5. S4b.5.

Fig. 14. The Empress Jingō and her fleet. *c.* 1842–3. S21.5.

THE SUBJECTS

It would be quite impossible in a book of this kind to give a full narrative account of all the historical and legendary episodes illustrated by Kuniyoshi. But to some of them he returns repeatedly, and what follows is an attempt to provide a basic outline of the passages in the mainstream of Japanese history which are most often encountered in his work. The account is not intended to be strictly historical; it is simply a companion, telling the stories as they are illustrated in the prints, which are frequently based on popular historical fiction or theatrical versions. Even so, many subsidiary episodes are necessarily omitted through lack of space.

I. Early History

(a) PRINCE YAMATO-TAKE-NO-MIKOTO

He was the third son of the Emperor Keikō and was said to have lived 81–113. He early displayed a mixture of high courage and absolute ruthlessness in a series of exploits against the aborigines, who were still a serious threat to the immigrant Japanese. On being sent against the aborigines of the eastern provinces by the Emperor, he first visited his aunt Yamato-hime, high priestess of the Ise shrine, and she lent him the famous sword *Ame no murakumo no tsurugi* ('sword of the clustering clouds of heaven'). This sword had been taken from the tail of an eight-headed dragon formerly slain by the brother of the Sun-Goddess (S17.5), and, together with the Mirror and the Jewel, formed the Japanese Imperial regalia. In the course of his expedition the Prince found himself suddenly surrounded by fire, the aborigines having surreptitiously set alight the dry grass all round him, fanned by a strong breeze. The sword leaped spontaneously from its scabbard and mowed down the burning grass, thus enabling him to make his escape (Fig. 13). Meanwhile the wind changed, and the unfortunate barbarians found themselves hoist with their own petard. In commemoration of this incident the sword was renamed *Kusanagi-no-tsurugi* ('grass-mowing sword'), and it remained in the Imperial regalia till 1185, when it went to the bottom of the sea with the boy-Emperor Antoku, the Mirror, and the Jewel at the battle of Dan-no-ura (see p. 23). The Mirror and the Jewel were recovered by divers, but the Sword was never found (T134). However, some authorities maintain that the sword lost at Dan-no-ura was a copy made in the reign of the Emperor Sūjin (97–29 BC), and that the original is still in the Ise shrine.

(b) THE EMPRESS JINGŌ

She was the daughter of Prince Okinaga-no-sukune, and was divinely inspired at the beginning of her reign (200–269) to 'chastise the West', that is, to invade Korea. This she did, assembling a large fleet under the command of her minister Takeshiuchi-no-sukune (Fig. 14). At this time Korea was divided into three kingdoms, Silla, Pekché, and Koryö. The Japanese landed in Silla, whose king immediately proffered his allegiance, in which prudent course he was soon followed by the other two. Some accounts, however, maintain that a certain amount of fighting was involved (T51, T145).

(c) PRINCE SHŌTOKU TAISHI

This Prince (572–621), sometimes called Umayado ('born in the stable'), was the second son of the Emperor Yōmei, and is celebrated as an early champion of Buddhism, recently imported into Japan from the mainland. Kuniyoshi was mainly concerned with his struggle against Mononobe no Moriya, protagonist of the old order (S14, T279).

II. The Rebellion of Masakado

Masakado (d. 940) was an early scion of the Taira clan, and a man of inordinate ambition and arrogance. He was at first in the service of the regent Fujiwara no Tadahira, but the latter was a weak character, and, failing to obtain from him a lucrative post he had requested, Masakado withdrew to the province of Shimosa. Here, by a series of intrigues, battles, and murders, he secured the headship of his clan, and proclaimed himself Heishinnō, or 'new Taira emperor', having by this time brought the provinces of Shimosa, Kōdzuke, and Shimotsuke under his sway. When his brother Kintsura tried to restrain him from this treasonable course, Masakado expelled him with ignominy from his court (S61.5, T23, T252). To deal with this rebellion Taira no Sadamori, whose father Masakado had murdered, and Tawara Tōda Hidesato were put in command of the Imperial troops. In spite of using a number of 'doubles' (*kagemusha*) dressed in similar armour, the real Masakado was defeated, cornered, and slain.

He left a son, Yoshikado, and a daughter, Takiyasha, both of whom practised witchcraft (T138, T166), joining the robber gang of Iga no Jutarō (T89, T111, T219). Their adventures formed the subject of a play, *Sōma dairi* ('The Palace of Sōma'), staged at the end of 1844, which no doubt inspired some of Kuniyoshi's illustrations of the story.

III. Raikō and his Four Retainers

Minamoto no Yorimitsu (944–1021), more familiarly known as Raikō, was the son of Mitsunaka, belonging to the branch of the great Minamoto clan that traced its descent from the Emperor Seiwa (859–77). Under the rather weak rule of the Emperor Murakami (947–68) the country had become infested with bandits, and Raikō was commissioned to get rid of them. He surrounded himself with four stout retainers, known as the *Shitennō*, or 'four heavenly kings': Watanabe no Tsuna, Usui no Sadamitsu, Urabe no Suyetake, and Sakata no Kintoki. Hirai no Yasumasa is sometimes found as a supernumerary. Japanese legend has magnified the various bandit chieftains into supernatural monsters. The Shuten-dōji ('great drunken boy') was the most notorious; he had his lair in the mountains of Ōyeyama in the province of Tamba, where he was attended by demon-retainers, and kept captured ladies for his pleasure, feeding on human flesh. Raikō and his companions gained access to the monster in the guise of travelling monks, entertained him with dancing, and made him drunk on *sake* (T21, T305). When he was thoroughly stupefied the warriors donned their armour, which they had carried in their monks' travelling-cases; Raikō struck off the monster's head which sprang in the air and descended full on the hero's helmet, in which it buried its fangs (S1a.3, T261, T298). He was only saved by an inner steel skull-cap given him by the Spirit of Sumiyoshi. His retainers made short work of the attendant demons, and the grisly head was carried in triumph to the capital (T280). Another bandit chieftain was called the Earth-Spider (*Tsuchi-gumo*), presumably because he was one of the cave-dwelling aborigines, and he is represented as haunting and tormenting Raikō during a period of sickness (S88.19, T4, T128). The Four Retainers, however, tracked him to his lair and slew him (T46), and their master's health was immediately restored.

Many stories are told of the Four Retainers individually. Yasumasa, for example, had a brother named Yasusuke, who went to the bad, learned witchcraft from the *tengu*, and became a robber under the name of Kidō Maru (S1f.1). One day the latter stole up behind his brother, intending to kill and rob him, but Yasumasa was playing the flute, and the sweet sounds so softened the villain's heart that he stole away (S35.11, S74.42). Later Kidō Maru conceived a great hatred for Raikō, who had derided him when he was in temporary captivity. He therefore concealed himself under a buffalo-hide and lay in wait on

Fig. 15. The strong boy Kwaidō Maru. 1860. S93.3.

Fig. 16. *Triptych:* Tametomo shipwrecked by a great fish. 1851–2. T263.

the moor of Ichihara, where he knew Raikō would pass. As the party approached he sprang out and made a desperate rush for Raikō, but was overpowered and slain by the Four Retainers (S8.6, S17.2, S88.28, T3, T169, T262). Kintoki started life as Kintarō, or Kwaidō Maru ('wonder child'), a boy of enormous strength (hence conventionally represented with red skin) brought up in the Ashigara mountains by his widowed mother Yayegiri, or Yama-uba ('old woman of the mountain'). He used to test his strength by wrestling with a bear-cub or a giant carp (S1d.1, S93.3 Fig. 15), and being observed at exercise one day by Tsuna, was persuaded to join Raikō's retinue (T44). Tsuna himself had a frightening experience at the Rashōmon gate in Kyoto. It was reputed to be haunted, and he undertook to spend the night there. Nothing happened till near dawn, when he suddenly felt himself seized by the hair (S1a.16). His blade was out in a flash, and he made a sweeping backward cut, whereupon there fell to earth a huge hairy severed arm. Tsuna treasured this grim trophy in a box, but the demon eventually recovered it by impersonating the hero's old nurse.

IV. Kiyomori in Power

Taira no Kiyomori (1118–81) was the greatest and most ruthless of the Taira clan. He first came to prominence during the war of Hōgen (1156) in which the Emperor Sutoku, forced by his father to abdicate in favour of a younger brother, attempted to regain the throne. He was defeated by the partisans of his rival Go-Shirakawa, and died in exile (S19.77). Kiyomori had been on the winning side, and soon became all-powerful. Among the Minamoto clansmen who opposed him were Yoshitomo and his eldest son Yoshihira; but they were defeated in the war of Heiji (1160), and Yoshitomo was killed by treachery. On hearing of his father's death, Yoshihira returned secretly to the capital, hoping for an opportunity to kill Kiyomori, but he was arrested by the latter's son Shigemori (T195), and the tyrant ordered his immediate decapitation. At the moment of death his ghost sprang into the air in a sulphurous explosion, and his executioner was struck dead by a thunderbolt (S1c.4, T10).

Kiyomori was a great builder, and besides erecting for himself the magnificent palace of Fukuhara, he restored at great expense the famous temples of Miyajima on the Inland Sea. Impatient at the slow progress of the work, he arrested the setting sun by incantations, so that the workmen could continue uninterrupted (S52.3, T83; *Lieftinck*, No.8). He maintained a splendid court, and kept a succession of mistresses, amongst whom were Tokiwa-gozen, former mistress of Yoshitomo and mother of Yoshitsune (T155), Hotoke-gozen, Giō, and Ginyo. In the end he was seized by a violent fever and died miserably (T139).

V. Tametomo the Great Archer

Minamoto no Tametomo (1139–70) was the eighth son of Tameyoshi, and a younger brother of Yoshitomo. He was a giant in size and strength and had a wonderful skill with the bow; having his left arm four inches longer than the right, he was able to make a longer draw and speed his arrows with greater force. Owing to his unruly conduct, he was sent to the western province of Higo, where he wooed and married Shiranui-hime, daughter of the local chieftain (T91, T223), and soon made himself master of the whole of Kyūshū. But he was on the losing side in the war of Hōgen and was exiled to Ōshima. Here too, however, he contrived to carve out a little empire among the surrounding islands. An expedition was sent to apprehend him, but he sank the leading boat with a single heavy arrow (T113, T254) and then performed *seppuku*.

But Kuniyoshi's illustrations of Tametomo's more fantastic adventures are taken from Bakin's romance *Yumihari-dzuki* (S64), including his shipwreck by a monstrous fish and rescue by the *tengu* (T30, T263 Fig. 16).

VI. Youthful Exploits of Yoshitsune and Benkei

Tokiwa-gozen, the beautiful mistress of Minamoto no Yoshitomo, had borne him three sons before he was killed in the war of Heiji (1160). She fled through the snow with the three little boys, Yoshitsune, less than a year old, clasped to her breast (S20.23 etc.), and took refuge in a remote village. Kiyomori, however, found means to bring her to court (T155), and she became his concubine in order to save her children's lives. In due course the boys' heads were shaved and they were packed off to various monasteries to be brought up and educated as monks.

The youngest was known at first as Ushiwaka Maru ('young ox'), then as Shanaō, and finally, from 1174, as Minamoto no Kurō Yoshitsune. He was sent to the monastery at Kuramayama, but the monastic life bored him, and he used to climb out at night to practise military exercises in the neighbouring pine-woods. There he met the *tengu* and their king, under whose instruction he gained an almost superhuman agility and skill with the sword (S1f.11, S65.2, S88.8, T20, T264, T351). He eventually contrived to run away from the monastery altogether, and joined a gold-merchant on his way to the northern province of Mutsu. On the way they were attacked at an inn (the name of the post-station varies in different accounts, but seems to have been in the province of Mino) by a gang of robbers under a giant renegade monk named Kumasaka Chōhan. Ushiwaka displayed all his boldness and skill, slew Chōhan and dispersed his followers (T5, T40, T53, T224 Fig.17). At a later stage of the journey, outside a large house, he heard the sweet strains of a *koto* exquisitely played. He took out his flute (which was named *Taitō Maru*) and improvised an accompaniment, and soon a maid came out with a lantern and invited him to enter (T85, T108), when he found himself in the presence of the fair *koto*-player Jōruri-hime ('pure emerald princess'). Ushiwaka seduced her, and they were happy for ten days, but after that he abandoned her to pursue his journey to Mutsu, and in the most popular version of the story poor Jōruri drowned herself in the Yahagi river nearby. Eventually he reached Hiraidzumi in Mutsu, and presented himself before the powerful local magnate, Fujiwara no Hidehira, (T93) who received him kindly and gave him some useful advice and instruction in military matters.

We must now turn to Musashi-bō Benkei, the son of a monk of Kumano who had contracted a somewhat scandalous liaison with a nobleman's young daughter who had come to pay her devotions at the Kumano shrine. Thus, like Ushiwaka, he was brought up in a monastery, but soon evinced a preference for fencing and other military exercises; he quarrelled incessantly with the monks, and at last, after knocking a number of them about in a general mêlée (T178), he strode off to the capital, leaving the temple in flames. He grew to be of giant size and strength, and when in Kyoto he formed a design of collecting 1,000 swords. This, of course, involved the use of force on their owners, and rumours were soon circulating in the capital of a demon-monk of enormous size by whom unwary travellers were liable to be waylaid. The chronology of these stories is often doubtful, but it seems that this was the time when Ushiwaka was at Kuramayama, and on one of his nightly outings he met Benkei on Gojō bridge by moonlight. Benkei had only one more sword to get in order to achieve his goal, and he therefore attacked the frail-looking youth who, as he observed, was wearing a splendid weapon. But the skill and agility Ushiwaka had learned from the *tengu* enabled him to baffle his enormous assailant completely (S28.4, S65.9, S65.10, S76.1, T47, T54, T194), and the latter was soon flat on his back. Benkei had imagined himself invincible, and he now swore eternal allegiance to his young vanquisher.

Another incident belongs to the period between the fight on Gojō bridge and the linking up of Yoshitsune and his brother Yoritomo against the Taira. Wishing, in a fit of remorse, to benefit the monastery in which he had grown up, Benkei decided to present it with the great bell of Miidera. This bell hung in the

Fig.17. *Triptych:* Ushiwaka fighting Chōhan at the inn. 1849–52. T224.

monastery of Onjōji, where it had been dedicated by Hidesato after he had received it from the Dragon King as a reward for killing the giant centipede of Seta (S44.54, T354). Without further ceremony, Benkei cut its ropes and proceeded to drag it away (S49.1, S84.5, T150). After a while he rested and tried the bell, which, however, would only utter a moaning sound that seemed to say, 'I want to go back to Miidera.' In disgust Benkei heaved it over into the valley below, from which the Onjōji monks eventually recovered it.

VII. Yorimasa and the Beginning of the Taira–Minamoto War

Minamoto no Yorimasa (1106–80) was fifth in descent from Raikō (see p.18), and when, in 1153, the Emperor Konoye was disturbed at night by strange noises above his head, he was instructed to deal with the situation. That night he saw a dense black cloud settle on the palace roof, and loosed an arrow into the middle of it (S48.6, T112). Immediately there fell to earth a monster called the *Nuye* (S74.72, T7), with a monkey's head, a badger's body, a tiger's legs and claws, and a snake for a tail (T7), which was quickly dispatched by the squire Ii no Hayata (S4a.6). Yorimasa was rewarded with a magnificent sword and the hand of the lady Ayame (T107). In 1180, chafing under the tyranny of Kiyomori, he rose in revolt together with Prince Mochihito, but on 18 June, after a gallant struggle, he was defeated by vastly superior numbers at the battle of the Uji river bridge. He retired to a nearby temple where he wrote a farewell poem, and performed *seppuku* (S46.8). A feature of the battle was the spirited defence of the broken bridge by two warrior-monks, Tsutsui Jōmyō and Ichirai-hōshi (S8.3, S73.10).

On 8 September of the same year, Minamoto no Yoritomo opened his campaign against the Taira by a successful attack on the mansion of Kanetaka at Yamaki in the province of Idzu (S92.4, T88, T123, T239, T312), but was defeated a few days later at Ishibashiyama (T39). The two outstanding incidents at this battle were the struggle between Sanada Yoichi Yoshitada (or Yoshisada) and the Taira champion Matano Gorō Kagehisa, in which the former was killed by other Taira troops after getting his opponent down (S1a.13, S1c.8, S1f.6, S8.1, S95b.1, T28, T94, T197); and the hiding of Yoritomo and his companions in a large hollow tree, from which his pursuers were diverted by Kajiwara Kagetoki (S73.9, T320), who transferred his allegiance on this occasion from the Taira to the Minamoto. Meanwhile Yoshitsune, immediately on hearing of the rising, hurried southwards from Mutsu, and the brothers met on 10 November to concert their plans (T56).

Fig.18. *Triptych:* Nagamochi and the apparition of the Thunder-God. 1849–52. T240.

VIII. The Career of Yoshinaka

Minamoto no Yoshinaka (1154–84) was a first cousin of the brothers Yoritomo and Yoshitsune. He was brought up among the Kiso mountains, and is hence usually known as Kiso Yoshinaka. On 27 September 1180 he raised his standard against the Taira in the province of Shinano (T25), and after a series of spectacular victories drove them from the capital in the summer of 1183 (Fig. 18). His most famous victory was at Kurikaradani (T303) on 2 June 1183, where, after throwing the Taira into confusion by driving oxen among them with flaming straw attached to their horns (T300), so that many of them fell over a cliff (T146), he grappled with their general Tomonori; they rolled down a steep precipice together, and Yoshinaka killed his man (S9.2, T43).

Once established in Kyoto, he quarrelled with the ex-Emperor Go-Shirakawa, and gave his rough mountain troops free rein in the city, which they speedily transformed into a scene of murder, rapine, and confusion. News of this sorry state of affairs and of Yoshinaka's overweening ambition was soon conveyed to Yoritomo, the head of the clan, at Kamakura, who sent a strong force under his brothers Yoshitsune and Noriyori to bring his troublesome cousin to heel. They found his army occupying a strong position on the further bank of the Uji river, near Kyoto; a frontal attack was launched, the two rival generals Takatsuna and Kagesuye racing to be first across the river to engage the enemy (T18, T62, T191, T217, T334), who were soon driven off. Yoshinaka made his last stand on the neighbouring moor of Awadzu on the shore of Lake Biwa, where, as always, he was ably backed by his warrior-mistress Tomoye-gozen (T265, T315); but he was again defeated, and shot in the forehead under the peak of his helmet as he attempted to get away across a frozen bog (S73.8). This was on 5 March 1184.

IX. The Destruction of the Taira

After the elimination of Yoshinaka, Yoritomo could concentrate on his ultimate objective, the total destruction of the Taira clan. The Taira had fled westwards after being driven out of Kyoto by Yoshinaka, taking with them the little boy-Emperor Antoku. Yoritomo again placed Yoshitsune and Noriyori in command, and they marched out only ten days after their victory over Yoshinaka. They soon learned that the Taira had fortified themselves in the neighbourhood of Ichi-no-tani on the coast of Settsu province, with their fleet moored off shore. A preliminary engagement took place in the forest of Ikuta, at the eastern end of the Taira position, and here Kajiwara Kagesuye again distinguished himself, conspicuous with a spray of plum-blossom in his quiver in honour of his lady-love Umegaye (S28.32). But eventually he was so hard pressed by the Taira that he lost his helmet and had to be rescued by his father Kagetoki (T153 Fig.19).

But the most dramatic episode in the fighting at Ichi-no-tani was the descent of the precipitous defile of Hiyodori-goye by Yoshitsune with a body of picked men, who were thus able to take the Taira unexpectedly in the rear, 'like the Persians at Thermopylae' as Laurence Binyon observed (T65, T84). Benkei had found a local youth, Kumaō Maru ('bear king'), who acted as their guide, and on whom Yoshitsune bestowed the name of Washi-no-o Saburō (T64). Though thrown into confusion by this surprise attack (T226), the Taira fought fiercely on the shore (T38, T156), and most of them managed to get aboard their ships, which sailed off to Yashima. But Mukwan-no-tayū Atsumori, a youth of fifteen who had fought bravely in the battle, found himself left behind, and was challenged to single combat by the seasoned Minamoto warrior Kumagaye Naozane (T228). Having overthrown Atsumori, Naozane would have spared his life but for the taunts of his comrades standing by. As it was, he dealt the fatal stroke, and took Atsumori's head to Yoshitsune (T66). Later, overcome by remorse, he shaved his head and became a monk (S44.23, T48).

The Taira now took up their position on the other side of the Inland Sea at Yashima in the province of Sanuki. Yoshitsune, however, pressed his attack with such speed that they were at first taken by surprise, and the battle began with the Minamoto riding out into the shallows to attack the Taira as they were taking to their boats. One boat, about a hundred yards off shore, displayed a fan attached to the top of a bamboo pole fixed in the bows, beneath which sat a beautiful court lady named Tamamushi-no-maye. The Minamoto regarded this as a challenge, and, on the orders of Yoshitsune, Nasu no Yoichi, a celebrated archer, rode into the sea as far as he could and brought down the fan with his first arrow (S21.3, T179). Meanwhile the Taira giant, Noto no Kami Noritsune, determined to kill Yoshitsune, took careful aim and loosed off a heavy arrow; but Satō Tsuginobu saw it coming, interposed his body, and saved his lord's life at the cost of his own (T109, T256). During the ensuing engagement Yoshitsune dropped his bow in the sea, and in going after it and trying to retrieve it with the handle of his riding-whip, he exposed himself to great danger, but at length he got it back safely (T221, T339 Fig.20). After the battle he was reproved for his rashness by some of the older warriors, but replied laughing, 'It was not that I grudged the

Fig.19. *Triptych:* Kagesuye fighting at the forest of Ikuta. *c.*1845. T153.

Fig.20. *Triptych:* Yoshitsune recovering his bow at Yashima. 1857. T339.

bow, only that I did not want such a weak one as mine to fall into the enemy's hands. They would have laughed and said, "Look at this wretched bow that belonged to the Minamoto leader!" '

The final and decisive battle took place at Dan-no-ura in the straits of Shimonoseki, between Kyūshū and the Main Island, on 25 April 1185. The tide-flow favoured the Minamoto. The engagement quickly became general as the two lines converged; according to the *Heike monogatari* the Taira had 1,000 ships and the Minamoto 3,000; even if these figures be accepted, it must be remembered that the great majority were no more than boats carrying perhaps six or eight warriors. But the Taira had one or two larger vessels of Chinese build, on one of which was the infant Emperor. As was their custom, the Taira flew red banners, and the Minamoto white. The Taira had the advantage of the first exchanges, but they were dismayed by an omen in the form of a white cloud, like a banner, that descended from heaven and settled on the stern of one of the Minamoto ships. There were also some serious defections to the Minamoto side, so that after a while things began to look increasingly black for the Taira, whose ships were further encumbered with numbers of court ladies. Their gallant commander Tomomori was on board the Imperial barge when he received news of impending disaster (T96), and so was Kiyomori's widow Nii no Ama, who was looking after the child-Emperor, her grandson. She had already made her decision; taking up the Imperial regalia of the Sword, the Mirror, and the Jewel, and clasping little Antoku in her arms, she plunged into the waves and was seen no more. The Emperor was only eight years of age.

One after another the Taira champions fell, often taking one or more of their foemen to the bottom with them. Noritsune made a last desperate effort to kill Yoshitsune, but the latter escaped him, leaping from boat to boat with his customary agility (T68, T222, T230), and the giant had to content himself with grasping two Minamoto warriors, one under each arm, and so plunging to his death. Tomomori himself, sorely wounded and at his last gasp (S1f.7, S36.68, S45.40), seeing that he could do no more, tied himself to a huge anchor and flung himself into the sea (T144); his example was followed by a number of other Taira notables. No quarter was asked or given; those who survived the battle (including the craven Munemori, nominal head of the clan) were carried captive before Yoritomo to be inevitably beheaded, while their allies and supporters throughout the country were systematically hunted down.

After this terrible battle it is no wonder that the sea and shore at Dan-no-ura have been haunted for nearly 800 years. As Lafcadio Hearn has written, there are 'strange crabs found there, called Heike [i.e. Taira] crabs, which have human faces on their backs, and are said to be the spirits of the Heike warriors [cf. T144]. But there are many strange things to be seen and heard along that coast. On dark nights thousands of ghostly fires hover about the beach, or flit above the waves—pale lights which the fishermen call *oni-bi*, or demon-fires; and whenever the winds are up, a sound of great shouting comes from the sea, like a clamour of battle.' (*Hearn*, p.9.)

X. Yoritomo in Power

(a) THE PERSECUTION OF YOSHITSUNE

It might be thought that after the battle of Dan-no-ura by which the Minamoto supremacy was finally assured, and Yoritomo securely established in the position soon to be known as Shōgun, the supreme military ruler, he would have welcomed his younger brother, who had gained him the victory, and raised him to some honourable post. Nothing of the sort happened. The brothers were as different as could be; Yoshitsune was honest, direct, enthusiastic, and loyal, whereas Yoritomo was cold, scheming, ruthless, and suspicious. Yoshitsune's brilliant conduct of the war had aroused jealousies among some of the Minamoto

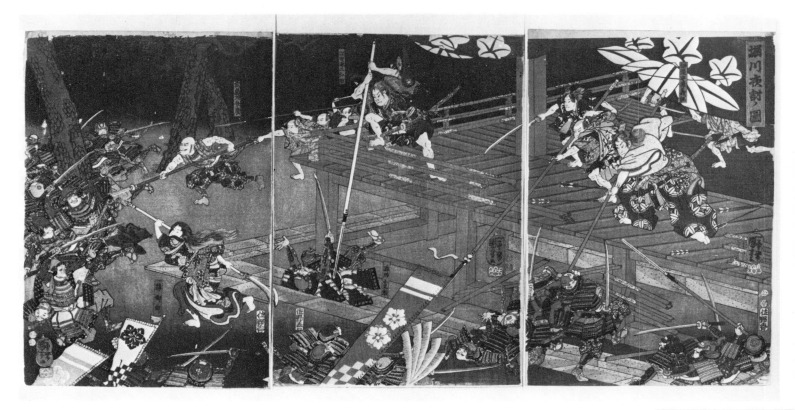

leaders, especially Kajiwara Kagetoki, who did not hesitate to poison the ears of the elder brother against the younger. Yoshitsune was not even allowed into his brother's presence at Kamakura after his great victory (but see T45), but was detained at Koshigoye, where he composed a pathetic letter to Yoritomo, reminding him of the signal services he had rendered, and protesting his absolute loyalty (T117). (It was at Koshigoye, incidentally, that Yoshitsune's head was exposed by his brother four years later.) He was finally directed to Kyoto, where he lodged in the Horikawa palace.

Meanwhile the slanders continued, and Yoritomo secretly ordered a ruffianly warrior-monk named Tosa-bō Shōshun to attack the Horikawa palace with a body of troops and to kill Yoshitsune. By chance one of the latter's retainers, Yeda Genzō, encountered the party on its way and, his suspicions aroused, learned of its purpose through one of the accompanying porters. He hastened to give the alarm, but nevertheless Yoshitsune spent the evening drinking and slept soundly. He was soon awakened, however, by his mistress Shizuka, who had heard the approach of Shōshun and his men (T16, T97, T135, T185). A bloody fight ensued (T267 Fig.21), and Yeda Genzō was killed in a desperate defence of his master (S4a.18, S76.6), but in the end Shōshun's men were slain or scattered, whilst he himself, seized by Benkei, was dragged before Yoshitsune and summarily beheaded (T282).

Yoshitsune had no alternative but flight. He set sail for Shikoku, but in Daimotsu bay, off the coast of Settsu, a terrible storm burst upon the ship, flickering spirit-fires appeared among the waves, and the ghosts of the Taira warriors slain or drowned at Dan-no-ura rose from the depths about the ship, trying to sink it (T1, T70, T147, T242, T266 Fig.22). Benkei's priestly training saved them; grasping his rosary (or, in another version, loosing off a number of arrows) he recited the proper exorcisms, the ghosts sank back into the sea, and the storm subsided. His subsequent wanderings found Yoshitsune among the snows of Mount Yoshino (T133) when he found it necessary to part from his faithful mistress Shizuka (S21.2, T127). She made her way to Kyoto, but was soon discovered and taken to Kamakura where, though in an advanced

state of pregnancy, she was forced to dance before Yoritomo and his assembled nobles (T86). As soon as the child was born Yoritomo had it killed. Meanwhile, still in the Yoshino mountains, Yoshitsune was saved by the devotion of his retainer Satō Tadanobu (whose brother had already given his life for him at Yashima), who impersonated his lord by wearing his armour and holding off a number of hostile warrior-monks, while Yoshitsune made good his escape (S8.2, S65.16, S89.8, T2, T257). Tadanobu then betook himself to Kyoto and sought shelter with a former mistress. She pretended to shield him, but betrayed him to the authorities. A body of men arrived to arrest him, and Tadanobu, caught unarmed, defended himself for some time with a *go*-board (S4a.15, S16.2, S46.31, T168, T321 Fig.23), but finally cut himself open before them all, having killed his faithless mistress. After this, Yoshitsune and his little party, now disguised as wandering monks, were stopped at the Ataka Barrier in the province of Kaga, a situation from which they were delivered by the ingenuity of Benkei, who beat Yoshitsune to allay the suspicions of the officer in charge (T164, T327) and then pretended to read a subscription-list of the alms the party were supposed to be collecting for charity (S95d.2, T126). This incident is known as *Kwanjinchō* ('The Subscription-List') and is the subject of several plays.

In the end the party found refuge with Yoshitsune's old friend and protector Fujiwara no Hidehira in the far north, but when the old man died his sons sought the favour of Yoritomo by betraying their guest, whom they attacked in his castle of Takadachi (T124, T338). At the last battle of Koromogawa, on 16 May 1189, Yoshitsune's few remaining retainers were overwhelmed by an attacking force of 30,000 men; after a heroic resistance (S4a.1) several of them performed *seppuku*, and Benkei died at his post, riddled with arrows. Yoshitsune himself cheated his treacherous assailants by suicide, taking with him his faithful wife and two infant children; his head was cut off and sent to his relentless brother at Kamakura. Yoritomo however, with cynical inconsistency, was enraged on receiving the news, and beheaded every member of the delegation who brought him the head. In the following year his men marched north under Hatakeyama Shigetada (T268), and wiped out the domain of Hidehira's unworthy sons.

(b) THE GREAT HUNTING-PARTY AND THE SOGA BROTHERS' REVENGE

In 1177 a certain Kudō Suketsune murdered his relative Sukeyasu, a famous wrestler and father of two sons, then aged five and three. Their mother remarried, her new husband being Soga Sukenobu, whose family name was conferred on the boys. Throughout their short lives the brothers trained and planned to take revenge on Suketsune, who had meanwhile achieved a high place in the entourage of Yoritomo. They had to wait till 1193, when they saw their opportunity in a great hunting-party held by the latter on Suso moor at the base of Mount Fuji (T71). With the assistance of two girls, Tora-gozen and Tegoshi no Shōshō (T125 Fig.24, T328), they found their way to Suketsune's tent on a night of pouring rain (S8.7, S74.61), and slew him (T132, T304). But the alarm was given, and after a desperate fight (T35, T103, T104, T159, T269, T349) Jurō, the elder, was killed by Nitta Tadatsune, while Gorō, the younger brother, trying to reach Yoritomo himself, was tripped by Gorō Maru, the latter's bodyguard, captured, and sentenced to be beheaded with a blunt sword.

Two other remarkable adventures befell Tadatsune during the same hunting-party. A monstrous wild boar was roused by the beaters, whom it tossed in all directions as it charged straight at Yoritomo. Without hesitation Tadatsune placed himself directly in its path, leaped on its back, and killed it with his dirk (T72, T73, T99, T200). Later, in company with some friends, he penetrated into the interior of Mount Fuji through a subterranean cavern, and there met the goddess of the mountain, accompanied by her dragon (T143). His companions were overcome, but Tadatsune held a conversation with her, and she congratulated him on his valour. This latter incident is sometimes dated to 1203.

Fig.21. *Triptych:* Yoshitsune defending the Horikawa palace. 1851–2. T267.

Fig.22. *Triptych:* The Taira ghosts preparing to attack Yoshitsune. 1851–2. T266.

Fig.23. *Triptych:* Tadanobu resisting arrest. 1855. T321.

(c) ASAHINA SABURŌ THE STRONG MAN

Asahina Saburō Yoshihide, a man of enormous strength, was the son of Wada Yoshimori who, though a Taira by birth, had been prominent in the Minamoto ranks throughout the war. His mother is said to have been Tomoye-gozen, the warrior-mistress of Kiso Yoshinaka (see p.22) whom Yoshimori had captured after the battle of Awadzu, but chronological difficulties make this attractive story improbable. Yoshihide distinguished himself by fighting a couple of sea-monsters resembling crocodiles which appeared at Kotsubo-no-hama near Kamakura, under the eyes of the Shōgun Yori-iye (T119, T218). He later took part with his father in the revolt of Idzumi Chikahira against the Hōjō in 1213, and when Yoshimori attacked the palace of Hōjō Yoshitoki, it was Asahina who broke down the great gate (T281, T342). Hōjō reinforcements arrived, however, and Yoshimori and two of his sons perished. Asahina escaped, and is said to have spent some years travelling in outlandish places (T31).

Fig.24. *Triptych:* The Soga brothers and Tegoshi no Shōshō. *c.*1842–3. T125.

XI. The Tragedy of Kesa-gozen

Kesa-gozen was the faithful young wife of Watanabe Wataru, a palace guard; she was a paragon of virtue and beauty, but unfortunately attracted the amorous attention of her cousin Yendō Musha Moritō, then (*c.*1140) a youth of eighteen. She rejected his advances, and even threats (T129), but eventually he became so pressing that she decided, her honour being at stake, to bring matters to a conclusion. She therefore pretended to agree to his proposals, stipulating, however, that he must first kill her husband. Wataru was due for promotion, and that evening, in honour of the occasion, Kesa made him a special feast, ensuring that he had plenty to drink so that he soon felt drowsy and went to bed. Kesa then cut off her long hair and tied up what remained in male fashion (S20.15); she then lay down in the darkness in a small room she had pointed out to Moritō as her husband's usual sleeping-place. At midnight he arrived, entered the little room, felt about, and soon found the apparently sleeping figure. With a quick stroke he severed the head, stowed it in his ample sleeve, and made off. It was not till the next morning that he looked at the head and realized what he had done, though in some accounts he held it up in the moonlight immediately on coming out of Wataru's house (S1e.6, S24.2, S46.44). Horror-struck, he went straight to Wataru, confessed his terrible crime, and offered his neck to the bereaved husband's sword. But the latter merely said, 'My only wish now is to pray for the dead. Do not trouble me with thoughts of vengeance, only get out of my sight.'

The wretched Moritō shaved his head and became a monk. For three years he attempted to expiate his crime by the harshest austerities, standing under the icy Nachi waterfall in winter, his endurance strengthened by Fudō ('the immovable') and his two acolytes Seitaka and Kongara (S1e.14, S93.4, T253). On becoming a priest he took the name of Mongaku Shōnin, and spent the rest of his long life in pilgrimages and the collection of money for the restoration of temples and other charitable causes (S15.6). His bold and fearless reproof of all kinds of evil and corruption, even in the highest circles, made him rather less than popular, and he died in exile on the island of Sado soon after 1200.

XII. The Wars of the Nitta and the Kusunoki

The next series of episodes that we find extensively illustrated in Kuniyoshi's prints arose from the division of the Empire under a Northern and a Southern Court early in the fourteenth century. This began with the two sons of the Emperor Go-Saga (reigned 1242–6). The elder became Emperor on his father's abdication, but the younger was Go-Saga's favourite, and in 1259 he forced Go-Fukakusa to abdicate, and Kameyama was enthroned in his stead. (In medieval

Japan a retired Emperor often wielded more power than the one actually on the throne.) For a time the two lines alternated, the succession being largely regulated by the regents (*shikken*) of the Hōjō family, till the Emperor Go-Daigō of the Southern line felt himself strong enough to defy the Hōjō, whose cruelty and extravagance had made them unpopular. But his plans became known to Hōjō Takatoki, who defeated the Imperial forces, and sent Go-Daigō into exile on the island of Oki. Kōgon, a scion of the Northern branch, was elevated in his stead.

But there was much sympathy and support for the exiled Emperor, and Nitta Yoshisada, formerly an officer under the Hōjō, was persuaded by Go-Daigō's son, Prince Morinaga (popularly known as Ōto-no-miya, or 'prince of the great pagoda'), to espouse his father's cause. Yoshisada accordingly led an army against Kamakura, the Hōjō capital, and, having secured a calm passage for his ships by the sacrifice of his sword to the sea-gods (S73.4, T142), took the city and burnt it on 22 May 1333. Hōjō Takatoki together with his family and followers to the number of over 200 committed suicide in the Tōshōji temple. Go-Daigō returned from exile; the famous warriors Ashikaga Taka-uji and Kusunoki Masashige joined Yoshisada in supporting him; Kōgon abdicated; and the returned Emperor entered the capital in triumph.

But due to his extravagance and favouring of the courtiers at the expense of the military, the Emperor's popularity melted away, so that in 1335 Ashikaga Taka-uji rebelled, and his brother Tadayoshi (S22.4), who held Prince Morinaga in captivity, caused his prisoner to be murdered by Fuchibe Yoshihiro (S1c.5, S16.5, S74.38). The Prince put up a stout fight, and even bit off the point of the assassin's sword in the struggle, but was dispatched with a dagger. Go-Daigō sent Nitta Yoshisada against the Ashikaga rebels, but his army was destroyed, and Go-Daigō fled when the Ashikaga entered the capital. Gathering a fresh army, however, Yoshisada managed to drive them out again, and Ashikaga Taka-uji withdrew for a time to Kyūshū. He there assembled an enormous host, and on 4 July 1336 a vast fleet bore them in to attack the heavily outnumbered Imperial troops, led by Nitta Yoshisada (T244) and Kusunoki Masashige, near the modern port of Kobe (T78). The decisive battle of the Minatogawa followed, in which the loyalist forces were annihilated after a heroic struggle (T26, T344); Masashige, wounded in eleven places, performed *seppuku*, and Yoshisada fled to Echizen, where he died in battle three years later.

Supreme power was now in the hands of the Ashikaga, but the legitimate Emperors of the Southern line still had their loyal adherents. Kusunoki Masatsura, son of Masashige, marched out a small force to meet the Ashikaga host under Kō no Moronao (T79), which Taka-uji hoped would obliterate the Southern branch and its supporters. After some brilliant preliminary successes (T34, T105, T333), Masatsura found himself surrounded by overwhelming numbers, and at the battle of Shijō-nawate in the province of Kawachi in 1348 the Kusunoki died to a man under a pitiless hail of arrows (T271, T346, T347). There still remained Nitta Yoshioki, the second son of Yoshisada, to maintain the loyalist cause. In 1352 he drove Ashikaga Moto-uji from Kamakura, but the city was recovered by Taka-uji; and Yoshioki, whose forces were badly thinned by desertions, was captured and put to death. One account says that he was executed by drowning, whilst another makes a renegade betray him into entering a boat at the Yaguchi crossing in the province of Musashi, not far from modern Tokyo. But the boat was holed and began to fill with water, while volleys of arrows were fired at Yoshioki by the Ashikaga troops in ambush on the river-bank (S28.51, S44.3). Yoshioki contrived to perform *seppuku* in the boat before it sank, thus completing the last tragic act in the loyalists' patriotic struggle. The Ashikaga and, later, the Tokugawa Shōguns wielded supreme power for the next 500 years, and it was not till 1868 that the last Shōgun abdicated, and the Imperial power was restored in the Emperor Meiji.

XIII. The Sixteenth and Seventeenth Centuries

The sixteenth century in Japanese history is often known as *Sengoku*, 'the country at war', which describes it pretty accurately. The Ashikaga shōgunate was crumbling, power-hungry war-lords were fighting each other in the provinces, and the unfortunate peasantry were suffering under appalling conditions in consequence. In sixteenth-century Japan, as in Homeric Greece, *quicquid delirant reges plectuntur Achivi*.

Among these often petty squabbles one has been singled out by writers, dramatists, and painters for special attention. This was a local war of some ten years' duration (1553–63) fought in an area called Kawanakajima ('island between the rivers', sc. the Saigawa and the Chikumagawa) in the northern part of the province of Shinano (Fig. 25). The protagonists were two doughty warrior-monks, Takeda Shingen of Kai and Uyesugi Kenshin of Echigo. Many engagements were fought between them with indecisive results, both being skilled strategists, but the favourite episodes for illustration are: firstly, the irruption of Kenshin into Shingen's camp, where they fought for a while face to face, Shingen, who had been taken by surprise, defending himself with his war-fan (T162, T325 Fig. 26, T332); secondly, another face-to-face encounter either in the river or on the river-bank (T160, T165, T175, T345); and thirdly, the prowess (T161, T247, T259) and last stand (T190, T313) of Shingen's one-eyed general Yamamoto Kansuke, when, withdrawing with an exhausted remnant of his troops to a little hill, they were mown down by the Uyesugi musketeers, on 12 October 1561. Takeda Shingen seems to have been a pioneer of the strategic use of gunpowder (T246 Fig. 27), which had been introduced into Japan by the Portuguese in 1542, and during the sixteenth-century wars we find on the one hand the undaunted but unavailing courage of the old-style warrior against the new weapon (S62.36, S63.7), and on the other considerable sophistication in its use (S63.9). Kenshin, not to be outdone, had 'Three Master-Gunners' and a highly trained body of musketeers (S63.18, T190). The Japanese have always been quick learners.

The later sixteenth century is dominated by the figures of Oda Nobunaga (Harunaga in the prints) and Toyotomi Hideyoshi, who between them succeeded in pacifying the country. Most of the important characters in the wars of this period appear (with altered names) in S62, but outside this series Kuniyoshi has portrayed Imagawa Yoshimoto, whom Nobunaga crushed in 1560 (S76.7, S93.2), and Akechi Mitsuharu who seconded his cousin Mitsuhide in the treacherous killing of Nobunaga at the Honnōji temple in 1582, only to be defeated by Hideyoshi's men at Uchide-hama in the same year, after which he took his own life (T206). *Hawley* provides a full range of illustrations of the wars of Nobunaga and Hideyoshi.

Having completed the pacification of the country and assumed the high-sounding title of Taikō ('great lord'), Hideyoshi launched an invasion of the mainland in 1592, the first since that of the almost legendary Empress Jingō (see p. 17). The Japanese were at first uniformly successful, but the King of Korea obtained support and reinforcements from the Ming Emperor, and the tide turned against them; one of Hideyoshi's last acts (1598) was to recall the expedition. The chief commander in Korea was Katō Kiyomasa (Fujiwara no Masakiyo or Watōnai on the prints), and the feature of the campaign that particularly caught the Japanese imagination was the appearance of hungry tigers about his winter encampments. A number of Japanese soldiers were carried off by these famished beasts, and a great hunt organized by Katō Kiyomasa, in which many tigers were accounted for (T183, T317), is more vividly remembered than his barren victories over the Chinese and Koreans. In popular representations, and especially in Kuniyoshi's prints, a deliberate ambiguity is often introduced between Katō Kiyomasa and Takeshiuchi-no-sukune, the commander-in-chief of

Fig. 25. *Triptych:* The battle of Kawanakajima. 1852. T284.

Fig. 26. *Triptych:* Kenshin attacking Shingen at Kawanakajima. 1855. T325.

Fig. 27. *Triptych:* Shingen discharges his big gun. 1849–52. T246.

the Empress Jingō's expedition; the characteristic helmet with long backward-sloping crown, the *mon* of a broad ring, and the long spear with a single jutting blade below the main point (the corresponding blade on the other side is said to have been bitten off by a tiger) are common to both in the popular tradition (S8.5, T145, T234).

The last historical figure to be given full mythological treatment is the swordsman-poet-painter-craftsman Miyamoto Musashi (1583–1647). The son of a noted master of fence, he inherited his father's skill, to which he added from his experiences against other swordsmen. Finally he evolved a completely original style, the *nitō-ryū*, or two-sword style, using the long *katana* in the right, and the short *wakizashi* in the left hand (S53.6), in much the same way as his contemporaries in western Europe were using the rapier and *main-gauche* dagger. *Dening* gives a full account of his life and adventures, and his own *A Book of Five Rings*, admirably translated and edited by Mr Victor Harris of the British Museum (London, 1974), lays before us his precepts and philosophy (it also includes reproductions of S4b.3, S53.6, and T33). In popular tradition he carried out a vendetta against Sasaki Ganryū, who had waylaid and murdered his father; the final encounter took place on the sea-shore, and Musashi killed his man, though only using wooden swords against Ganryū's steel (S89.5, T335). This seems to be founded on fact, but there are also tales of Musashi's combats with a whale (T208), a pack of wolves (T358), a monstrous bat (S74.68), a *tengu* (S1f.4), and a huge lizard (S4b.3), which must be taken *cum grano*.

XIV. *Chūshingura*, 'The Treasury of Loyal Retainers'

The incidents on which this most celebrated and popular of all Japanese stories of 'fidelity in revenge' is based took place in the years 1700–3. The tale has often been told, first and, perhaps, best by Mitford as the first of his *Tales of Old Japan*. He gives the historical account; but the story was quickly adapted and embroidered for dramatic performance by the great playwright Chikamatsu Monzayemon and later (1748) by Takeda Idzumo, whose version in eleven acts is that most frequently illustrated. This, or something very like it, is the basis of *Dickins*, which is thus a better companion to the prints than *Mitford*. It was a Japanese convention, as we have seen, that when comparatively recent events became the subject of plays or popular prints, the names of the characters should be slightly altered, and the action moved back into an earlier period. Thus in the *Chūshingura* drama the events are supposed to take place in the fourteenth century; the first act (T248 Fig.28) involves the identification of the helmet of Nitta Yoshisada (see p.27), and the villain, actually Kira Kōdzuke no Suke Yoshinaka, becomes the Ashikaga general Kō no Moronao.

In barest outline the story is as follows, using the stage names, as they are the ones found on the prints, with the historical names in parentheses. There was a quarrel in the palace between a young nobleman, Yenya (Asano Takumi-no-kami), and an older one, Kō no Moronao (Kira Kōdzuke no Suke), in which the former drew his dirk and wounded the latter in the forehead. For this heinous offence he was condemned to perform *seppuku*. His forty-seven retainers automatically became *rōnin*, and under the leadership of Ōboshi Yuranosuke (Ōishi Kuranosuke) solemnly vowed revenge (T273). They patiently bided their time, secretly making themselves suits of armour, and engaging in various occupations that might make them familiar with the layout of Moronao's mansion (S58.2). Yuranosuke appeared to give himself up to a life of extravagant dissipation, and thus their enemy was thrown completely off his guard. They chose a night in the depth of winter for their attack, scaling the outer walls with rope-ladders (T13, T276) and taking Moronao's retainers by surprise. There was some brisk fighting in the garden (T12, T80, T249) and adjacent buildings where Moronao was hidden (T285), but at length he was extracted and invited to perform *seppuku* as a nobleman should (T260, T272); when he declined, Yuranosuke cut off his head without further ceremony. Dawn was breaking as the forty-seven comrades crossed Ryōgoku bridge (T14, T15, T209). Arriving at the temple Sengakuji (T210) they washed the head (T211), burnt incense (T186), and laid it on their lord's tomb (T81). All then gave themselves up, and all duly performed *seppuku*. They were buried in a ring round their master, and incense is still burnt and fresh flowers placed on their graves. 'A terrible picture of fierce heroism which it is impossible not to admire', as Mitford comments, and the continuing admiration is attested by the very large number of prints designed by Kuniyoshi throughout his career to illustrate it: nineteen triptychs and twelve series.

XV. The *Hakkenden* and Other Popular Fiction

Not unnaturally, many Japanese works of popular fiction partook of the qualities of the favourite historical stories, and were illustrated in the same manner. The greatest purveyor of such fiction was Bakin, 1767–1848 (*Papinot*, p.345), and the most famous and popular of all the 142 novels with which he is credited is the *Hakkenden*, or 'Story of Eight Dogs', published in 106 small volumes between 1814 and 1841. The enormous length of the *Hakkenden* and its complexity of plot preclude even a summary in a book of this kind. The framework of the story, however, is that the Lord of Satomi vowed to give his daughter Fuse-hime in marriage to whoever brought him the head of his enemy. The head was brought by a dog; the father was as good as his word; and Fuse-hime became the mother of eight sons, all of whom have Inu ('dog') as the first element in their names (see Index), and who represent the Eight Cardinal Virtues. The body of the novel is occupied by an account of their fantastic adventures (Fig.29). One of the favourite episodes is Inudzuka Shino's desperate defence on the Hōryūkaku roof against Inukai Kempachi, the chief of police, and his men (S4a.3/4, S5.1/2, S95f.3, T41). Needless to say, the *Hakkenden* provided material for a number of popular plays.

Some other favourite stories for illustration are supposed to rest on an at least semi-historical basis. Such is the story of the Lonely House of Adachi-ga-hara, inhabited by a terrible hag who preyed on travellers, especially young women, till one of them was saved by the intervention of Kwannon (see Index, s.v. Hitotsuya; also *Robinson 1961*, pp.21, 22). Most of the others are revenge stories of one kind and another, often culminating in a fight in which the villain is worsted, often before an audience. Typical examples are the Igagoye revenge story (T29, T106, T250, T290), the revenge of the daughters (or widow and daughter) of Yoshioka Ichimisai on Kyōgoku Takumi (T131, T137, T170), and the revenge of Yasubei, one of the Forty-Seven *Rōnin* (T148, T213 Fig.30). The first of these is fully told by Mitford as 'Kazuma's Revenge'.

Fig.28. *Triptych:* First act of the *Chūshingura* drama. 1849–52. T248.

Fig.29. Inuyama Dōsetsu amid flames. 1852–3. S74.4.

Fig.30. *Triptych:* The revenge of Horiguchi Yasubei. *c.*1847–50. T213.

PLATES

Plate 1. Inukai Kempachi, one of the eight heroes of the *Hakkenden*. c.1830. S4a.4.

Plate 2. Kane-jo stops the runaway temple-horse. *c.* 1825–30. SIa.5.

Plate 3. The *Suikoden* hero Rōshi Yensei. *c*.1827–30. S2.50.

Plate 4. Abe no Yasuchika exorcizing the fox-woman Tamamo-no-maye. *c*.1834–5. Sic. 1.

Plate 5. Fuse-hime saving the child Masashi from a thunderbolt. *c.*1836. S4c.3.

Plate 6. Inudzuka Shino fighting on the Hōryūkaku roof. *c*.1835. S5.1.

Plate 7. Kōmei conjuring the wind. *c.*1836. S10.1.

Plate 8. Struggle between Yoshinaka and Tomonori at Naminoyo. *c.* 1836. S9.2.

Plate 9. Tokiwa-gozen with her three children in the snow. *c*.1841–2. S20.23.

Plate 10. Nichiren and the Seven-faced Divinity. *c.* 1835–6. S6.6.

Plate 11. Appearance of a gourd-plant at the birth of Prince Shōtoku. *c.*1840. S14.1.

Plate 12. Kidō Maru learning magic from the *tengu*. *c.*1843. S1f.1.

Plate 13. Tomomori and the anchor with which he drowned himself. *c.*1845. S1f.7.

Plate 14. The Soga brothers at the tent of Kudō Suketsune. *c.*1836. S8.7.

Plate 15. Sasaki Takatsuna commandeering a farmer's horse. *c.*1840. S15.11.

Plate 16. Uneme exorcizing the monstrous serpent from the lake. *c.*1842–3. S23.23.

列猛傳
源三位頼政

Plate 17. Yorimasa shooting at the monster *Nuye*. *c*.1845. S48.6.

Plate 18. Taira no Koremochi and the demon-woman. *c*.1843. S28.7.

Plate 19. Tametomo on the beach at Ōshima. *c*.1845. S49.3.

Plate 20. Masakiyo blown up by a land-mine at Kawanakajima. *c.*1848–9. S63.9.

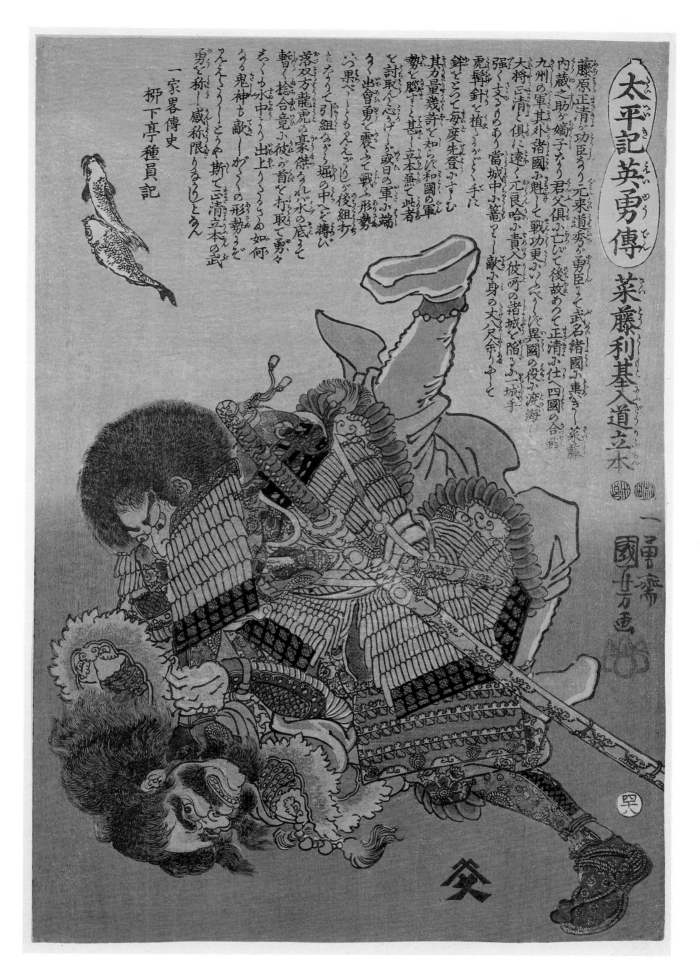

Plate 21. Saitō Toshimoto and a Chinese general struggling under water. *c.*1848–9. S62.31.

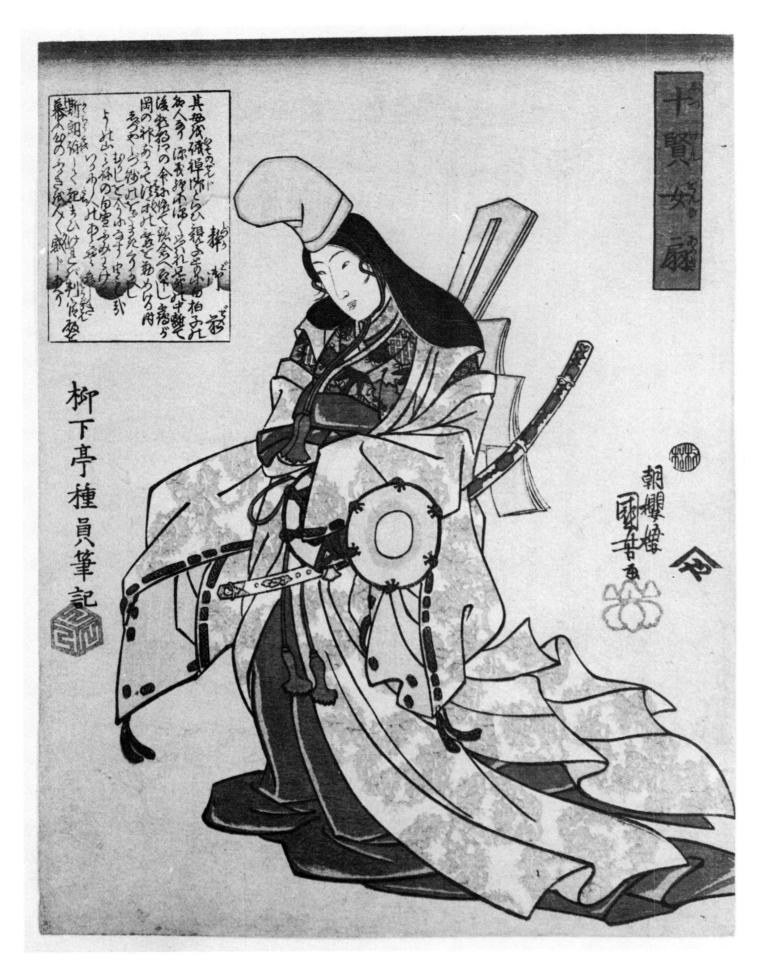

Plate 22. Shidzuka-gozen in the dancing dress of a *shirabyōshi*. *c*.1843. S25.3.

Plate 23. The *Hakkenden* hero Inukai Kempachi. *c.*1845–6. S37.6.

Plate 24. Oniwaka Maru and the giant carp. *c.*1848. S1f.10.

Plate 25. Yeda Genzō at the defence of the Horikawa palace. 1852. S76.6.

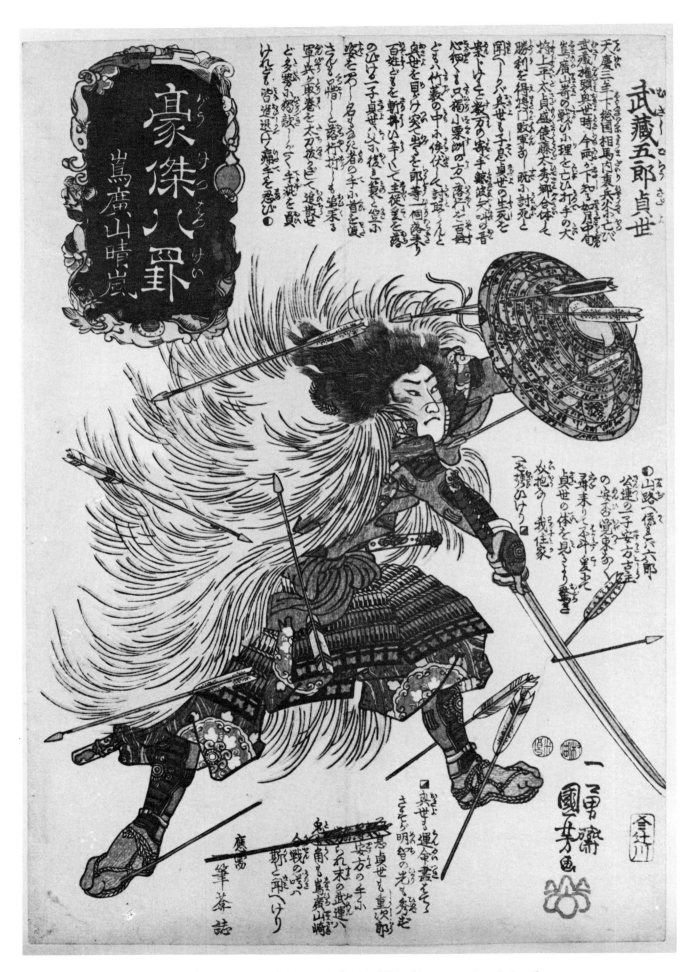

Plate 26. Musashi Gorō Sadayo at the battle of Shimahiro-yama. 1847–8. S52.6.

Plate 27. Death of Shundō Jiroyemon in the moment of revenge. 1847–8. S51.9.

Plate 28. Yamamoto Kansuke wounded to death at Kawanakajima. 1854. S84.2.

Plate 29. Mongaku Shōnin under the waterfall. 1860. S93.4.

Plate 30. Amakasu Ōmi no Kami, a general of the Uyesugi at Kawanakajima. *c.*1845. S34.9.

Plate 31. Kiyo-hime and the bell of Dōjōji. 1855. S87.4.

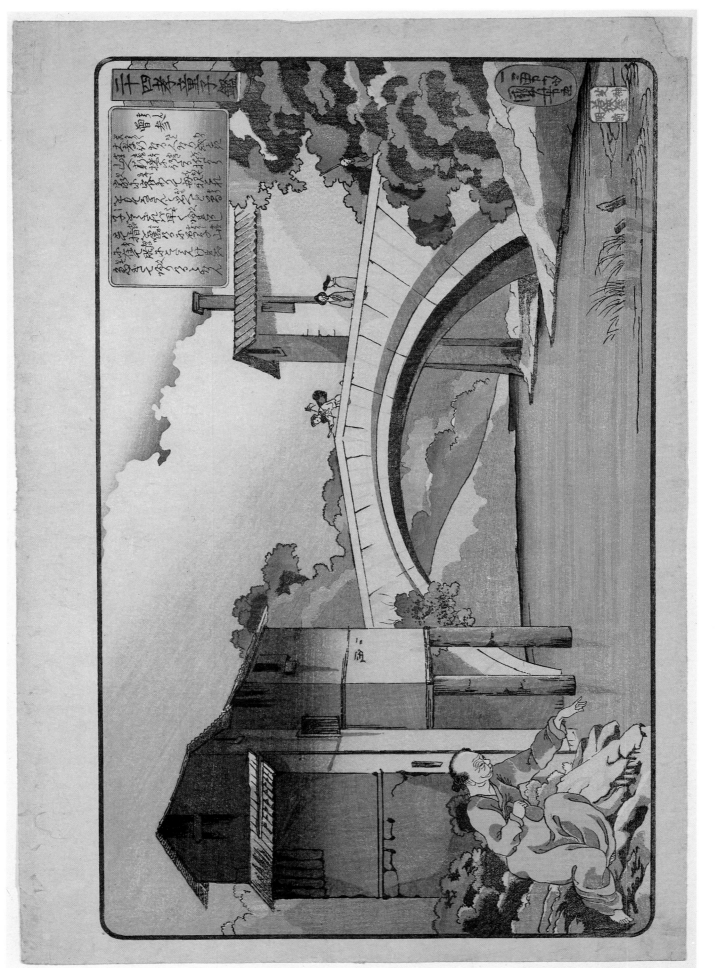

Plate 32. Sōshin returning to help his injured mother. c.1840. S13.4.

Plate 33. Triptych: Sanada Yoichi fighting Matano Gorō at Ishibashiyama. c.1835. T28.

Plate 34. *Triptych*: The Earth-Spider tormenting the sick Raikō. *c.*1820. T4.

Plate 35. *Triptych:* Yorimasa shooting down the monster *Nuye. c.* 1820–5. T7.

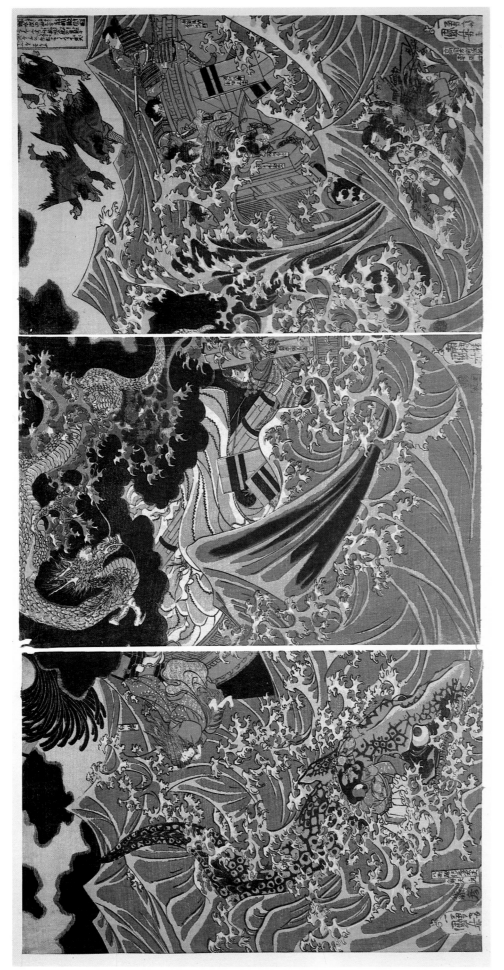

Plate 36. *Triptych: Tametomo's shipwreck. c.*1836. T30.

Plate 37. *Triptych*: The Earth-Spider slain by Raikō's retainers. *c.*1838. T46.

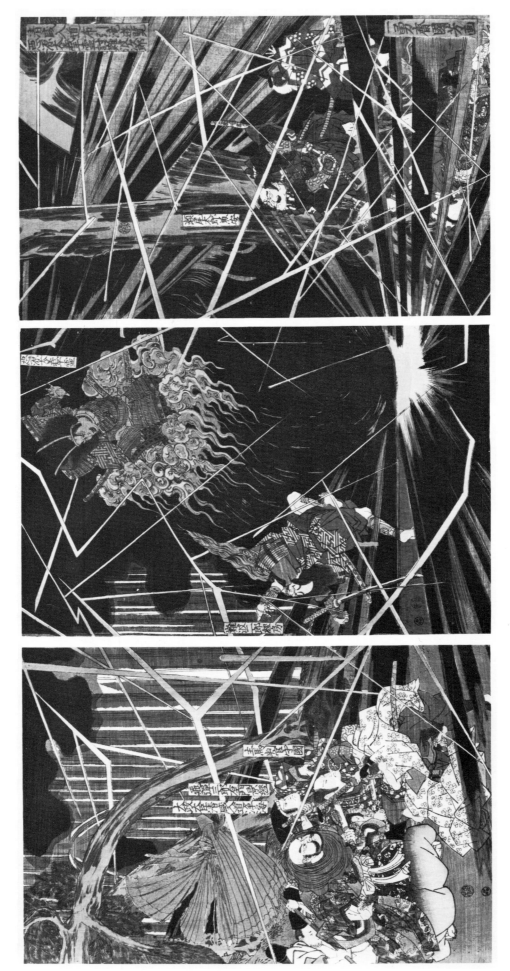

Plate 38. *Triptych*: The ghost of Yoshihira at the Nunobiki waterfall. *c*.1825. T10.

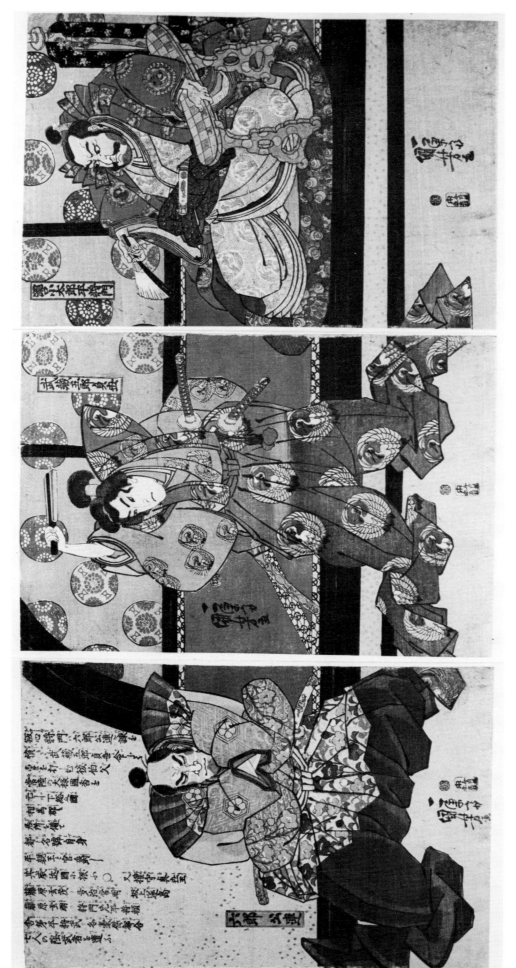

Plate 39. *Triptych:* Sadayo striking Kintsura before Masakado. *c.*1833-4. T23.

Plate 40. *Triptych*: Ushiwaka and Benkei fighting on Gojō bridge. *c*.1839. T47.

Plate 41. *Triptych*: Kiyomori arresting the sunset by incantations. *c.*1842–3. T83.

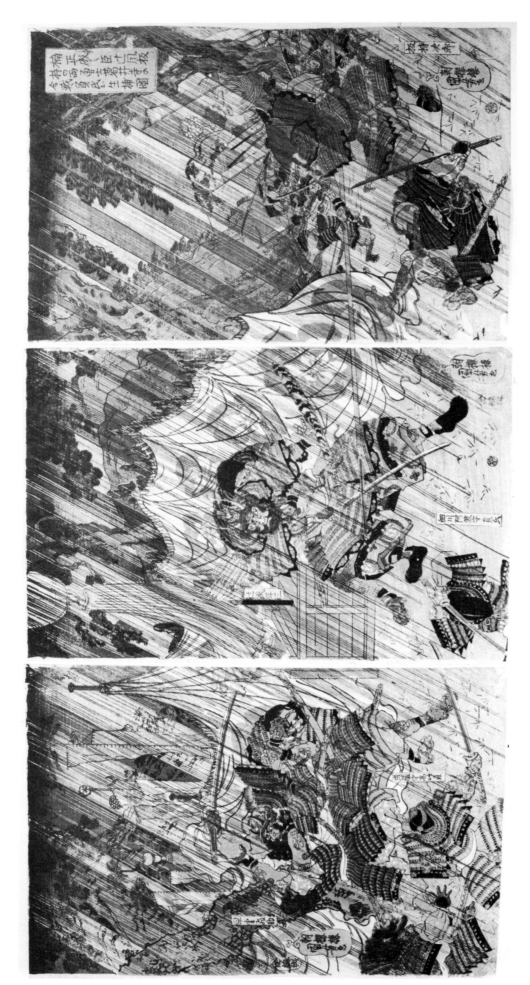

Plate 42. *Triptych*: The battle of Fujiidera in driving rain. *c.* 1836. T34.

Plate 43. *Triptych:* Inudzuka Shino at bay on the Hōryūkaku roof. *c.*1836–7. T41.

Plate 44. *Triptych: The Ashikaga fleet sailing in to attack Nitta. c.*1839–41. T78.

Plate 45. *Triptych*: Ushiwaka visiting Jōruri-hime. *c.*1842–3. T108.

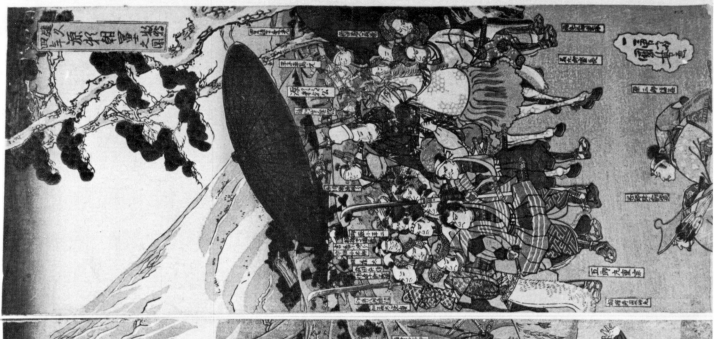

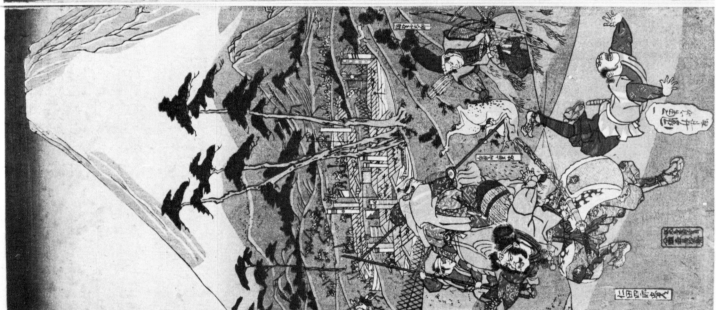

Plate 46. *Triptych*: Tadatsune and the giant boar. *c.*1839–41. T72.

Plate 47. *Triptych:* Tametomo's master-shot. *c.*1844. T140.

Plate 48. *Triptych*: Bridge of boats at the battle of the Nagaragawa. *c.*1842–3. T105.

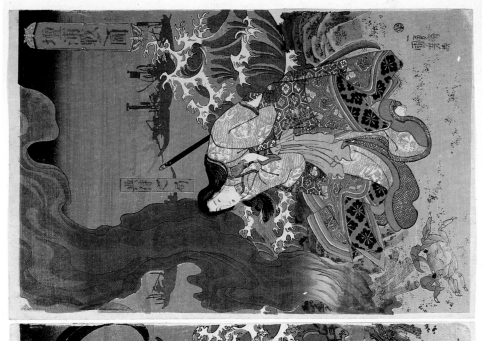

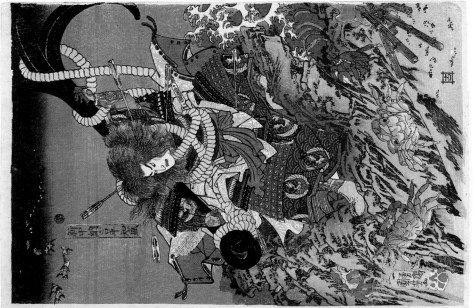

Plate 49. *Triptych*: Death of Tomomori at Dan-no-ura. *c.*1844. T144.

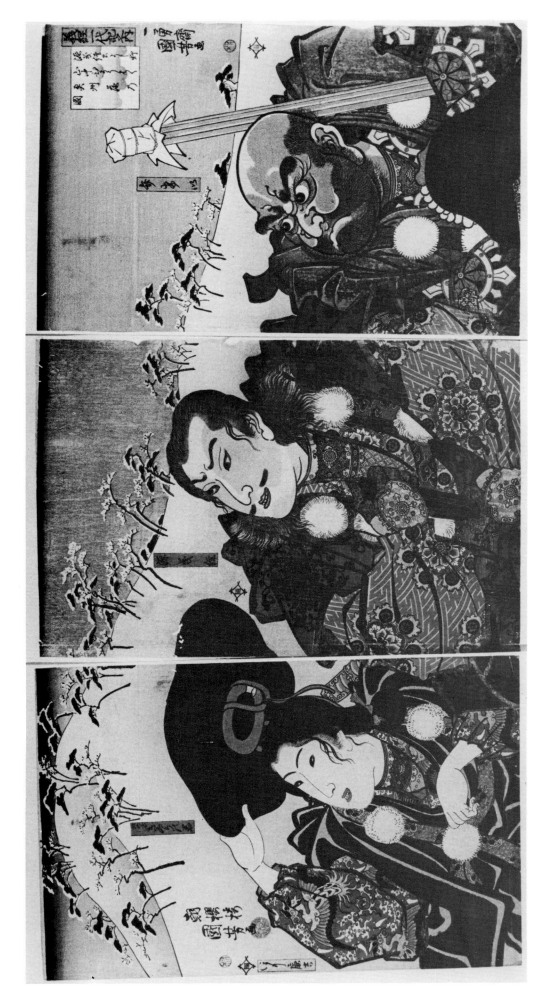

Plate 50. *Triptych*: Yoshitsune, his wife Kita-no-kata, and Benkei in the snow. *c.*1844. T133.

Plate 51. *Triptych*: Takiyasha and her brother Yoshikado learning toad-magic. *c.*1845. T166.

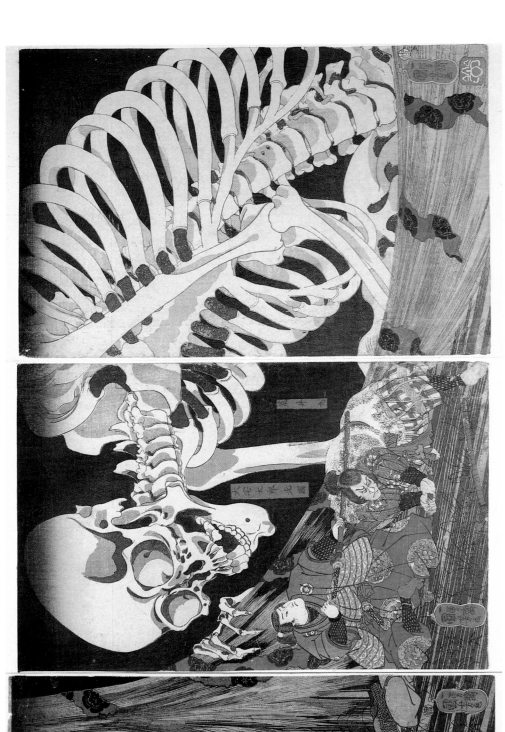

Plate 52. *Triptych*: Takiyasha the witch and the skeleton-spectre. *c.*1844. T138.

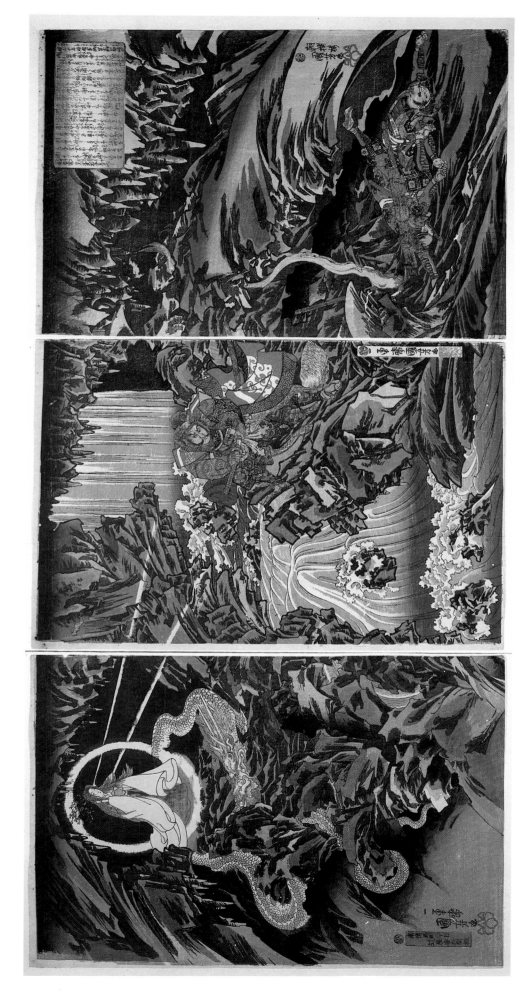

Plate 53. *Triptych: Tadatsune and the goddess of Mount Fuji. c.*1844. T143.

Plate 54. *Triptych*: Oniwaka Maru about to slay the giant carp. *c.*1845. T171.

Plate 55. *Triptych*: Japanese troops attacking a Korean city. *c.*1845. T145.

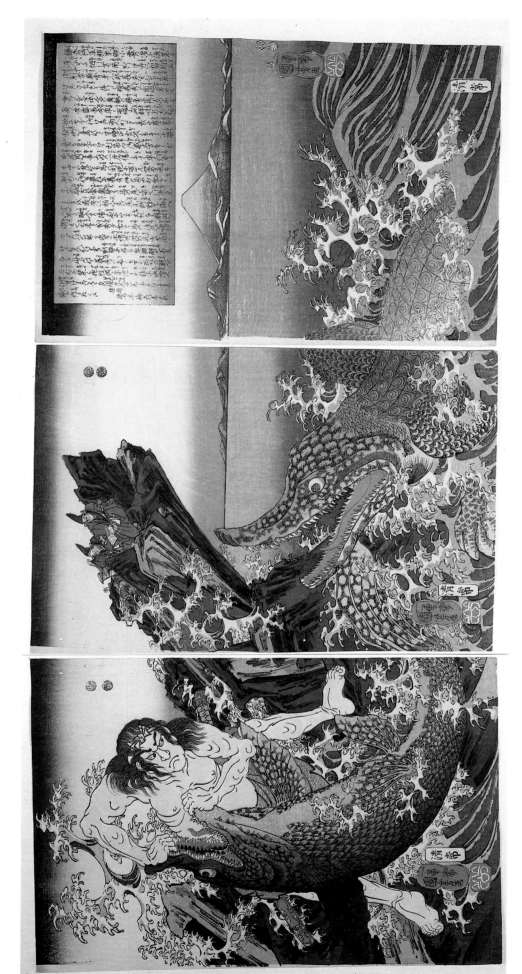

Plate 56. *Triptych:* Asahina Saburō and the crocodiles. 1849. T218.

Plate 57. *Triptych*: Kamei Rokurō and the black bear in the snow. 1849. T215.

Plate 58. *Triptych*: Katō Kiyomasa and the tiger in the snow. *c*.1846. T183.

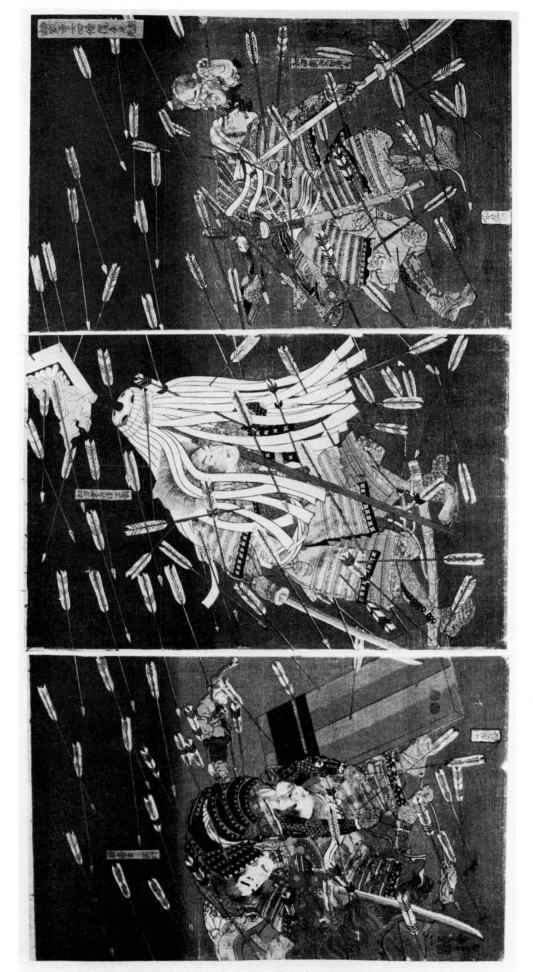

Plate 59. *Triptych*: Last stand of the Kusunoki clan at Shijō-nawate. 1851–2. T271.

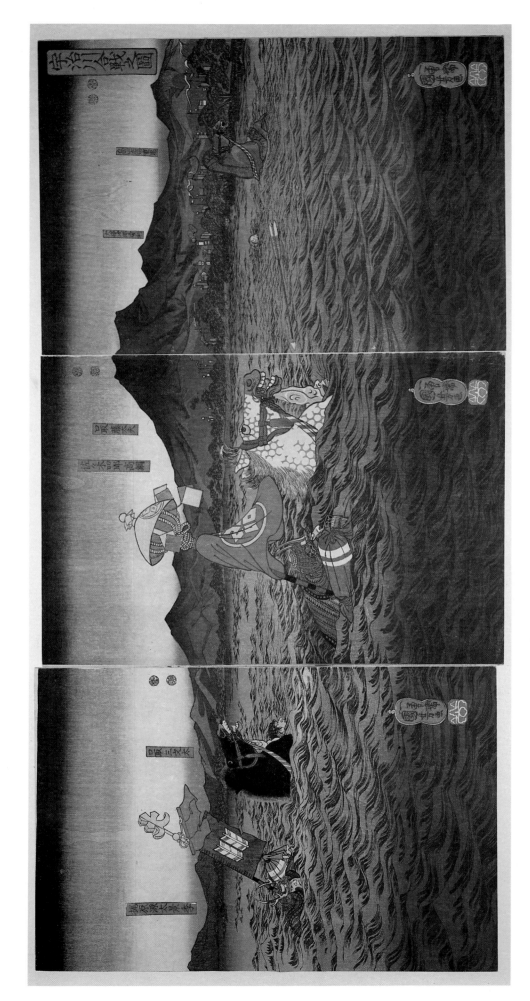

Plate 60. *Triptych*: The rival generals fording the Ujigawa. 1849. T217.

Plate 61. *Triptych:* Gentoku leaping his horse into the gorge of Tan. 1853. T296.

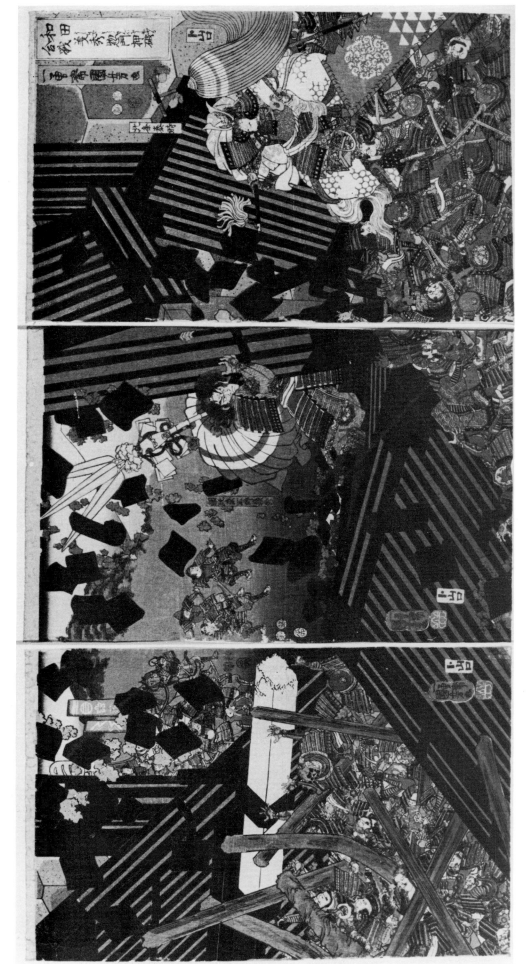

Plate 62. *Triptych*: Asahina Saburō breaking down the gate. 1852. T281.

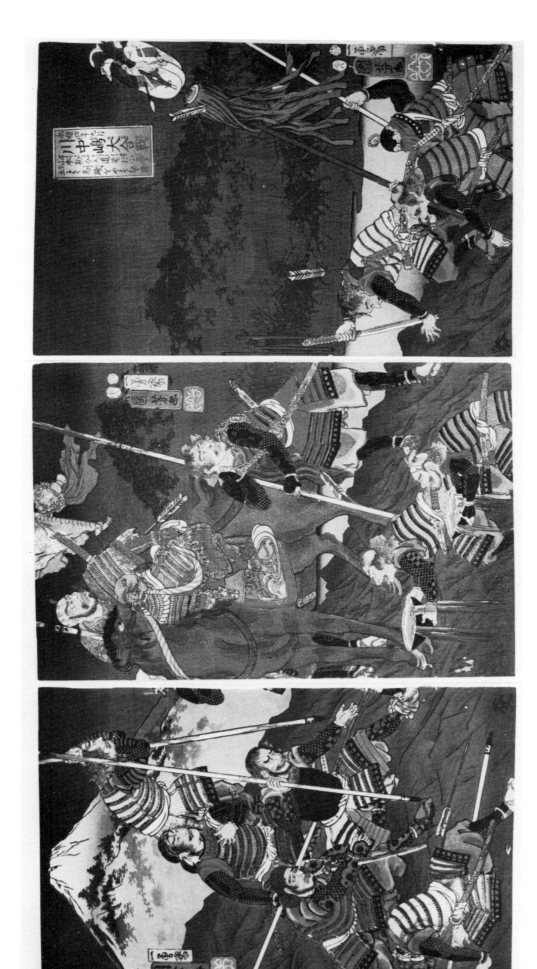

Plate 63. *Triptych:* Yamamoto Kansuke preparing for his last stand. 1854. T313.

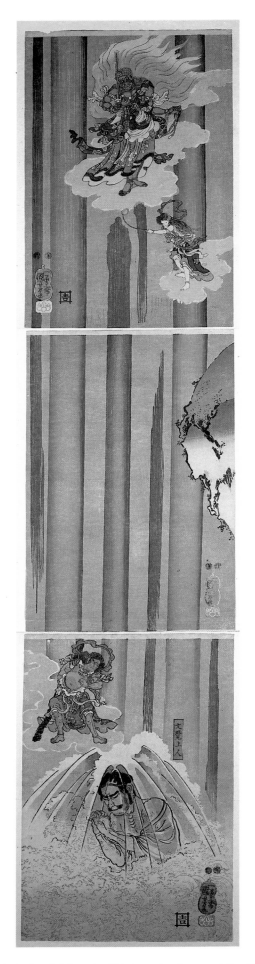

Plate 64. *Vertical triptych:* Mongaku Shōnin under the waterfall. 1851–2. T253.

CATALOGUE

Note on Catalogue Entries in Part I

The series are arranged, so far as possible, in chronological order of publication. At the end of each entry are noted, in abbreviated form, the institutions etc. possessing copies of the print, as follows:

B   Bidwell Collection, Museum of Fine Arts, Springfield, Mass.
Baur   Collections Baur, Geneva.
BM   British Museum, London.
MFA   Museum of Fine Arts, Boston, Mass.
PC   Private collections, auction sales, dealers' stocks, etc.
RSM   Royal Scottish Museum, Edinburgh.
VAM   Victoria and Albert Museum, London.

After this come references to reproductions in the publications listed in the Bibliographical References. If the print is reproduced in this book, as either a Plate or an illustration in the Introduction (Fig.), a reference is included at the beginning of the entry, directly following the Catalogue number, or the subtitle, caption, etc., where one occurs. Other abbreviations used are:

Cens.   Censorship seal.
Eng.   Engraver.
Pr.   Printer.
Pub.   Publisher's seal or mark.

Part I : Single-Sheet Prints in Series

S1

(Untitled) *Ōban*. During the first thirty years of his working life, *c.*1815–45, Kuniyoshi produced a long succession of large and powerful heroic portraits without any series title. The earliest of these clearly look forward to the great *Suikoden* set (S2), and many of the later ones are reminiscent of it. They were evidently not conceived as a series, but issued more or less at random. However, among them are one or two small groups with similar inscription arrangements, as noted below. In some cases his signature and style of 1830–40 are found combined with the post-1842 censors' seals. This is often due to the later reissue of the prints concerned, the blocks having been acquired by a different publisher, and the censors' seals inserted to replace the earlier *kiwame*. Thus we find a number of them with the mark of Nishimura-ya Yohachi combined with *kiwame*, and then the same designs reprinted *c.*1845 with the mark of Idzumi-ya Ichibei and a single censor's seal. On the other hand, where no earlier printing is known, we may suppose that Kuniyoshi kept a number of finished drawings by him ready for a publisher's sudden demand. Such indeed are the two magnificent drawings in the Victoria and Albert Museum (*Robinson 1961*, Pls.84, 85) which are uniform in all respects with nos. S1c.7–9 below, but which were never produced for publication. Various pub. and cens.; *c.*1820–45.

S1a (*c.*1820–30)

1. Ōta Sayemon-dayū Mochisuke (*sic*; *Papinot* and *Edmunds* give Sukenaga), usually known by his later name of Dōkwan, with the maiden offering him a spray of *yamabuki* when he asked to borrow a straw rain-cloak. The *yamabuki* has no seeds (*mino*), and indicated that she had no straw cloak (*mino*) to offer him. Pub. Nishimura-ya Yohachi; cens. *kiwame*; *c.*1815–20.
   VAM; MFA. *Robinson 1961*, Pl.6.

2. Oki Jirō Hiroari killing a huge *tengu* against a black background with swirling flames issuing from the *tengu*'s mouth. Pub. Idzumi-ya Ichibei; cens. *kiwame*; *c.*1820.
   MFA; PC. *Robinson 1961*, Pl.7.
   NOTE. In this and the preceding print Kuniyoshi uses the *gō* of Saihōsha; this is very rare,

S1a. 1

and seems to be confined to his earliest work.

3. The severed head of the Shuten-dōji swooping on the helmet of Raikō. Pub. Idzumi-ya Ichibei; cens. *kiwame*; *c.*1820.
   MFA; B. *Bidwell 1968*, Pl.2; *Riccar 1978*, 49; *Bidwell 1980*, 2.

4. Takeda Katsuchiyo Maru (Shingen in boyhood) making a slash at a wolf. Pub. Kawaguchi-ya Uhei; cens. *kiwame*; *c.*1825–30.
   VAM.

5. (Pl.2) Kane-jo stopping the runaway temple-horse by stepping on its trailing rein, while the incompetent groom grovels on the ground. Pub. Kawaguchi-ya Uhei; cens. *kiwame*; *c.*1825–30.
   PC. *Geneva 1978*, 26.

6. Sasaki Saburō Moritsuna, holding a dirk in his mouth, strangling the fisherman Tōdayū, who has shown him the ford over the Inland Sea. Pub. Kawaguchi-ya Uhei; cens. *kiwame*; *c.*1825–30.
   VAM; PC. *Kruml*, 20.73.

7. Tenjiku Tokubei seated on a giant toad in a magic-making attitude, backed by swirling flames. Pub. Kawaguchi-ya Uhei; cens. *kiwame*; *c.*1825–30.

VAM; MFA; B; PC. *Illing 1978*, 11; *Riccar 1978*, 54; *Bidwell 1980*, 49.

8. Kamigashi-hime thrusting her spear down on an earth-spider, which has emerged from its hole below her to drink from a stream. Pub. Tsuta-ya Kichizō (later edition, Sano-ya Kihei); cens. *kiwame*; *c.*1825–30.
   MFA; B; PC.

9. Saitō Oniwaka Maru (Benkei in boyhood), a dirk held in his teeth, fighting the giant carp. Pub. Tsuta-ya Kichizō; cens. *kiwame*; *c.*1825–30.
   PC. *Illing 1980*, 123.

10. Washi-no-o Saburō, in a close-fitting straw hat, overcoming a huge boar with his bare hands. Pub. Tsuta-ya Kichizō; cens. *kiwame*; *c.*1825–30.
    B; PC. *Düsseldorf 1961*, 10; *Riccar 1978*, 51; *Kruml*, 20.74.

11. Kumagaye Naosada overcoming a black bear in the mountains of Musashi. Pub. Tsuru-ya Kiyemon; cens. *kiwame*; *c.*1825–30.
    MFA; PC. *Kruml*, 22.51.

12. Asahina Saburō shouldering the gate of Hōjō Yoshitoki's palace. Pub. Idzumi-ya Ichibei; cens. *kiwame*; *c.*1825–30.
    PC.

13. Matano no Gorō Kagehisa and Sanada no Yoichi Munesada (*sic*) wrestling at the battle of Ishibashiyama (1180). Pub. Tsuru-ya Kiyemon; cens. *kiwame*; *c.*1825–30.
    MFA.

14. (Frontispiece) Higuchi Jirō (Kanemitsu) on a wooded mountainside struggling with a giant monkey which grips his sword-blade between its teeth. Pub. Tsuta-ya Kichizō; cens. *kiwame*; *c.*1825.
    PC. *Illing 1978*, 10.

15. Matano Kagehisa thrown at wrestling by Kawadzu Sukeyasu; tent drapery above bearing the Kudō *mon*. Pub. Idzumi-ya Ichibei; cens. *kiwame*; *c.*1825.
    MFA.

16. Takiguchi U-toneri Watanabe no Tsuna about to cut off the arm of the demon of Rashōmon, who grasps his hair. Pub. Kawaguchi-ya Uhei; cens. *kiwame*; *c.*1825.
    VAM; MFA.

S1b.1

S1c.4

S1b (1830–3)

1. Musashi-bō Benkei, fully armed, by moonlight, with bats flying; plain background. Pub. Tsuru-ya Kiyemon; cens. *kiwame*; *c*.1832.
   PC.

2. Minamoto no Yoshitsune seated on a camp-stool in full armour, beneath a blossoming plum-tree. Pub. Idzumi-ya Ichibei; cens. *kiwame*; *c*.1833.
   PC.

S1c (1834–5)

1. (Pl.4) Abe no Yasuchika, court robes flying, exorcizing the Nine-tailed Fox, in the form of the lady Tamamo-no-maye, using a mirror in which the reflection of the Fox appears. Pub. Nishimura-ya Yohachi; 1834–5.
   BM; MFA; PC.

2. (Fig.3) Koshibe no Sugaru, amid lightning and flames, captures a *raijū* in the village of Toyora, which he presented to the Emperor Yūryaku. Pub. Nishimura-ya Yohachi (later edition, Idzumi-ya Ichibei); cens. *kiwame*; 1834–5.
   PC.

3. Usui Matagorō slays a giant white monkey in the mountains of Hida, a long stream of black smoke curling up from the monster's mouth. Pub. Nishimura-ya Yohachi; 1834–5.
   BM; MFA; B; PC. *Or.Art*, Spring 1961, p. 25; *Riccar 1978*, 52; *Bidwell 1980*, 42 (Pl.3).

4. The (rather unghostly) ghost of Akugenda Yoshihira executes vengeance with a thunderbolt on his slayer, Namba Jirō. Pub. Nishimura-ya Yohachi; cens. *kiwame*; 1834–5.
   BM; MFA.

5. The death-struggle of Ōto-no-miya with his murderer, Fuchibe Iga no Kami. Pub. Nishimura-ya Yohachi (later edition, Idzumi-ya Ichibei); cens. *kiwame*; 1834–5.
   BM; MFA; PC.

6. Takagi Toranosuke capturing a *kappa* under water in the Tamura river in the province of Sagami. Pub. Kawaguchi-ya Uhei; cens. *kiwame*; 1834–5.
   MFA; PC.

7. Kusunoki Tamon Maru Masatsura at the age of seven, with his companion Chikudō Maru, killing an old badger that took the form of a lay priest, in the palace yard. Pub. Kaga-ya Kichiyemon (later edition, Iba-ya Sensaburō); cens. *kiwame* (later, Watari); 1834–5.
   MFA; PC.

8. Struggle between Matano Gorō Kagehisa and Sanada Yoichi Yoshitada on the shore at Ishibashiyama. Pub. Yamaguchi-ya Tōbei; cens. *kiwame*; 1834–5.
   PC.

9. Idzumo no Imaro killing a sea-monster (*wani*) to avenge his daughter who had been devoured by one; he killed 100 of them altogether. Pub. Yamaguchi-ya Tōbei; cens. *kiwame*; 1834–5.
   MFA; PC.

10. Wada Heita Tanenaga killing a huge python by a waterfall. Pub. Yamaguchi-ya Tōbei; cens. *kiwame*; 1834–5.
    MFA; PC.

11. Hasebe Chōhyōye Nobutsura fighting over fallen foemen at the Taira attack on the Takakura palace, Kyoto (1180), from which he helped Prince Mochihito to escape. Pub. Sano-ya Kihei; cens. *kiwame*; 1834–5.
    PC.

12. Hangami Danjō-no-jō Arakage killing a giant salamander in the Tontagawa river in the province of Idzumo. Pub. Kawaguchi-ya Chōzō; cens. *kiwame*; 1834–5.
    BM; PC.

13. Ariō Maru on the sea-shore, sword in hand, struggling with a giant octopus while on his way to Kikai-jima in search of his exiled master Shunkwan (1177). Pub. Kawaguchi-ya Chōzō; 1834–5.
    BM; PC.

14. Asahina Saburō Yoshihide tugging at the armour of Soga Gorō Tokimune. Pub. Ise-ya Sanjirō; cens. *kiwame*; 1834–5.
    VAM; PC.

15. Taira no Koremochi killing the demon-woman. Pub. etc. not noted (Christie's, September 1971); 1834–5.
    PC.

16. Nagasaki Kangayu-sayemon, riddled with arrows, and a dragon. Pub. etc. not noted; 1834–5.
    B.

S1d.1

S1d (c.1836)

1. Sakata Kwaidō Maru struggling with a huge carp in a waterfall. Pub. Kaga-ya Kichiyemon; cens. *kiwame*; *c*.1836.
   MFA; B; PC. *Boller*, opp. p.138; *Riccar 1978*, 55; *Bidwell 1980*, 22; *Kruml*, 20.70; 21.61.

2. Ono no Komachi praying for rain. Pub. etc. not noted; *c*.1836.
   B.

3. The *Rakan* Nakasaina Sonja seated on a rock, with a dragon emerging from the bowl

he holds. Pub. Kaga-ya Kichiyemon; cens. *kiwame*; *c.*1836.
PC.

S1e (1838–41)

1. Watōnai Sankwan overcoming a tiger under a pine-tree. Pub. Sano-ya Kihei; cens. *kiwame*; *c.*1840.
PC.

2. Nikki Gennosuke with an umbrella in a downpour of rain observes the apparition of a dead man behind a tree, a closed fan in his mouth, whilst at the same time placing his foot on the neck of one of two thunder-beasts which attempt to molest him. Pub. Tsuta-ya Kichizō; cens. *kiwame*; *c.*1840.
PC.

3. Kamada Matahachi killing a monstrous cat in the mountains of Ise province. Pub. Tsuta-ya Kichizō; cens. *kiwame*; *c.*1840.
PC.

S1e.4

4. Keyamura Rokusuke struggling with three *kappa* on the bank of a river in which a fourth *kappa* swims. Pub. Tsuta-ya Kichizō; cens. *kiwame* (later edition, Tanaka); *c.*1836.
PC.

5. Satō Shirō Tadanobu, wearing the armour of Yoshitsune, on the balcony of the Yoshino temple pagoda, amid snow. No pub. visible; *c.*1840.
PC.

6. Yendō Musha Moritō, skirts looped up and sleeves tied back, in the moonlight amid falling maple-leaves, holding up the severed head of Kesa-gozen. Pub. Sōshū-ya Yohei; cens. *kiwame*; *c.*1840.
PC.

7. Kashiwade no Hanoshi in full armour glaring down at the tiger, which clings to the edge of a snowy precipice. Pub. Yamamoto-ya Heikichi (later edition, cens. Mera–Murata); *c.*1840.
MFA; PC.

8. Tomoye-gozen struggling with Musashi Saburozayemon Arikuni on a rock by a waterfall. Pub. Yamamoto-ya Heikichi (later edition, cens. Mera–Murata); *c.*1840.
MFA; PC.

9. Hako-ō Maru (Soga Gorō in boyhood) reading a scroll by a waterfall. Pub. Yebi-Ne; *c.*1840.
VAM.

10. Usui Sadamitsu holding a beam and treading on a wolf. Pub. Yebi-Ne; *c.*1840.
VAM.

11. Kwaidō Maru overcoming a wild boar with a huge axe; plain background, and poem above. Pub. Jōshū-ya Kinzō; *c.*1840.
PC.

12. Taira no Tadamori and the oil-thief. Pub. etc. not noted; *c.*1840.
B.

13. Momotarō with the monkey and the pheasant, the Precious Things before him; the dog offers *sake*. Pub. etc. not noted; *c.*1840.
MFA.

14. Mongaku Shōnin under the waterfall. Pub. Maru-ya Seijirō; cens. *kiwame*; *c.*1840.
MFA (key-block pull only).

S1f (1842–50)

1. (Pl.12) Kidō Maru seated cross-legged on the head of a giant python, his hands clasped and two wrapped pine-sprigs (*aomatsuba*) in his mouth; into the python's head a dirk has been driven, round which smaller snakes are writhing; four *tengu* watch from below. Pub. Tsuta-ya Kichizō; cens. Tanaka (earlier edition, *kiwame*); *c.*1843 (design *c.*1840).
MFA; PC.

2. The *ama* Tamatori, who had penetrated the Dragon King's palace under the sea to recover the sacred jewel, plunging through the waves, dirk in hand, hotly pursued by a dragon and various fish. Pub. Tsuta-ya Kichizō; cens. Tanaka (earlier edition, *kiwame*); *c.*1843 (design *c.*1840).
MFA; PC. *Inouye*, Pl.109; *UMS*, 10; *Suzuki–Oka*, 47.

3. Musashi-bō Benkei overcome by Onzōshi Ushiwaka Maru on Gojō bridge by moonlight. Pub. Tsuta-ya Kichizō; cens. Tanaka; *c.*1843.
PC.

4. Miyamoto Musashi cuts the wing from a *tengu*-like creature (called *bake-yamabushi*, 'ghostly warrior-monk', in the caption) in the mountains. Pub. Jō-Yasu; cens. Fu; *c.*1843 (design *c.*1835).
PC.

5. Raigō Ajari, watched with apprehension by

Ōye no Kunifusa-kyō, destroying the Buddhist scrolls at Miidera temple. Pub. Jō-Yasu; cens. Fu; *c.*1843 (design *c.*1835).
RSM; PC.

6. Matano Gorō Kagehisa and Sanada Yoichi Yoshisada struggling on the rocks by a waterfall at Ishibashiyama. Pub. Maru-ya Seijirō; cens. Muramatsu; *c.*1845 (design *c.*1840).
PC.

7. (Pl.13) Shinchūnagon Tomomori clasping the great anchor, whose rope entwines him, arrows sticking in his armour. Pub. Yamashiro-ya Heisuke(?); cens. Mura; eng. Jirokatsu (?—last character damaged); *c.*1845.
PC.

S1f.8

8. Wada Heita Tanenaga, dirk in hand, struggling with a huge python; plain brown background. Pub. Yamashiro-ya Heisuke; cens. Mura; *c.*1845.
PC.

9. The *Suikoden* hero Kokusempū Riki, with flying hair and beard, armed with two large axes. Pub. Daikoku-ya Heikichi; cens. Hama; *c.*1845.
PC.

10. (Pl.24) Oniwaka Maru (Benkei in boyhood) raising his dirk to kill the giant carp of Ko-ike ('ancient lake'). Pub. Yamamoto-ya Heikichi; cens. Mera–Murata; *c.*1848 (design *c.*1840).
PC.

11. Onzōshi Ushiwaka Maru (Yoshitsune in boyhood) prostrating himself before the *tengu* king, Sōjō-bō, in the woods of Kuramayama, his retainer Kisanda in the background. Pub.

Yamamoto-ya Heikichi; cens. Mera–Murata; *c.* 1848 (design *c.* 1840).

MFA.

12. Shimamura Danjō Takanori in full armour pierced with arrows and leaning on his *naginata* as he rides over the waves on the backs of a number of large crabs. Pub. Maru-ya Seiyemon; cens. Muramatsu; *c.* 1845 (design *c.* 1840).

PC. *Illing 1980*, 110.

13. Sugawara no Michizane standing in full court robes, 'from a picture by Ise Sadabumi'. This painter does not appear in the standard reference books, and may perhaps be a legendary contemporary of Michizane. No pub. visible; cens. Tanaka; *c.* 1845.

PC.

The following have also been noted, but without particulars, from sale catalogues etc.

14. Shirafuji Hikoshichirō.

15. Yamanaka Dankurō.

16. Tegoshi no Shōshō.

17. Kiyo-hime turning into a dragon as she lifts the bell of Dōjōji. Pub. cut off only available copy; cens. Yoshimura; *c.* 1845.

VAM.

S2
Tsūzoku Suikoden gōketsu hyaku-hachi-nin no hitori (or ***ichinin***) ('The hundred and eight heroes of the popular *Suikoden*, one by one'). *Ōban*.

Title on a narrow oblong cartouche framed with irregular decorative motifs top and bottom; name of character adjoining; short text, sometimes enclosed in panel. Generally large single figures, but a few with two. Pub. Kaga-ya Kichiyemon; cens. *kiwame*; *c.* 1827–30. One or two added later, 1836 and *c.* 1845. The publication of this series was the turning-point of Kuniyoshi's career. For a complete treatment of this set and its derivatives, from the pen of Mr Suzuki Jūzō, see *Riccar 1979*.

1. Bizenkō Shutō, an iron truncheon in his mouth, tying his girdle on some steps under a brocade curtain.

BM; B; PC. *Riccar 1979*, 8.

2. Bokutenō Riō wielding a mace with a chained weight, and Botsusharan Bokkō, with tattooed back, preparing to make a sword-stroke (forms triptych with nos. 17 and 59 below).

VAM; B; PC. *Riccar 1978*, 45; *Riccar 1979*, 7; *Kennedy*, 1980.46.

3. Botaichū Kodaisō having her wounded arm attended to by the aged physician Shini Andōzen.

BM; PC. *Robinson 1963*, Pl.2; *Riccar 1979*, 48.

Botsusharan Bokkō, see no.2.

4. Botsu-usen Chōsei, armoured on a plung-ing horse, throwing stones out of a bag (forms diptych with no.14 below).

BM; B; PC. *Düsseldorf 1961*, 5; *Riccar 1979*, 11.

5. Boyasha Sonjirō, the amazon, binding an opponent whom she has overthrown together with her horse in the snow; she was the wife of no.55 (forms pentaptych with nos.44, 56, 65 and 71).

BM; B; PC. *Riccar 1979*, 69.

6. (Gyōja) Bushō of Seika-ken, brown-skinned and half-naked, killing a huge tiger with his bare fists at the hill of Keiyō.

BM; PC. *Riccar 1979*, 10.

7. Byōkwansaku Yōyū, a sword between his teeth, strangling his erring wife and her maid, one with each hand.

BM; B; PC. *Riccar 1979*, 29; *Bidwell 1980*, 9.

8. Byōtaichū Setsuyei, half-naked and tattooed, in a furious bare-fisted struggle with Shōsharan Bokushun.

BM; B; PC.

9. Byō-utsuchi Sonryū, grasping a foeman by the scruff of his neck, threatens him with his drawn sword.

BM; VAM; MFA; B; PC. *Riccar 1979*, 38; *Kruml*, 22.47.

10. Chinsanzan Kōshin, bestriding a rock, feels the edge of his sword (forms diptych with no.74).

BM; B; PC. *Riccar 1979*, 37.

11. Chitasei Goyō, robed and making a magic gesture with his right hand, standing by a celestial globe and quadrant.

BM; MFA; B; PC. *Riccar 1979*, 2; *Bidwell 1980*, 7.

12. Chōkanko Chintatsu, in full armour and armed with a spear, falling headlong from his black horse (forms triptych with nos.18 and 42). See also no.41.

PC. *Riccar 1979*, 57; *Kruml*, 13.36.

13. Chūsenko Teitokuson driving his sword with both hands into an enormous snake.

BM; B; PC. *Robinson 1961*, Pl.10; *Riccar 1978*, 46; *Riccar 1979*, 59; *Kruml*, 9.3.

14. Daitō Kwanshō, fully armoured, using the butt of his enormous glaive to parry stones flung by Botsu-usen Chōsei at the battle of Tōshōfu (forms diptych with no.4).

BM; MFA; B; PC. *Apollo*, January 1949, p.3; *Robinson 1961*, Pl.11; *Düsseldorf 1961*, 5; *Crighton*, V53; *Riccar 1979*, 4; *Bidwell 1980*, 14.

15. Dakoshō Richū in armour holding a spear, a half-naked retainer kneeling before him.

BM; B; PC. *Riccar 1979*, 63.

16. Dokkakuryū Sūjun, with gun and trophies of the chase, whispers to Sōkokatsu Kaihō, who holds a bamboo pole from which lanterns are suspended; they are about to enter the castle of Peking to rescue their imprisoned comrades.

BM; MFA; B; PC. *Riccar 1979*, 32.

Dokkwasei Kōryō, see no.73.

17. Gyokkirin Roshungi, armoured, raising his sword with both hands (forms triptych with nos.2 and 59).

BM; VAM; MFA; B; PC. *Strange* (1st edn.), Pl.41; *Speiser*, p.25; *Crighton*, V54; *Riccar 1979*, 1; *Discovering Antiques*, No.72, p.1717; *Kennedy*, 1980.46.

18. Hakkwaja Yōshun on horseback with a spear; Jinkigunshi Shubu in front of him in long robes holding a feather fan (forms triptych with nos.12 and 42).

PC. *Riccar 1979*, 36; *Kruml*, 13.36.

19. Hakujisso Hakushō, half-naked and tattooed, lifting a box of snakes above a foeman with whom he is struggling; several snakes have escaped and writhe over him.

BM; B; PC. *Riccar 1979*, 71.

20. Hakumenrōkun Teitenju in full armour levering a mass of rock with an iron bar; a flight of arrows descends behind him.

BM; B; PC. *Riccar 1979*, 58.

21. Hitentaisei Rikon in armour, holding a long-handled axe, scanning the landscape from a lofty rock.

BM; VAM; MFA; B; PC. *Robinson 1963*, Pl.1; *Riccar 1979*, 55.

22. Hōtenrai Ryōshin, in armour, discharging a huge cannon, the flaming linstock in his hand.

BM; MFA; B; PC. *Riccar 1979*, 45; *Kennedy*, 1980.48.

23. Hyōshitō Rinchū, in voluminous robes, grasps a foeman by the throat, a drawn sword in his other hand (forms triptych with nos.46 and 70).

BM; B; PC. *Riccar 1979*, 5.

24. Jinkigunshi Shubu, bareheaded and wearing a gorgeous robe of brocade, puts a small demon to flight with the magic of his sword (see also no.18).

BM; MFA; B; PC. *Riccar 1979*, 35.

25. Jinkyōtaihō Taisō, with a discomfited foeman at the base of a castle wall, holds the rope taut (forms vertical diptych with no.58). *c.* 1836.

MFA; PC. *Riccar 1979*, 15.

26. Ju-unryū Kōsonshō holding up a short sword and making a magical gesture with his other hand; a dragon surrounds the rock on which he stands.

BM; B; PC. *Riccar 1979*, 3.

27. Kanchikotsuritsu Shuki, half-naked and tattooed, on a balcony overlooking a wide river, fitting to his bow a humming-bulb arrow containing a concealed message.

BM; B; PC. *Riccar 1979*, 67; *Bidwell 1980*, 8.

28. Kikenji Tokyō, half-naked and tattooed,

lifting a huge temple bell above a cowering foeman.

PC. *Riccar 1979*, 65.

29. Kimmōken Dankeijū, half-naked and tattooed, watches the departure of an armed gang of horse-thieves, a flaming torch at his feet.

BM; B; PC. *Riccar 1979*, 73.

30. Kimpyōshi Yōrin after the battle of Kōtōshū, in a straw cloak on a windy day, carrying a barbed and hooked pole-arm.

BM; MFA; B; PC. *Riccar 1979*, 44.

31. Kinsempyōshi Tōryū the smith, half-naked and seated on a mat by his fire and anvil, tests the straightness of an iron bar.

BM; B; PC.

32. Kinsōshu Jonei cutting down sparrows on the wing with his hooked spear; two spectators of distinctly western appearance.

BM; B; PC. *Riccar 1978*, 47; *Riccar 1979*, 13.

33. Kojōsō Jisen in a tree by moonlight, shining his lantern towards the ground.

BM; B; PC. *Riccar 1979*, 72; *Kennedy*, 1980.47.

34. Kokusempū Riki in a drunken fury attacking the gate of the Hakuryōjin temple with a huge axe; another axe already buried in the woodwork (he had been expelled from the temple, of which he was formerly a priest).

BM; MFA; B; PC. *Riccar 1979*, 17.

35. Konkōryū Rishun, in the water half-naked, upsets a boat with a foeman in it.

BM; B; PC. *Riccar 1979*, 22.

36. (Fig.1) Konseimaō Hanzui, spear in hand and his rearing black horse behind him, recoils from a shower of stones and an apparition of demons.

BM; MFA; B; PC. *Riccar 1979*, 51.

37. Kosanryō Ichijōsei, a sword in either hand, cuts flying arrows, her horse behind her; she was the daughter of the general Kotaikō.

BM; B; PC. *Riccar 1979*, 50; *Bidwell 1980*, 12.

38. Kwakubimba Ōteiroku overcoming three foemen, one of whom he lifts above his head.

BM; B; PC. *Riccar 1979*, 70.

39. Kwaoshō Rochishin, brown-skinned, half-naked and tattooed, smashing through a pine-trunk with his great iron club; he was formerly called Rotatsu.

BM; MFA; B; PC. *Robinson 1961*, Pl.8; *Riccar 1979*, 9; *Kruml*, 13.37.

40. Kwatsuyenra Genshōshichi, in a boat, sheltering from flying arrows under a tiger-skin.

BM; MFA; B; PC. *Düsseldorf 1961*, 3; *Riccar 1979*, 28; *Kruml*, 22.46.

41. Kyumonryō Shishin, half-naked and tattooed, armed with a pole, overthrows an armoured foeman, Chōkanko Chintatsu (see no.12).

BM; VAM; MFA; B; PC. *Robinson 1961*, Pl.9; *Riccar 1979*, 19.

42. Kyumonryō Shishin seated on a vanquished adversary, parrying a flying sword with his pole (forms triptych with nos.12 and 18).

PC. *Riccar 1979*, 20; *Kruml*, 13.36.

43. Kyumonryō Shishin, chest and right arm bared and holding a drawn sword, seated on a vanquished foeman, Kyūshō-otsu Hitenyasha; in the background Rochishin (no.39) in pursuit of the enemy, and the burning Gwaranji temple. Pub. Iba-ya Sensaburō; cens. Watari; c.1845.

PC. *Riccar 1979*, 20.

44. Kyūsempō Sakuchō at the battle of Peking, armoured on a black horse plunging through the snow, and wielding a large axe forms pentaptych with nos.5, 56, 65 and 71).

BM; B; PC. *Riccar 1979*, 14; *Kruml*, 22.49.

45. Ma-unkinshi Ōbō with a drawn sword seizes an adversary by the scruff of the neck in the castle of Seishū.

BM; VAM; MFA; B; PC. *Riccar 1979*, 43.

46. Mochakuten Tosen, right arm and shoulder bare, draws his sword from behind his back (forms triptych with nos.23 and 70).

BM; B; PC. *Takagi*, 3; *Bidwell 1968*, Pl.6; *Riccar 1979*, 62.

47. Mōtōsei Kōmei throttling a sentry under the wall of Peking castle (forms diptych with no.73).

BM; MFA; B; PC. *Riccar 1979*, 52.

48. Nyūbinata Kōjū armoured, with spear, on a prancing horse; background of stormy wind.

BM; B; PC. *Riccar 1979*, 54; *Lewis*, 1975.2.

49. Rōrihakuchō Chōjun, half-naked and tattooed, with a sword between his teeth, forces apart the bars of a water-gate. (Later edition, pub. Iba-ya Sensaburō; cens. Watari; c.1845.)

BM; MFA; B; PC. *Riccar 1979*, 27; *Bidwell 1980*, 13.

50. (Pl.3) Rōshi Yensei, half-naked and tattooed, on a roof by moonlight, hurling stones on a pursuing gang of thieves. (Later edition, pub. Iba-ya Sensaburō; cens. Watari; c.1845. The original is *unsigned*; the later version has signature added in Kuniyoshi's handwriting of the period.)

BM; B; PC. *Riccar 1979*, 34.

51. Rōshi Yensei, half-naked and tattooed, lifts a huge beam above a prostrate adversary.

RSM; PC. *Riccar 1979*, 33; *Kruml*, 9.6 (key-block pull); *Lewis*, 1975.cover.

52. Ryōtōja Kaichin the hunter, in a shower of rain, binding a fallen enemy general with a corded missile.

BM; MFA; B; PC.

53. Ryūchitaisai Genshōji in a boat, attacked by grappling-hooks on cords, thrown by his opponents.

BM; MFA; B; PC.

54. Saijinki Kwakusei, of markedly simian appearance, armed with a spear on a plunging horse, with a banner charged with a winged horse (forms diptych with no.63).

BM; MFA; B; PC. *Riccar 1979*, 47.

55. Saiyenshi Chōsei, half-naked and tattooed, carrying a pole, looks down from a lofty rock.

BM; PC. *Riccar 1979*, 49; *Kennedy*, 1980.49.

56. Seibokkan Kakushibun, bareheaded in armour in the snow, wields his sword with both hands (forms pentaptych with nos.5, 44, 65 and 71).

BM; B; PC. *Riccar 1979*, 40.

57. Seimenjū Yōshi by the Tenkanshū bridge poising his sword over a fallen adversary, who raises a protesting hand; the latter had ridiculed his poverty in going to sell his sword.

BM; MFA; B; PC. *Riccar 1979*, 12.

58. Seishushosei Shōjō, a sword suspended in his teeth, descending the wall of Peking castle by a rope in the moonlight (forms vertical diptych with no.25). c.1836.

PC.

59. Sekibakki Ryūtō armoured and raising his sword for a stroke (forms triptych with nos.2 and 17).

BM; VAM; MFA; B; PC. *Riccar 1979*, 16; *Kennedy*, 1980.46.

60. Sekishōgun Sekiyū throttling a foeman at the base of a waterfall, both fully armoured. c.1840.

MFA; PC. *Riccar 1979*, 74.

61. Senkwaji Chō-ō, half-naked and tattooed, about to slay the enemy general Hōtentei with his sword, looks back on a supernatural flame that plays on the torrent behind him.

BM; B; PC. *Riccar 1979*, 24.

62. Shameisaburō Sekishū, in a wide hat and black robe, and holding a *mokugyo* and stick, with his foot on the neck of the prostrate monk Haijokai at the back gate of the palace of Yōyū.

BM; VAM; MFA; PC. *Or.Art*, Spring 1961, p.25; *Riccar 1979*, 30; *Kruml*, 9.5.

Shini Andōzen, see no.3.

63. Shō-onkō Ryohō, three-quarter back view, armoured on a galloping horse, and armed with a long spear, his banner charged with a newt (forms diptych with no.54).

BM; B; PC. *Riccar 1979*, 46.

64. Shōrikō Kwayei standing by a hill and shooting at wild geese with his bow and arrows.

BM; MFA; B; PC. *Riccar 1979*, 6; *Lewis*, 1975.1.

Shōsharan Bokushun, see no.8.

65. Shūgumba Sensan, armoured but bareheaded, in the snow, carrying a pole-arm

with a ring head barbed on the inside (forms pentaptych with nos. 5, 44, 56 and 71).

BM; B; PC. *Riccar 1979*, 39.

66. Shutsurinryō Sūyen, his helmet crested with long pheasant's feathers, in a furious hand-to-hand struggle with an opponent.

BM; VAM; RSM; MFA; B; PC. *Riccar 1979*, 66.

Sōkokatsu Kaihō, see no. 16.

67. Sōshiko Raiō gripping the Lady Hakushūyei by the throat, and about to strike her with his fist.

MFA; PC. *Riccar 1979*, 21.

68. Sōtōki Sōsei, half-naked and tattooed, wielding a long pole, with kitchen utensils and provisions behind him.

BM; MFA; B; PC. *Riccar 1979*, 61.

S2.69

69. Tammeijirō Genshōgo, half-naked and tattooed, grappling with an armoured foeman under water.

BM; VAM; PC. *Inouye*, Pl. 108; *Or. Art*, Spring 1961, p. 25; *Hillier*, 47; *UMS*, 8; *UT*, 171; *Riccar 1978*, 48; *Riccar 1979*, 26; *Bidwell 1980*, 10; *Kruml*, 9.4.

70. Tammeijirō Genshōgo, half-naked and tattooed, kneels on a fallen foeman, a drawn sword in his hand (forms triptych with nos. 23 and 46).

BM; B; PC. *Riccar 1979*, 25; *Bidwell 1980*, 11; *Illing 1980*, 127.

71. Temmokushō Hōki in a black bear-skin cloak in the snow, stretching a cord with a noose at the end (forms pentaptych with nos. 5, 44, 56 and 65).

BM; B; PC. *Riccar 1979*, 41.

72. Tettekisen Barin lifting a stag above his head and at the same time overthrowing a

monstrous monkey; this he was able to do by means of the black arts.

BM; B; PC. *Riccar 1979*, 56.

73. Unrikongō Sōman, under the wall of Peking castle, holds up a burning match; Dokkwasei Kōryō crouches behind him with a short bamboo pole (forms diptych with no. 47).

BM; MFA; B; PC. *Riccar 1979*, 53; *Kruml*, 22.48.

74. Waikyakko Ōyei on a rock overhanging a torrent, a drawn sword in his hand (forms diptych with no. 10).

BM; B; PC. *Riccar 1979*, 49.

S2a
Suikoden gōketsu hyaku-hachi-nin no hitori ('The hundred and eight heroes of the *Suikoden*, one by one'). *Chūban*.

Reduced versions of the designs in the preceding series, with wide decorative margins. No pub. visible on any of those seen, but Suzuki (*Riccar 1979*) gives Yamazaki Kimbei. Originally issued *c*. 1830 (cens. *kiwame*), but later edition *c*. 1842 (cens. Mura); all designs *c*. 1830 with the possible exception of no. 2, the only one that does not retain the design of the original series.

1. Bushō of Seikaken. Cens. *kiwame* and Mura.

VAM; PC. *Riccar 1979*, 24.

2. Chūsenko Teitokuson. Cens. Mura.
VAM; MFA; PC.

S2a.3

3. Hakujisso Hakushō. Cens. Mura.
VAM; PC.

4. Hyōshitō Rinchū.
MFA.

5. Kokusempū Riki (called Ritetsu Gyu).
MFA.

6. Kwaoshō Rochishin.
VAM; PC.

7. Kwatsuyenra Genshōshichi. Cens. *kiwame*.
VAM; PC.

8. Ryōtōja Kaichin. Cens. Mura.
VAM; PC.

9. Ryūchitaisai Genshōji. Cens. *kiwame*.
VAM; PC.

10. Sekibakki Ryūtō.
MFA.

11. Sōshiko Raiō.
MFA.

12. Tammeijirō Genshōgo. Cens. Mura.
VAM; PC.

NOTE. In these *Suikoden* series the readings of the names are those given on the prints themselves; in a few cases they differ slightly from those given by Suzuki in *Riccar 1979*.

S3
Suikoden gōketsu hyaku-hachi-nin ('The hundred and eight heroes of the *Suikoden*'). *Ōban*.

Title on oblong cartouche (sometimes with rounded corners). Twelve numbered sheets, each with a group of nine heroes, on plain blue ground. Pub. Kaga-ya Kichiyemon; cens. *kiwame*; *c*. 1830 (later edition, pub. Iba-ya Sensaburō; cens. Watari; *c*. 1845). In the following list the heroes are named from the top clockwise.

1. Kohōgi Sōkō holding a scroll; Chitasei Goyō seated with folded hands; Sōsōshō Tōhei with a spear, grimacing; Daitō Kwanshō with a large glaive; Kokusempū Riki with two axes; Botsu-usen Chōsei with a bag of stones; Sōbenshō Koyenshaku with a ribbed staff; Hekirekkwa Shimmei with a spiked mace; and Hyōshitō Rinchū seated with a closed fan.

MFA; PC. *Riccar 1979*, 35.

2. Shinkigunshi Shubu seated with a feather fan; Chōkanko Chintatsu seated grasping his sword; Kimmōko Yenjun seated with a spiked mace; Waikyakko Ōyei with hand on hip; Ichijōsei Kosanjō (woman) with a glaive; Hakumenrōkun Teitenju with an iron club; Dakoshō Richū seated with a pole; Shōhaō Shūtsū with a spray of leaves; and Hakkwaja Yōshun seated with a spear.

MFA; PC. *Riccar 1979*, 39.

3. Seibokkan Kakushibun with a barbed ring pole-arm; Shūgumba Sensan with a fancifully headed mace; Dokkwasei Kōryō breathing on the blade of a knife; Shutsudōkō Dōi drawing his sword; Hōtenrai Ryōshin with a large gun; Honkōshin Dōmō stooping; Kojōsō Jisen with a large bell; Mōtōsei Kōmei seated clasping his knees; and Hei-ichi (Byō-utsuchi) Sonryū with a scythe-like weapon.

MFA; PC. *Riccar 1979*, 40.

4. Chinsanzan Kōshin with a big mallet; Kingampyō Shion holding his sword in both hands; Sekishōgun Sekiyū with clenched fists; Heidaichū (Byōtaichū) Setsuyei seated with a pole and a yellow cylinder; Kendōjin Ikuhōshi with bared chest and right arm; Shōsharan Bokushun examining a sword; Dokkakuryō Sūjun with a cloth bag; Shutsurinryō Sūyen pointing at his sword; and Sōmonjin Hōkyoku putting on his topcoat.

MFA; PC. *Riccar 1979*, 41.

5. Shōsempū Saishin seated with an iron club; Seimenjū Yōshi testing the edge of his sword; Sōshiko Raiō, brown-skinned, holding his sword; Kyumonryō Shishin half-naked and tattooed; Kwaoshō Rochishin, brown-skinned, with a long iron club; Sōbikatsu Gaihō with a dead hare on a bamboo pole; Shingyōtaihō Taisō resting his chin on his stick; Ryōtōda Gaichin (Ryōtōja Kaichin) adjusting his leggings; and Bizenkō Shutō seated in contemplation.

MFA; PC. *Riccar 1979*, 36.

6. Kinsōshu Jonei with a pole and a sickle-like weapon; Shōriko Kwayei with bow and arrows; Senkwaji Chō-ō wiping his sword; Ryūchitaisai Genshōji with a net and shuttle; Rōrihakuchō Chōjun half-naked and tattooed; Kwatsuyenra Genshōshichi with a basket of fish; Tammeijirō Genshōgo, half-naked and tattooed, twisting a thread round his toe; Kongōryō Rishun holding a helmet and sword; and Bokutenchō Riō with his hand to his sword-hilt.

MFA; PC. *Riccar 1979*, 37; *Kruml*, 9.7.

S3.7

7. Kwachōko Kyō-ō with a spear of curious design; Chūsenko Teitokuson with a long

spear and fur-trimmed hat; Tessenshi Sōsei with clasped hands and a bow; Shōmenko Shubu smiling and holding up his hands; Kyūbiki Tōsō-ō examining his sword; Mochakuten Tosen, in profile, with a spear; Botsumemmoku Shōtei, half-naked, feeling his shoulder; Unrikongō Sōman testing an arrow; and Shinsanshi Shōkei in a tiger's head helmet with a curly-headed spear.

MFA; PC. *Riccar 1979*, 42.

8. Gyokkirin Roshungi seated with an axe; Ju-unryō Kōsonshō, an old man with a small dragon; Kyūsempō Sakuchō in a spiked breastplate; Shameisanrō Sekishū in black with a gong-stick; Gyōja Bushō seated with a large pearl necklace; Byōkwansaku Yōyū seated with a pole; Botsusharan Bokkō with folded arms and a red wig; Sekihakki Ryūtō with right shoulder and chest bare; and Rōshi Yensei, half-naked and tattooed, with a pole surmounted by a ball.

MFA; PC. *Riccar 1979*, 38 (the later edition, where it is numbered 9).

9. Seisuishō Tanteikei in a spotted coat with frilled collar; Shinkwashō Giteikoku adjusting his sleeve; Hyakushōshō Kantō seated in full armour; Tekkyōshi Rakkwa standing in full armour; Kimpyōshi Yōrin seated, shouting; Kimmōken Dankeijū holding a coiled cord; Kwaganshunkei Tōhi seated with his hand to the back of his head; Temmokushō Hōki seated, resting his chin on his fan; and Maunkinshi Ōbō in a black helmet with half-mask.

MFA; PC. *Riccar 1979*, 43 (where it is numbered 8—see above).

10. Konseimaō Hanzui with magically clasped hands emitting lightning; Hitendaisei Rikon leaning on the shaft of his weapon; Tettekisen Barin seated in armour; Shō-onkō Ryohō seated, with a spear; Hakujisso Hakushō bending a bamboo for a bow; Saijinki Kwakusei with a spear and weighted cord; Tetsubihaku Saifuku seated, with a curved bamboo; Itsushikwa Saikei seated, three-quarter back view; and Hatsubinada Kōjū, half-naked, holding up a sword.

MFA; PC. *Riccar 1979*, 44 (where it is numbered 7—see above).

11. Tetsumenkōmoku Haisen with a scroll; Shini Andōzen, an old man with a staff; Gyokuhishō Kindaiken wearing spectacles; Seiganko Riun feeling the edge of his sword; Kinsempyōshi Tōryu, half-naked, with a long hammer; Sōtōki Sōsei scaling a fish; Shisempaku Kōhotan seated in contemplation; Tsūbiyen Kōken pointing upwards; and Seishushosei Shōjō seated with hands clasped round his knees.

MFA; PC. *Riccar 1979*, 45.

12. Kanchikotsuritsu Shuki testing a bow; Shō-utsuchi Sonshin seated in helmet and striped armour; Bodaichū Kodaisō (woman) holding up a lantern; Saimeihangwan Riryū in

armour expounding from a book; Gyokuban-kan Mōkō, left arm and shoulder bare, in a horned helmet; Kwakuzemba Ōteiroku with a straw-wrapped fish; Kigenji Tokō with a trident; Boyasha Sonjirō (woman) feeling the edge of her sword; and Saiyenshi Chōsei in a helmet covered with spikes.

MFA; PC. (Not in *Riccar 1979*.)

S4
Honchō Suikoden gōyū happyaku-nin no hitori ('Eight hundred heroes of our country's *Suikoden*, one by one'). *Ōban*.

Title on oblong cartouche with narrow yellow reeded border; name of character on similar panel adjoining; short text fitted into the design. Single figures (a few with two or more) of historical and dramatic characters in a large bold style, closely following that of S2. Pub. Kaga-ya Kichiyemon, but some reprints issued *c*.1845 by Iba-ya Sensaburō. The set seems to have been published in three batches, and is so divided in the lists below. Cens. *kiwame*.

S4a.1

S4a (*c*. 1830)

1. Fujinoye at the battle of Takadachi castle (1189), sword in one hand and *naginata* in the other, amid flying arrows, overthrows Yemoto Jurō and Nagasawa Uyemon-tarō on the castle steps.

BM; PC.

2. Hayakawa Ayunosuke damming the Ayu-kawa river in order to strand the fish in the open fields. (Later edition, cens. Watari.)

BM; VAM; MFA; PC.

3. Inudzuka Shino Moritaka resisting arrest on the Hōryūkaku roof (forms vertical diptych with no.4).

BM; B; PC.

4. (Pl. 1) Inukai Kempachi Nobumichi, an iron truncheon in his mouth, directs the attempted arrest of Shino on the roof (forms vertical diptych with no.3).
BM; B; PC.

5. Inuzaka Keno Tanetomo holding down Tsunahei, with a sword in his hand; he has written on the adjacent wall 'Written by Inuzaka Keno Tanetomo, aged fifteen, on the sixteenth day of the fifth month of the eleventh year of the period Bummei' (6 June 1479).
BM; VAM.

6. I no Hayata Hironao seizing the monster *Nuye* as it falls to the ground amid clouds and lightning (1154).
BM; B.

7. Kadzusa no Suke Hirotsune bestriding the Nine-tailed Fox on Nasu moor; the beast has already been struck by two arrows.
BM.

8. Kashiwade no Hanoshi killing the Korean tiger that had devoured his daughter.
BM; VAM; PC.

9. Kitashirakawa Iwabuchi Tankai in combat with Ushiwaka Maru before the Tenjin temple at Gojō, Kyoto.
BM; PC.

10. Ōanamuchi-no-mikoto killing a monstrous eagle which had been attacking and damaging passing ships.
BM. *Robinson 1961*, Pl. 12.

11. Odai Matarokurō (Yorisada) breaking a huge *sake*-jar with his spear; Iwadzu Tetsuyemon (Shigenobu) drinking in the background; this was during his war with Takeda Shingen (*c*. 1540).
BM.

12. Ogata Shuma Hiroyuki (later known as Jiraiya), with a heavy gun, overcoming a huge snake which had preyed on his friends the toads.
BM; VAM; PC.

13. Oniwaka Maru (Benkei in boyhood) as an apprentice monk at Shōshazan discomfiting the monks with whom he had quarrelled.
BM; VAM; PC.

14. Ōtani Furuinosuke at the age of fifteen killing a giant boar with his bare fists.
BM; VAM; PC.

15. Satō Shirobyōye Tadanobu, crushing two armed assailants under a large *go*-board, heaves another up by the girdle.
BM.

16. Shimose Kaga tying up a man in a horned mask who had pretended to be a demon at Rokkakudō in Kyoto (*c*. 1510).
BM; PC.

17. Tengan Isobei throwing Yasha Arashi in a wrestling-bout.
PC. *Illing 1980*, 60.

18. Yeda Genzō Hirotsuna defending the Horikawa palace, Kyoto, against the attacking force of Tosa-bō Shōshun (1185).
BM; VAM; PC.

S4b (1834–5)

1. Doki Taishirō Motosada wrestling with a *Niō* (temple guardian) at the haunted shrine of Maōdō at Inohanayama in the province of Kai.
PC.

S4b.2

2. Inumura Daikaku Masanori killing the monstrous witch-cat of Kōshin-yama.
PC.

3. Miyamoto Musashi killing a huge lizard on the borders of the provinces of Echizen, Mino, and Hida. (Later edition, cens. Watari.)
BM; PC. *Riccar 1978*, 53; *Bidwell 1980*, 21.

4. Sagi-no-ike Heikurō wrestling with a huge serpent at the lake of Sayama (or Hazama) at Tondabayashi in the province of Kawachi. (Later edition, cens. Watari.)
BM; MFA; PC.

5. (Fig. 13) Yamato-take-no-mikoto, with his 'grass-mowing sword' (*Kusanagi-no-tsurugi*) about to cut down the grass which the eastern barbarians had ignited around him.
PC.

6. The Crown Prince Gon-no-suke Sumimoto struggling with Tai no Jurō Masaharu, a retainer of Minamoto no Mitsunaka.
PC.

S4c (*c*. 1836)

1. Inuda Kobungo Yasuyori wrestling a huge bull during the festival bull-fight at Nijū, Koshi-gōri, in the province of Echigo.
PC.

2. Inuyama Dōsetsu Tadatomo raising the

S4c.2

famous sword *Murasame* as a fire of branches burns behind him; he was a fire-magic adept.
PC.

3. (Pl. 5) Inuye Shimbyōye Masashi snatched up by the ghost of his grandmother Fuse-hime, to save him from a thunderbolt.
PC. *Robinson 1961*, Pl. 13.

S5

Kyokutei-ō seicho Hakkenshi zui-ichi ('The one and only Eight Dog History of old Kyokutei [Bakin], best of refined authors'). *Ōban*.

Title on the cover of a scroll which carries descriptive text by Rekitei Kingyo and stretches across the top of each print. Set of eight, depicting the 'Dog Heroes' in action, and designed to form four diptychs. Pub. Nishimura-ya Yohachi; cens. *kiwame*; *c*. 1835.

1 (Pl. 6) and 2. Inudzuka Shino Moritaka defending himself against Inukai Kempachi Nobumichi and his men on the Hōryūkaku roof; a flight of pigeons (l.).
VAM; RSM; PC.

3 and 4. Inuda Kobungo Yasuyori and Inuye Shimbei Masashi (the latter a child on the shoulder of his protector) attacked by a gang of roughs.
RSM; MFA; PC.

5 and 6. Inukawa Sōsuke Yoshitō cuts off the corner of a stone tank with his sword, revealing a shining jewel, whilst Inuyama Dōsetsu Tadatomo raises his sword for another blow.
RSM; MFA; PC.

7 and 8. Inuzaka Keno Tanetomo struggling with four assailants, all armed with swords, whilst Inumura Daikaku drives his dirk into a monstrous witch-cat.

S5.8

RSM; MFA; B; PC. *Düsseldorf 1961*, 7; *Cologne 1963*, 6; *Bidwell 1968*, Pl.63.

S6

Kōsō go-ichidai ryaku dzu ('Illustrated abridged biography of Kōsō'). *Ōban yokoye*.

Title and brief caption on r.h. margin, the former printed in black, red, or blue. Scenes from the life of the Buddhist priest and saint, Nichiren (Kōsō), 1222–82. Set of ten. Pub. Ise-ya Rihei; cens. *kiwame*; *c.* 1835–6.

1. 'Nichiren converting the spirit of a cormorant fisherman on the Isawa river in the province of Kai.' The saint seated on the rocky river-bank; fishermen in a boat below, and a large pine-tree across the foreground, left.

BM; B; Baur; PC. *Inouye*, Pl.91; *Bidwell 1968*, Pl.20; *Riccar 1978*, 187; *Kruml*, 9.17.

2. 'Komatsu moor, Tōjō, 2 December 1264.' Nichiren, attacked by Tōjō no Sayemon and his men, throws them into confusion by holding up his shining rosary; his disciple Nikkyō crouches in the background.

BM; B; Baur; PC. *Inouye*, Pl.86; *Riccar 1978*, 179.

3. 'The Star of Wisdom descends on the night of the thirteenth of the ninth month.' Nichiren with his rosary before an old plum-tree in which appears a shining apparition of Buddha; behind him two officials and a group of armed men exhibit signs of alarm.

BM; B; Baur; PC. *Inouye*, Pl.89; *Riccar 1978*, 182.

4. 'The prayer for rain on the headland of Reisan, Kamakura, 1271.' Nichiren's prayer on the rocky headland is answered by a downpour of rain; an attendant holds an umbrella over him.

BM; MFA; B; Baur; PC. *Inouye*, Pl.87;

Robinson 1961, Pl.22; *Robinson 1963*, Pl.3; *Bidwell 1968*, Pl.19; *Riccar 1978*, 180; *Bidwell 1980*, 29; *Kruml*, 9.16.

5. 'At Komuroyama, 4 July 1274.' Nichiren stands, dignified and impassive, whilst a huge rock, lifted over him by the magic of a warrior-monk, whose small attendant carries his enormous axe, remains suspended in the air.

BM; VAM; MFA; B; Baur; PC. *Inouye*, Pl.90; *Riccar 1978*, 188; *Kruml*, 9.15.

6. 'Apparition of the Seven-faced Divinity at Minobuzan, October 1277.' (Pl.10) Nichiren presiding at a crowded service in the temple hall, with a dragon emerging in a dark cloud from the inert body of a woman who had disturbed his devotions.

BM; B; Baur; PC. *Inouye*, Pl.92; *Riccar 1978*, 189; *Bidwell 1980*, 34; *Lewis*, 1975.4.

7. 'The defeat of the Mongol army in 1281, prophesied by Nichiren.' As here shown, their ships were battered by a terrible storm, and those who had managed to land were slain on the shore by the Japanese.

BM; B; Baur; PC. *Inouye*, Pl.93; *Riccar 1978*, 190; *Bidwell 1980*, 35.

8. 'At Tatsunokuchi in the province of Sagami.' Nichiren in prayer on the shore under a pine-tree, whilst his would-be executioner's sword is shattered and the rest of the party thrown into confusion by rays emanating from the sun.

BM; B; Baur; PC. *Inouye*, Pl.88; *Riccar 1978*, 181; *Bidwell 1980*, 30; *Kruml*, 9.19.

9. 'On the waves at Kakuda on the way to Sado.' Nichiren, in a boat with terrified companions among mountainous waves, projects the invocation *namu myōhō renge kyō* upon the surface of the water to calm it.

BM; VAM; B; Baur; PC. *Inouye*, Pl.85;

Robinson 1961, Pl.23; *Düsseldorf 1961*, 11; *Bidwell 1968*, Pl.18; *Crighton*, V14; *Illing 1976*, 79; *Riccar 1978*, 183; *Ronin*, 74; *Kruml*, 9.13, 14; 12.50; 13.35.

10. 'Tsukahara in the province of Sado in snow.' Nichiren toils alone up a snow-covered hillside, the huts of the village on the shore below. The earlier state of this print has a horizon line bounding sea and sky, which was later removed, causing them to merge into each other.

BM; MFA; B; Baur; PC. *Inouye*, Pl.84; *Bidwell 1968*, Pl.17; *Speiser*, p.41; *Riccar 1978*, 184/186; *Bidwell 1980*, 31/33.

S7

Buyei mōyū kagami ('Mirror of military excellence and fierce courage'). *Ōban*.

Title on oblong red cartouche with narrow yellow border; subtitles on smaller coloured oblong panels adjoining figures. Single combats, in a bold style. Pub. Ise-ya Sanjirō; cens. *kiwame*; *c.* 1836.

1. Hirotsune, the Taira turncoat, and Yukiuji.
   BM.

2. Kintoki and the serpent.
   BM.

3. Seizure of Soga Gorō Tokimune by Gozen Gorō Maru Shigemune.
   BM; PC.

4. Tomoye-gozen throttling Uchida Saburō by a waterfall.
   BM.

5. Minamoto no Ushiwaka Maru and Musashi-bō Benkei on Gojō bridge, with bats flying across a full moon.
   MFA; PC.

S6.3

S7.5

S8.5

S9.5

S8

Yōbu hakkei ('Military brilliance for the Eight Views'). *Ōban*.

Title on oblong cartouche incorporating subtitle; on an adjoining oblong panel with cut corners are two poems. Historical scenes. Pub. Tsuru-ya Kiyemon; cens. *kiwame*; *c*.1836. (Cf. S76.)

1. 'Autumn Moon at Ishibashiyama.' Sanada Yoichi Yoshitada about to kill Matano Gorō Kagehisa, Nagao Shinroku Sadakage approaching from behind; moon, waves, and distant Fuji.

VAM; RSM; MFA; PC.

2. 'Lingering Snow on Mount Yoshino.' Satō Tadanobu, in the armour of Yoshitsune, overthrowing the monk Yokogawa Kakuhan in the snow by a waterfall.

VAM; MFA; PC.

3. 'Evening Glow at Uji Bridge.' Ichirai-hōshi standing on the shoulders of Tsutsui Jōmyō, defending the broken bridge against the Taira; setting sun behind a mountain.

MFA; PC.

4. 'Vesper Bell at Suma Temple.' Kurō Hangwan Minamoto no Yoshitsune and Musashi-bō Benkei seated under the cherry-blossom after the battle of Ichi-no-tani.

PC.

5. 'Returning Boats from Korea.' Takeshiuchi-no-sukune, the Empress Jingō's commander-in-chief, on the prow of his ship after his triumphant campaign in Korea.

PC. *Robinson 1961*, Pl.24.

6. 'Clearing Weather on Ichihara Moor.' Kidō Maru's murderous attack on Raikō foiled by the latter's retainers; wind sweeps across the moor.

MFA; PC.

7. 'Night Rain on Suso Moor.' (Pl.14) The Soga brothers, in a downpour of rain, about to enter the tent of Kudō Suketsune; in the background is Hanzawa Rokurō, who gave the alarm.

PC. *Or.Art*, Spring 1961, p.26.

8. 'Homing Geese at Kanazawa.' Hachimantarō Yoshi-iye and his followers watching the flight of geese at Kanazawa, by which the position of his foes, the Kiyowara, was betrayed (*c*.1085).

PC.

S9

Buyū hyaku den ('A hundred stories of military valour'). *Ōban*.

Title, subtitle (name), and short text in three gourd-shaped cartouches. Historical scenes. Pub. Fujioka-ya Hikotarō; cens. *kiwame*; *c*.1836.

1. Chinzei Hachirō Tametomo overthrowing a wild boar in the snowy mountains of Mashiki in the province of Higo, watched from a distance by Takama Harutsugu.

PC.

2. (Pl.8) Kiso Yoshinaka and the Taira commander Mikawa no Kami Tomonori, locked in struggle, tumble down a precipitous hillside at the battle of Naminoyo in the province of Kaga.

PC; Graz, Landesmuseum.

3. Momotarō and his companions in the demons' stronghold.

Graz, Landesmuseum.

4. Shirafuji Hikoshichirō lifts a struggling white horse on to his shoulders in the course of his pursuit of Ashikaga Taka-uji to the Fukkai-ji temple on Wada cape, Hyōgo (shown in the background).

RSM; PC.

5. Onzōshi Ushiwaka Maru encounters Ise Saburō Yoshimori and his gang on the Suzuka bridge in the province of Ise, by moonlight.

BM; RSM; PC. *Robinson 1961*, Pl.25.

S10

Tsūzoku Sangokushi yeiyū no ichi-nin ('Heroes of the popular History of the Three Kingdoms, one by one'). *Ōban*.

Title on oblong cartouche with narrow yellow edges; text on rectangular panel with similar edge. One or two large figures of Chinese warriors in action. Pub. Jōshū-ya Kinzō; cens. *kiwame*; various eng.; *c*.1836.

1. (Pl.7) Kōmei, the scholar and teacher of strategy, praying for wind at the altar of Seven Stars. Eng. (Ishikawa) Tokubei.

BM; PC. *Geneva 1978*, 52.

2. Kwanu grasping his huge glaive and easily subduing a band of rebel traitors on the entrance-steps of a castle. Eng. Ishikawa Tokubei.

PC.

3. Mōki Bachō killing the mother of Kyūjo of Rekijō, after becoming a follower of Gentoku. Eng. Okamoto Yeiji.

B; PC.

4. Chōkō and Chō-un fighting in a red glare on a hillside. Eng. Tetsuzō.

PC.

5. Gentoku, on his black horse Tekiro, leap-

S10.3

ing into the gorge of Tan (the horse shaded in western style). Eng. Sashichi.

MFA; PC.

6. Hōsen Ryofu, mounted, hair and clothes flying, spears a fallen foeman after the defeat of Sōsō. No eng. visible.

PC. *Düsseldorf 1961*, 13.

7. Chōhi glaring, mounted on a black horse and grasping his formidable spear, on Chōhan bridge. Eng. Sashichi.

MFA; B.

8. Shusō and Hōtoku fighting under water. Eng. Ishikawa Tokubei.

PC. *Lewis*, 1975.5 (key-block pull only).

S11

Shū-yeki hakke-ye ('Universal divination by the Eight Trigrams, illustrated'). *Ōban.*

Title and subtitle on oblong cartouche with convex top and concave bottom. Large single figures. Pub. Jōshū-ya Kinzō; cens. *kiwame*; *c.*1837–8. (See *Koop*, p.107.)

1. *Shin-Rai.* Raijin the Thunder-God brandishing his drumsticks as he storms through the sky accompanied by a thunder-beast. Eng. Ishikawa Tokubei.

B. *Bidwell 1968*, Pl.72; *Riccar 1978*, back cover; *Bidwell 1980*, 99 (Pl.6).

2. *Son-Fū.* Fūten the Wind-God manipulating his swirling bag; below him a storm-bird.

B. *Riccar 1978*, front cover; *Bidwell 1980*, 100.

S12

Kintarō dzukushi ('Set of Kintarō'). *Ōban.*

Title and subtitle on horizontal or vertical

S11.1

S12.2

rectangular cartouche. Scenes from the childhood of Kintarō (Kintoki). Pub. Tsujioka-ya Bunsuke; *c.*1840.

1. *Kwanu mitate* ('Kwanu Selection', i.e. imitation of Kwanu). Kintarō seated proudly on a rock with two attendant demons, one carrying his large axe.

MFA.

2. *Sagami no dzu* ('Picture of Sagami', the province where Kintarō was brought up). Kintarō, a demon and a *tengu* behind him,

umpiring a wrestling-match between a hare and a monkey.

B; PC. *Riccar 1978*, 56.

S13

Nijūshi-kō dōji kagami ('Mirror of the Twenty-Four Paragons of Filial Piety'). *Ōban yokoye.*

Title on red oblong cartouche; text in shaded oblong panel with narrow yellow border and rounded corners. Scenes with strong landscape element and western influence. Pub. Wakasa-ya Yoichi; *c.*1840.

1. Taishun (T'a Shun) hoeing a field with the help of elephants; lake, village, and mountains in the background.

PC. *Illing 1976*, 78; *Ronin*, 77; *Kruml*, 9.23.

2. Mōsō (Mêng Tsung) with his hoe in the snow going to find bamboo-shoots to feed his mother.

BM; B; PC. *Bidwell 1968*, Pl.69; *Riccar 1978*, 201; *Bidwell 1980*, 137; *Kruml*, 21.59.

3. Binshiken (Min-tzŭ-ch'ien) sweeping snow outside the house where his mother stands with two younger children.

BM; PC. *Inouye*, Pl.29; *Or.Art*, Spring 1961, p.26; *Kruml*, 9.24; 12.53.

4. (Pl.32) Sōshin (Ts'êng Shên) hurrying home across a bridge to the assistance of his mother (foreground, left) who has injured her finger. Largely copied from an Italian original.

BM; B; PC. *Takagi*, 7; *Apollo*, July 1949, p.10; *Robinson 1961*, Pl.34; *Robinson 1963*, Pl.5; *Riccar 1978*, 203; *Bidwell 1980*, 139; *Illing 1980*, 114.

5. Ōshō (Wang Hsiang) seated in the snow on a river-bank with two admiring relatives, having caught a fish through the ice for his ailing mother.

BM; PC. *Inouye*, Pl.28; *Robinson 1961*, Pl.35; *Kruml*, 9.22.

6. Rōraishi (Lao-li-tzŭ) playing with toys and acting as a child to amuse his aged parents; extensive landscape with high mountain.

BM; B; PC. *Riccar 1978*, 202; *Kruml*, 21.56.

7. Kyōshi (Chiang Shih) netting fish for his mother in the river outside her cottage.

BM; PC. *Cologne 1963*, 25; *Speiser*, p.45; *Ronin*, 76.

8. Tōfujin (T'ang Fu-jên, 'the Chinese Lady', i.e. Ts'ui Shih) suckling her grandmother amid buildings of western appearance. (A later printing has cens. Taka.)

BM; MFA; PC. *Kruml*, 12.54.

9. Yōkō (Yang Hsiang) placing himself in the path of a huge tiger to enable his father to escape.

BM; B; PC. *Riccar 1978*, 204; *Bidwell 1980*, 140; *Illing 1980*, 131; *Kruml*, 9.21; 20.69.

10. Tōyei (Tung Yung). The Heavenly

S13.5

Weaver, having helped Tōyei to pay for his father's funeral by weaving for him, returns to the sky.

BM; MFA; B; PC. *Inouye*, Pl.27; *Illing 1978*, 32; *Bidwell 1980*, 138; *Kruml*, 21.57.

11. Kwakkyo (Kuo Chü) and his wife unearthing a pot of gold; the surrounding buildings and landscape of markedly western type.

BM; PC. *Ronin*, 75.

12. Rikuseki (Lu Chi) stoops to pick up money for his aged father; European architecture; lake, ship, and mountains in the background.

BM.

13. Gomō (Wu Mêng) carrying a smoking pot to keep the mosquitoes from his father, who reclines on a bamboo couch.

BM; PC. *Düsseldorf 1961*, 14; *UT*, 85; *Kruml*, 9.26; 13.39; 21.58.

14. Ōhō (Wang P'ou) visiting the tomb of his mother to comfort her spirit during a thunderstorm; terrified peasants flee the lightning.

BM; MFA; PC. *Kruml*, 12.52; 22.43.

S14
Shōtoku Taishi go-ichidaiki ('Biography of Prince Shōtoku'). *Ōban yokoye.*

Title (when it occurs) in upper margin; text in shaded oblong panel with rounded corners. Scenes from the life of Prince Shōtoku (572–621). Pub. Jōshū-ya Jūzō; *c.*1840.

1. (Pl.11) Country-people and ladies in travelling-veils stopping to admire the miraculous gourd which appeared at the time of the Prince's birth, with its guardian snake and a horse nibbling the leaves.

B; PC.

2. Lightning flashing from a great tree about to be felled by Kawabe no Omi, to build a ship for the Prince.

B; PC. *Bidwell 1968*, Pl.68; *Riccar 1978*, 85; *Bidwell 1980*, 95.

3. The attempt to smash the relic before the Emperor in the palace.

MFA; PC.

4. The Prince vanishes into a tree (on which his shadowy form appears) to escape pursuit by Moriya after an ambush.

B; PC. *Kennedy*, 1980.66.

5. The Prince directing the attack on the castle of Moriya.

MFA.

S15
Seisuiki jimpin sen ('Documented characters from the chronicle of the ups and downs', sc. of the Minamoto and Taira clans). *Chūban.*

Title in plain red cartouche with rounded corners, and adjoining text in rectangular panel also with rounded corners. One or more figures; the set here arranged alphabetically. Pub. Yeshima; *c.*1840.

1. *Heike no kaburo* ('the Taira pages'), of whom three are shown, one holding a plum-blossom spray and another with a parrot(?). There were as many as 300 of these youths in Kyoto under Kiyomori, to whom they would report any sign of dissidence (*Sadler*, p.24; *Heike*, p.16).

PC.

2. Hotoke-gozen, in nun's dress after her retirement, holding a rosary; geese flying across the moon.

MFA; PC.

3. Jijū of Matsuyoi (the poetess Kojijū) in court dress seated on a wooden balcony.

VAM; MFA.

4. Katōji Kagekado, fully armed and holding a *naginata*, standing under a pine-tree by a stone lantern.

VAM; MFA.

5. Aki no Kami Taira no Kiyomori in hunting dress on Rendai moor encounters an apparition of the fox-goddess Koki-tennō, who foretells his future greatness.

VAM. *Robinson 1961*, Pl.37.

6. Mongaku Shōnin demonstrating his rough method of collecting pious subscriptions in the palace, as he beats a cowering nobleman with his subscription-book (*Sadler*, pp.77ff.; *Heike*, pp.312ff.).

VAM; PC.

S14.4

S15.1

7. Chōhyōye-no-jō Nobutsura advancing over several prostrate foemen at the fall of the Takakura palace (*Sadler*, p.49; *Heike*, pp.241 ff.).
PC.

8. Komatsu Daifu Shigemori-kyō standing, in court robes of black brocade, whilst an attendant tries to catch a snake wriggling out of his sleeve.
VAM; PC.

9. Hosshōji-shugyō Shunkwan abandoned on the sea-shore with the boy Ariō Maru, his servant.
MFA; PC.

10. Taira no Tadamori Ason, in court robes of black brocade, examining a sword by the light of a lamp; three courtiers behind. In so doing, he forestalled a plot by jealous noblemen to assassinate him (*Heike*, pp.7ff.).
MFA; PC.

11. (Pl.15) Sasaki Shirō Takatsuna commandeering a farmer's horse in order to go to war.
MFA; PC.

12. Gen Sammi Yorimasa picking up gold coins, watched by Kinyoshi-kyō, in black court robes.
VAM; MFA.

S16

Buyū go-gyō ('Heroes for the Five Elements'). *Chū-tanzaku.*

Title on narrow red cartouche with yellow reeded edge and shaped ends, adjoining which is a disc bearing one of the characters for the *Jikken* ('Ten Stems'; see *Koop*, p.63, and for the Five Elements p.103), two of which are allotted to each of the Elements. Historical and legendary characters; very similar in form and content to S17. Pub. Minato-ya Kohei; *c.*1840.

1. *Ki-Kō.* Bingo Saburō writing on the trunk of a cherry-tree a message of encouragement to the captive Emperor Go-Daigō.
B; PC.

2. *Ki-Otsu.* Satō Tadanobu using the *go*-board as a weapon as he resists arrest, and sending the pieces and their boxes flying.
MFA; PC.

3. *Hi-Hei.* Kusunoki Masashige seated on a stool, watching fox-fires on a dark hillside opposite.
B. *Riccar 1978,* 76.

4. *Hi-Tei.* Koga Saburō suspended over a

S16.4

chasm in a basket; he holds up a torch and watches a dragon below.
B; PC. *Riccar 1978,* 77; *Bidwell 1980,* 95.

5. *Tsuchi-Bō.* The murderer Fuchibe Yoshihiro approaching the cell where Ōto-no-miya (Prince Morinaga Shinnō) is reading the scriptures.
B; PC.

6. *Tsuchi-Ki.* The wrestling-match between Matano Gorō Kagehisa and Kawadzu Saburō Sukeyasu, umpired by Yebina Gempachi Hirotsuna.
B; PC. *Riccar 1978,* 78.

(No subsequent numbers have been noted.)

S17

Buyū mitate jūnishi ('Choice of heroes for the Twelve Signs'). *Chū-tanzaku.*

Title in narrow oblong cartouche with cut corners; character for the Sign in adjoining red square with cut corners. Historical or legendary characters. Pub. Minato-ya Kohei; *c.*1840.

1. The Rat. Raigō Ajari at the Onjōji monastery, Miidera, turning the Buddhist scriptures into rats in his disappointment of the Emperor's favour; the latter's envoy, Ōye no Masafusa, looks on in dismay.
VAM; MFA; B; PC.

2. The Ox. The robber Kidō Maru by moonlight, disguised under the buffalo-hide in which he attempted to ambush and kill Raikō, looking at his reflection in water.
VAM; MFA; B; PC. *Inouye,* Pl.96; *Bidwell 1968,* Pl.71.

3. The Tiger. Kashiwade no Omi Hatebe (*sic,* usually Hadesu) engaging the tiger that had killed his daughter.
VAM; MFA; B; PC.

4. The Hare. Iga Jutarō, the elderly retainer of Sōma Yoshikado, sacrificing a hare in a Buddhist temple.
VAM; MFA; B; PC.

5. The Dragon. Susa-no-o-no-mikoto ('the impetuous male'), standing on a rock with drawn sword, watching a dragon moving under the waves; this is probably intended for the eight-headed dragon he slew in Idzumo.
MFA; B; PC. *Inouye,* Pl.97; *Robinson 1961,* Pl.32b; *Riccar 1978,* 74; *Bidwell 1980,* 97.

6. The Snake. Nitta Shirō (Tadatsune), having penetrated the interior of Mount Fuji during Yoritomo's great hunting-party (1193), encounters snakes and a vision of the goddess of the mountain.
MFA; B; PC. *Inouye,* Pl.98; *Riccar 1978,* 73; *Bidwell 1980,* 98.

7. The Horse. Soga Gorō (Tokimune) galloping from Hakone to Mount Fuji, where he and his brother Jurō executed their revenge in the course of Yoritomo's great hunting-party (1193).
MFA; B; PC. *Inouye,* Pl.99; *Bidwell 1968,* Pl.70; *Riccar 1978,* 75.

S17.6

8. The Goat. The Chinese hero Kwanu (Kuan Yü) seated drinking under a pine-tree, with a goat before him.

VAM; MFA; B; PC. *Crighton*, V39; *Kruml*, 9.41.

9. The Monkey. The monkey-king Songoku (Sun Wu K'ung) conjuring an army of monkeys from the air to attack his enemy the pig.

VAM; MFA; B; PC.

10. The Cock. Kwaidō Maru (the boy Kintoki) umpiring a fight between a cock and a young *tengu*.

VAM; MFA; B; PC. *Crighton*, V40.

11. The Dog. Hata Rokurozayemon, a follower of Nitta Yoshisada, armed with a variety of weapons, and accompanied by his faithful dog.

VAM; MFA; B; PC.

12. The Boar. Yūryaku Tennō, the twenty-first Emperor (457–80), by a waterfall, killing a huge boar without using a weapon; this is said to have occurred on Mount Katsuragi in 461 (*Nihongi* I, p.344).

MFA; B; PC.

NOTE. The complete series is illustrated in colour in *Weber*, s.v. Zodiaque.

S18

Gempei seisuiki ('History of the ups and downs of the Minamoto and Taira'). Triptychs. See T58, T59, T60, T109, T123.

S19

Hyaku-nin isshu ('The Hundred Poets'). *Ōban*.

Title, incorporating poet's name, on red cartouche to the right of a shaded panel of poem and descriptive text, oblong with rounded corners. Scenes, the majority in a rather refined court style, illustrating sometimes the poet's life, sometimes his poem, and sometimes some more abstruse allusion. Nearly all are numbered (one or two incorrectly, as noted below). Pub. Yebi-Ne. The series is remarkable for the variety of seals accompanying the artist's signature. *c.*1840–2.

1. Tenchi Tennō. Peasants harvesting grain; above, palace with courtiers, overlooking the sea. Eng. Katsu.

VAM; RSM; MFA; B; PC. *Bidwell 1968*, Pl.54.

2. Jitō Tennō. The Empress at a palace door looking out on the wooded mountain of Kaguyama; a maid with her writing-box.

VAM; RSM; PC.

3. Kakinomoto no Hitomaro. The aged poet, holding his brush and with writing-materials before him, watching a pheasant.

BM; VAM; RSM; PC.

4. Yamabe no Akahito. The poet with a page on a hill overlooking the bay of Tago, beyond which Fuji appears.

BM; VAM; RSM; B; PC.

5. Sarumaru-dayū. Peasant woman with two children looking over a river and rice-fields at a steep hill on which are deer and autumn maples.

VAM; RSM; MFA; PC. *Düsseldorf 1961*, 17.

6. Chūnagon Yakamochi. Ori-hime, the Weaving Princess, and her husband mounted on an ox, among the clouds and stars. This illustrates the legend of the Milky Way, of Chinese origin, which was celebrated in Japan

S18.T123

as the Tanabata Festival on the seventh day of the seventh month.

BM; VAM; RSM; MFA; PC.

7. Abe no Nakamaro. The poet in China, on a moonlit balcony overlooking the sea, with a Chinese official and two pages.

BM; VAM; RSM; B; PC.

8. Kisen-hōshi. The poet seated in his lowly hut, looking out over lake and mountains; a servant sweeping up fallen twigs.

BM; VAM; RSM; MFA; PC.

S19.9

9. Ono no Komachi. The poetess, seated by her writing-table, watches cherry-blossom scattered by the wind.

BM; VAM; RSM; PC.

10. Semimaru. The blind poet at the window of his hut, with travellers on the road outside; he listens to their sounds.

VAM; RSM; B; PC.

11. Sangi Takamura. Stern view of a large sailing-junk, with a rowing-boat in the foreground.

BM; VAM; RSM; MFA; B; PC. *Bidwell 1968*, Pl.56; *Kruml*, 22.37.

12. Sōjō Henjō. *Bugaku* performance before an audience of noblemen and the poet, with a large drum in the foreground.

BM; VAM; RSM; PC.

13. Yōzei-in. Two travellers viewing the Mina waterfall, pointed out to them by two peasants.

VAM; RSM; B; PC. *Bidwell 1980*, 78.

14. Kawara no Sadaijin. The poet, with a court page and attendant, examining rolls of Michinoku flower-printed cloth.

VAM; RSM; B; PC.

15. Kōkō Tennō. The Emperor walking in the snow with four attendants, the latter wearing wide-brimmed hats, and one holding up an umbrella. Several different printings have been noted.

VAM; RSM; MFA;. B; PC. *Bidwell 1968*, Pl.55; *Riccar 1978*, 192; *Kruml*, 9.30; 13.28.

16. Chūnagon Yukihira. The poet on the road with a page, looking across a valley to Mount Inaba, as does a woodcutter with his boy.

BM; VAM; RSM; PC.

17. Ariwara no Narihira Ason. The poet, with a page and attendant, on the banks of the Tatsuta river watching the floating autumn maple-leaves.

BM; VAM; MFA; PC. *Robinson 1961*, frontispiece; *Crighton*, V42; *Bidwell 1980*, 79.

18. Fujiwara no Toshiyuki Ason. The poet, with a page and attendant, viewing the drum-bridge of Sumiyoshi temple among pine-trees above a band of mist.

BM; VAM; B; PC. *Kruml*, 13.21.

19 and 20. (not seen)

21. Sosei-hōshi. The poet seated on a mat addressing his page, who carries his writing-box; rocky mountain in the background.

BM; VAM; PC.

22. Bunya (Fumiya) no Yasuhide. The poet with page and attendant under a willow-tree; in the foreground an umbrella-merchant has most of his stock carried off by the wind.

BM; VAM; RSM; MFA; B; PC. *Robinson 1961*, Pl.30; *Iserlohn 1963*, 22; *Cologne 1963*, 38; *Ronin*, 79; *Kruml*, 9.37; 13.22.

23. Ōye no Chisato. Two bearers on the road with an empty palanquin; above them is the autumn moon surrounded by a ring or halo.

BM; VAM; MFA; B; PC. *Or.Art*, Spring 1961, p.26; *Bidwell 1968*, Pl.57; *UMS*, 7; *Riccar 1978*, 191; *Kruml*, 9.35/36.

24. Kanke. The poet leading a procession of courtiers and attendants escorting a white horse to a Shintō shrine on a hill.

BM; VAM; RSM; PC.

25–31. (not seen)

32. Harumichi no Tsuraki. Lady-pilgrim walking with her little maid; beyond a band of conventional mist is a rugged hillside with waterfall, pines, and maples.

BM; VAM; B; PC. *Riccar 1978*, 197.

33. Ki no Tomonori. The poet, with page and attendant, watching falling cherry-blossoms in the spring sunshine; sea, with sailing-boats, in the background.

BM; VAM; PC.

34. Fujiwara no Okikaze. The old poet walking along the shore on a rainy night by the ancient pine-tree of Takasago.

BM; VAM; B; PC. *Apollo*, May 1949, p.125; *Kruml*, 9.32.

35–37. (not seen)

38. Ukon. The poetess in walking dress carrying a wide-brimmed black hat; beyond a band of conventional mist, a wooded hillside.

BM; VAM; B; PC. *Kruml*, 13.29.

39. (not seen)

40. Taira no Kanemori. The poet taking refreshment with a priest in a palace interior.

BM; VAM; B; PC.

41. (not seen)

42. Kiyowara no Motosuke. The poet, accompanied by his lady, by a pine-tree on a cliff-top, pointing out over the sea.

VAM; PC. *Kruml*, 13.25.

43. Gonchūnagon Atsutada. The poet, by a screen, receiving a love-message brought by his page.

BM; VAM; B; PC.

44. Chūnagon Asatada. The poet, kneeling on a palace veranda with bowls of water and his court cap on a box, lacquering his teeth black. Cens. Taka.

VAM; PC.

45–47. (not seen)

48. Minamoto no Shigeyuki. The poet standing on a rocky cliff path watching the raging waves on the rocks below; Fuji in the background.

BM; VAM; RSM; MFA; B; PC. *Kruml*, 12.51.

49. Ōnakatomi no Yoshinobu Ason. Three palace guards round their fire at night.

BM; VAM; B; PC. *Robinson 1963*, Pl.6; *Illing 1980*, 17; *Kruml*, 9.39; 13.26.

50. Fujiwara no Yoshitaka. The poet seated in reverie in the palace, his hand to his forehead.

VAM; B; PC.

51 and 52. (not seen)

53. The mother of Udaishō Michitsuna. The poetess looks out of her window as a noble lover comes to her gate.

VAM; B; PC.

54 and 55. (not seen)

56. Idzumi-shikibu. The poetess with an attendant maid walking past an enormous pine-tree in a shower of rain.

BM; VAM; MFA.

57. Dainagon Kintō. The poet, with a page and five attendants, viewing a waterfall with overhanging pine-tree.

BM; VAM; RSM; B; PC.

58 and 59. (not seen)

60. Koshikibu-no-naishi. The Shuten-dōji and his two sons on a terrace by the wooded mountainside of Ōyeyama.

BM; VAM; B; PC.

61. Ise-no-ōsuke (or, no-tayū). A priest and his attendant waylaid under a blossoming cherry-tree by three *yamabushi*.

VAM; B; PC.

62. Sagami. The poetess on her veranda in the

evening looking out over a river and mist. Cens. Tanaka.

VAM; PC.

63. Sakyō-no-daibu (or, no-tayū) Michimasa. Two court ladies on a veranda, one holding a fan, and the other examining a written scroll of paper; blossoming cherry behind.

BM; VAM; MFA; PC.

64. Gonchūnagon Sadayori. A peasant operating a fish-trap in the dawn mists of the Uji river. Several variant printings have been noted.

BM; VAM; RSM; MFA; B; PC. *Inouye*, Pl.48; *Riccar 1978*, 194; *Bidwell 1980*, 80, 81; *Kruml*, 9.33/34; 13.27.

65 and 66. (not seen)

67. Suō-no-naishi. A young court noble peeps and beckons through bamboo blinds to the poetess and a companion, who are seated in the palace.

BM; VAM; PC.

68. (not seen)

69. Nōin-hōshi. A party of travellers caught in a downpour of rain.

VAM; B; PC. *Kruml*, 9.27; 13.23.

70. Ryōzen-hōshi. The poet and a fellow-traveller on the road by the reedy shore of a lake, the latter pointing out features of the landscape.

BM; VAM; MFA; B; PC. *Inouye*, Pl.49; *Kruml*, 13.31.

71. (numbered 72) Dainagon Tsunenobu. The poet at the window of his study at night sees an apparition howling out a poem.

BM; VAM; MFA; PC. *Robinson 1963*, Pl.7; *Kruml*, 9.29.

72. (correctly numbered 72) Yūshi-naishinnō-ke Kii. The poetess on a rocky cliff-top under a pine-tree overlooking the sea.

BM; VAM; PC.

73. (not seen)

74. (numbered 72) Minamoto no Toshiyori Ason. Woman with a child on her back, and a young girl with an umbrella; cherry-blossom on a mountain beyond a band of conventional mist.

VAM; PC.

75 and 76. (not seen)

77. Sutoku-in. The ghost of the poet-Emperor with flying hair, on a rock above the waves in a storm at night.

BM; VAM; MFA; B; PC. *Robinson 1961*, Pl.31; *Riccar 1978*, 196; *Bidwell 1980*, 82; *Kruml*, 9.31.

78. Minamoto no Kanemasa. The poet with a page at a palace window overlooking the sea, with sailing-ships and a flight of *chidori*.

BM; VAM; PC.

79. Sakyō-no-dayū Akisuke. The poet on a palace veranda on a windy night, viewing the moon.

BM; VAM; MFA; PC. *Kruml*, 13.24.

80. (not seen)

81. Go-tokudaiji Sadaijin. The poet on a palace veranda looking out over a rocky bay, with the moon, a flying cuckoo, and bands of conventional mist.

VAM; PC. *Kruml*, 13.32.

82. Dōin-hōshi. The poet and a young acolyte seated by a screen painted with a deer under a pine-tree, the latter with a scroll of paper before him.

VAM; B; PC. *Kruml*, 13.30.

83. Kōtaikōgū-no-tayū Shunzei (Toshinari). The poet with a page and two armed attendants, one holding up a torch, by a palace entrance with bands of conventional mist.

VAM; MFA; PC.

84 and 85. (not seen)

86. Saigyō-hōshi. The poet under a willow-tree on a river-bank showing a group of children the golden cat given him by the Emperor.

VAM; B; PC.

87. Jakuren-hōshi. The poet and a page, both with open umbrellas, walking through a pine-wood in an evening shower of rain.

BM; VAM; MFA; B; PC. *Illing 1976*, 81; *Kruml*, 9.28.

88 and 89. (not seen)

90. Impu-monin-no-ōsuke. Two girls carrying pails of salt water along the sea-shore; Mount Fuji in the distance.

BM; VAM; B; PC. *Riccar 1978*, 193.

91–96. (not seen)

97. Gonchūnagon Sada-iye. The poet nursing his pet cat whilst a page prepares its food; a lady standing by.

VAM; B; PC.

98. (not seen)

99. Go-Toba-no-in. The Emperor and an assistant forging a sword-blade; a page and attendant seated behind.

VAM; PC. *Apollo*, December 1947, p.133.

100. (not seen)

S20

Kenjo reppuden ('Stories of wise women and faithful wives'). *Ōban.*

Title on red oblong cartouche with rounded corners, framed by delicate 'smooth dragons' in yellow; text in shaded rectangular panel with rounded corners, adjoining. Single figures of historical women, with accessories, the background often plain. Pub. Iba-ya Sensaburō; *c.*1841–2.

1. Anju-hime on the sea-shore carrying two buckets of salt water on a shoulder-pole; a flight of 'wave-birds' (*chidori*) above her.

PC.

2. Chiyo of Kaga, carrying a bucket, approaches a well-head where convolvulus has twined round the well-bucket; her extempore poem on this occasion is quoted in the text.

VAM; PC.

3. Giō and Ginyo, the sister *shirabyōshi* dancers, gathering flowers after their retirement as nuns.

VAM; PC.

4. Go-ō-hime holding a folded paper and a spray of blossom, while two sparrows fly before her. Cens. Muramatsu.

PC.

5. Hangaku-jo wearing a hair-band and *kimono* over armour, wooden shields (*tate*) and a sword behind her, and a water-tub and dipper in front. Cens. Yoshimura.

VAM; PC.

6. Hatsu-jo drinking from a dipper at a garden tank in a shower of rain.

VAM; MFA; PC.

7. (Fig.5) Hatsu-hana in prayer under the Gongen waterfall at Hakone, by which means she procured the recovery of her crippled husband.

BM; VAM; B; PC. *Robinson 1963*, Pl.8; *Illing 1976*, 80; *Riccar 1978*, 135; *Bidwell 1980*, 111.

8. Hotoke-gozen examining a poem written on the *shōji* by the light of a lantern.

VAM; MFA; PC.

9. Hyakuman of Nara, dancing with a fan and pulling a little cart full of toys, watched by her bewildered child.

VAM; PC.

10. Idzumi-shikibu, on a visit to the Kamo shrine, lifting her travelling-veil as her maid mends the cord of her sandal with paper. Cens. Yoshimura.

VAM; MFA; PC.

11. Idzutsu-hime seated by a brazier, a lamp behind her and a book on the floor in front.

VAM; MFA; PC.

12. Jōruri-hime standing under a lamp with streamers, one sleeve held to her mouth. Cens. Yoshimura.

VAM; MFA; PC.

13. Kaji of Gion seated on a bench with her fans and writing-brushes. Cens. Yoshimura.

B; PC.

14. Kane-jo, the strong woman, holding a caparisoned horse. Cens. Yoshimura.

VAM; PC.

15. Kesa-gozen seated before a mirror and candlestick, cutting her hair in male fashion in order to impersonate her husband, and be killed in his stead.

VAM; MFA; PC. *Robinson 1961*, Pl.28; *Geneva 1978*, 30.

16. Masaoka protecting her charge, Tsugichiyo Maru, from the apparition of an old warrior-monk grasping his rosary. Cens. Yoshimura.

MFA; PC.

17. Ōiko damming a stream with a huge rock

in order to irrigate the local paddy-fields.
VAM; MFA; PC.

18. Sayo-hime in distress on a rocky cliff at Matsu-ura in the province of Higo, watching the departure of her husband's ship for Korea. PC.

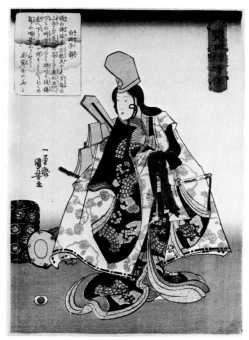

S20.19

19. Shidzuka-gozen wearing the full dress of a *shirabyōshi*, in which she danced before Yoritomo at Tsuru-ga-oka.
VAM; PC. *Düsseldorf 1961*, 15.

20. Take-jo the saintly servant-girl, a hanging pan forming a halo behind her head, sprinkling grain for the birds from a box. Cens. Yoshimura.
VAM; MFA; PC.

21. Tamayori-hime (usually Tamaori-hime) making fans in retirement after the death of her husband Atsumori. Cens. Muramatsu.
VAM; MFA; PC.

22. Terute-hime pulling the cart on which her crippled husband rode, whom she eventually cured at the Kumano-san hot springs.
VAM; PC.

23. (Pl.9) Tokiwa-gozen and her three children in the snow; a flight of herons above.
BM; MFA; B; PC. *Bidwell 1968*, Pl.74.

24. Tomoye-gozen seated on a padded mat supervising her young son Asahina Saburō at fencing practice.
VAM; RSM; PC.

25. Tora-gozen in a wind, her hat blowing away; after the affair of the Soga brothers she became a nun. Cens. Yoshimura.
VAM; MFA; PC.

26. Uneme in heavy court robes with a fan; a stand of *sake*-cups and ceremonial pourer are

near her (not the same Uneme as S23.23).
VAM; MFA.

27. Yamabuki-gozen seated on several shields (*tate*) by a log fire, mending the surcoat (*haori*) of her husband Yoshinaka.
VAM; MFA; PC.

28. The wife of Kajiwara Genda Kagesuye with a small girl-attendant carrying a branch of cherry-blossom.
VAM; MFA; PC.

29. The wife of Kusunoki Tei-i Masashige seated, restraining her young son Masatsura from performing *seppuku* after his father's death.
VAM; PC.

30. The wife of Idzumi no Saburō Tadahira (her name was Fujinoye) standing with a *naginata* while her attendant maid pours out hot drinks.
VAM; MFA; PC.

31. The daughter of Dainagon Yukinari seated at her drawing-table while her cat springs at a painting of a butterfly she has just executed, sending her brushes flying; so lifelike was the painting that the cat thought the butterfly was real. Cens. Muramatsu.
MFA; PC.

S21

Kenjo hakkei ('Virtuous women for the Eight Views'). *Chū-tanzaku.*

Title cartouche and text panel exactly similar to S20. Women of history and tradition. Pub. Iba-ya Sensaburō; single cens.; *c.*1842-3.

1. 'Autumn Moon on Saga Moor.' Kogō no Tsubone, driven from the court by intrigues, musing under the moon on the veranda of her rural retreat. Cens. Tanaka.
VAM; B; PC. *Inouye*, Pl.80; *Robinson 1961*, Pl.29b; *Cologne 1963*, cover; *Bidwell 1968*, Pl.86; *Speiser*, p.67; *Riccar 1978*, 161; *Bidwell 1980*, 120.

2. 'Lingering Snow on Mount Yoshino.' Shidzuka-gozen toiling through the snow after her last farewell to Yoshitsune. Cens. Tanaka.
VAM; B; PC. *Inouye*, Pl.83; *Robinson 1961*, Pl.29a; *Robinson 1963*, Pl.9a; *Speiser*, p.66; *Riccar 1978*, 159; *Geneva 1978*, 31.

3. 'Evening Glow at Yashima.' Tamamushi-no-maye watching the arrow of Nasu no Yoichi carry away the fan from the pole on her boat at the battle of Yashima. Cens. Tanaka.
B; PC. *Riccar 1978*, 163.

4. 'Vesper Bell at Uyeno.' The young poetess Shūshiki looks at the poem she has attached to a cherry-tree at Uyeno. Cens. Muramatsu.
B; PC. *Bidwell 1968*, Pl.85; *Riccar 1978*, 162.

5. 'Returning Boats at Tsukushi.' (Fig.14) The Empress Jingō, armed and in voluminous robes, watching the return of her victorious fleet from Korea. Cens. Tanaka.

S21.3

B; PC. *Cologne 1963*, 47; *Bidwell 1968*, Pl.84; *Riccar 1978*, 158; *Geneva 1978*, 32.

6. 'Clearing Weather at Mama.' The faithful wife of Mama in the province of Shimosa walking by a hillside in autumn. Cens. Tanaka.
B; PC. *Riccar 1978*, 165.

7. 'Night Rain at the Hunting-Ground.' Tegoshi no Shōshō waiting to guide the Soga brothers to their revenge; pouring rain outside. Cens. Tanaka.
VAM; B; PC. *Inouye*, Pl.82; *Robinson 1963*, Pl.9b; *Riccar 1978*, 164; *Bidwell 1980*, 119.

8. 'Homing Geese at Kanazawa.' The poetess Chiyo turns to watch a flight of wild geese while sweeping up autumn leaves; her poem is quoted:

hatsu kari ya	O the first wild goose!
narabete kiku wa	The chrysanthemums arranged—
oshiimono.	Something has been stol'n.

B; PC. *Inouye*, Pl.81; *Bidwell 1968*, Pl.87; *Speiser*, p.65; *Riccar 1978*, 160; *Bidwell 1980*, 118.

S22

Honchō bunyū hyaku-nin isshu ('A hundred poets from the literary heroes of our country'). *Chūban*.

Title on oblong coloured cartouche; descriptive text; poem on square patterned panel. A red *kakihan* associated with the character in question is also generally included. Heroes and historical figures who have written well-known verses. Pub. Mura-Tetsu; various cens., all singly; *c*.1842–3.

1. Abe Munetō wearing court robes over half-armour, holding a bow and arrows. Cens. Watari.
   PC.

2. Akugenda Yoshihira seated, glaring to the right. Cens. Tanaka.
   MFA; PC.

3. Asahina Saburō Yoshihide standing, in court robes, with fan. Cens. Hama.
   PC.

4. Ashikaga Tadayoshi seated before a large mirror, dressing for a *Nō* dance. Cens. Hama.
   MFA; PC.

5. Chinzei Hachirō Tametomo standing, in court robes and cap, with fan; a spray of cherry-blossom thrown at him by the maids at the time of his betrothal to Shiranui-hime. Cens. Mura.
   PC.

6. Kadzusa Akushichibyōye Kagekiyo standing, holding a closed fan and a wide straw hat. Cens. Mura.
   PC.

7. Kajiwara Genda Kagesuye standing, holding a wide straw hat. Cens. Mura.
   PC.

8. Komatsu Naidaijin Shigemori standing, in court robes of black brocade, holding the infant Emperor Antoku on his shoulder. Cens. Mura.
   PC.

9. Kō Musashi no Kami Moronao standing, holding a card on which is written his love-poem to the lady Kaoyo-gozen, as in the first act of the *Chūshingura*. Cens. Watari.
   PC.

10. Matsushima no Tsubone, seated, with her child before her. Cens. Mura.
    PC.

11. Minadzuru-hime, beloved of Yoshitsune, whom she helped to obtain copies of her father's scrolls of strategy (*Gikeiki*, p.53), standing barefooted, shielding a lantern with her sleeve. Cens. Muramatsu.
    MFA; PC.

12. Minamoto no Yoritomo standing, in court robes and cap, holding a fan and girt with a sword in tiger-skin sheath. Cens. Tanaka.
    MFA; PC.

13. Onzōshi Ushiwaka Maru seated, examining the strategic scroll *Sanryaku-no-maki* in the house of Ki-ichi Hōgen (cf. no.11 above). Cens. Muramatsu.
    MFA; PC.

14. Sarashina-hime with her son Shikanosuke and a bear-cub. Cens. Hama.
    PC. *Robinson 1961*, Pl.36.

15. Satō Shirobei Tadanobu seated, grasping his sword, his other hand on a *go*-board. Cens. Tanaka.
    PC.

16. Satsuma no Kami Tadanori seated at a writing-table, brush in hand. Cens. Mura.
    PC.

17. *Shirabyōshi* Mimyō, crouching, and holding a wide black hat amid falling cherry-petals. Cens. Watari.
    PC.

18. Shiranui-hime, wife of Tametomo, standing, with a branch of cherry-blossom (cf. no.6 above), and covering the lower part of her face with her sleeve. Cens. Watari.
    PC.

19. Soga Gorō Tokimune in boyhood, his hands clasped in prayer before an image of Fudō. Cens. Muramatsu.
    PC. *Kennedy*, 1980.79.

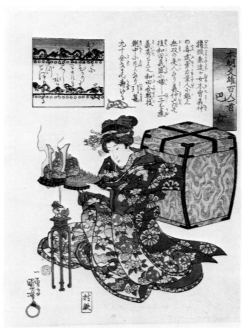

S22.20

20. Tomoye-jo seated, holding Yoshinaka's helmet in the smoke from a small incense-burner, an armour-box behind her. Cens. Muramatsu.
    PC.

S23

Honchō nijūshi-kō ('Twenty-Four Paragons of Filial Piety of our country'). *Chūban*.

Title on red cartouche with shaped ends, the name of the character on an adjoining blue panel, and descriptive text on a larger oblong panel, shaded and with rounded corners. Single figures and scenes. Pub. Mura-Tetsu; various cens. singly; *c*.1842–3.

1. Anju-hime and her younger brother Tsushiō Maru, she carrying two buckets on a pole over her shoulder, and he with a rake and a large basket of reeds on his back. Cens. Tanaka.
   PC.

2. Chiyonō-hime in a wind, holding a torch and a dirk, about to rescue her father from imprisonment after the rebellion of Aidzu no Tarō Nobuchika against Yoritomo. Cens. Fu.
   PC.

3. Chūjō-hime walking by a lotus-pond on a windy day. Cens. Tanaka.
   PC.

4. Hako-ō Maru (Soga Gorō) and his elder brother Ichiman Maru (Jurō) practising sword-strokes on a pile of snow in preparation for their revenge. Cens. Taka.
   PC.

5. Hino Kumawaka Maru, training to avenge his father, swinging on a bamboo across a stream. No cens.
   PC.

6. The dutiful girl (*kōjo*) of Hitotsuya, saved from the Hag of the Lonely House (*hitotsuya*) by an apparition of Kwannon. Cens. Fu.
   PC. *Inouye*, Pl.78.

7. Hitsu-no-saishō Haruhira on an embassy to China with his father Karu no Daijin, when the latter was drugged by the Emperor and forced to act as a lighthouse with a candle burning on his head. Cens. Hama.
   PC. *Kennedy*, 1980.71.

8. Homma Gennai-hyōye Suketada writing his farewell poem on a *torii* at Shitennōji with the blood of his finger after the death of his father Sukesada (*Taiheiki*, p.169). No cens.
   PC. *Kennedy*, 1980.70.

9. Ima-jo, a poor girl of Take-no-uchi village in the province of Yamato, catching a carp to feed her parents. Cens. Fu.
   PC.

10. Kamada Matahachi of Matsuzaka in the province of Ise fighting off wolves with a heavy iron bar in the Ashigara mountains of Idzu. Cens. Fu.
    VAM; PC.

11. Keyamura Rokusuke spending seven days under the Hikosan Gongen waterfall for the benefit of his mother. Cens. Muramatsu.
    VAM; MFA; PC.

12. (Takenori) Kinsuke seated, his bow behind him, and the court cap of a palace

guard before him; falling cherry-blossom. After some trouble over a bet on a horse-race, his father fled the court; Kinsuke eventually traced him, old and decrepit, and looked after him. Cens. Tanaka.

VAM; PC.

13. Kōju Maru seated, grasping a dirk and about to perform *seppuku*; travellers on a mountain behind. Cens. Hama.

PC.

14. Komatsu Sammi Shigemori-kyō in early youth. Cens. Muramatsu.

PC.

S23.15

15. Kusunoki Masatsura in court robes over armour, beside an armillary sphere on a starry night. Cens. Fu.

MFA; PC.

16. The dutiful girl of Matsuyama, named Karumo, looking with astonishment at a mirror on the floor in which she mistakes her own reflection for that of her dead mother. Cens. Muramatsu.

VAM; PC.

17. The dutiful youth of Mino province, holding an axe and a gourd, and with a bundle of wood on his back, watching wild geese fly across a waterfall. He had collected the wood in the mountains to warm his old father. Cens. Tanaka.

PC.

18. The dutiful girl Nobu by a boundary-stone, carrying a basket of rushes, her sickle on the ground. She looked after her old mother, and eventually became a nun. Cens. Fu.

PC.

19. Sono, daughter of Yoshioka Ichimisai, three puppies at her feet and carrying a *shakuhachi*, dressed as a nun, looking back at

wild geese flying across the moon. Cens. Tanaka.

B; PC.

20. Suketoki of Yamato holding a feather and a jar in front of a hydrangea-bush; two butterflies flutter about him. His father Suke-kuni had been passionately fond of flowers, and appeared to him, together with his mother, in the form of butterflies. Cens. Muramatsu.

PC.

21. Suō no Naishi, daughter of Ukon (both among the Hundred Poets), walking on a windy night. She served in the palace, and by her devotion her mother's sickness was cured. Cens. Muramatsu.

B; PC. *Riccar 1978*, 206.

22. Teruta-hime carrying a bucket of water through the snow. Cens. Muramatsu.

VAM; B; PC.

23. (Pl.16) Uneme of Atsuta exorcizing a monstrous serpent from a lake; she kneels on a rock above the water holding up a *gohei*, while lightning plays about her, and the serpent vanishes into the air in a swirling cloud. Cens. Hama.

B; PC. *Inouye*, Pl.79; *Bidwell 1968*, Pl.91; *Geneva 1978*, 56; *Riccar 1978*, 205; *Bidwell 1980*, 171.

24. The dutiful youth Yoji as a monkey-showman, leading his monkey, and watched by a child. By gaining a livelihood in this way he was able to help his sick mother. Cens. Tanaka.

PC.

25. Yuya holding a poem-card by a blossoming cherry-tree. She became a favourite of Taira no Munemori, while still caring for her old mother. Cens. Hama.

PC.

26. Zennojō of Shinano, with two demons and one of the Judges of Hell, sees a vision in a large mirror. His devotion to Jizō secured the recovery of his father from illness. Cens. Taka.

PC.

S24

Yeiyū Yamato Suikoden ('*Suikoden* of Japanese heroes'). *Chūban*.

Title on oblong red cartouche with narrow yellow border; name of character on adjoining coloured panel; text above. Single figures of heroes in action. Pub. Fujioka-ya Keijirō; single cens.; *c.* 1843.

1. (Uyesugi) Kenshin of Echigo standing, in armour, holding a general's baton (*saihai*). Cens. Tanaka.

MFA.

2. Yendō Musha Moritō, on the roof with a drawn sword, looks at the severed head of Kesa-gozen. Cens. Watari.

B. *Bidwell 1980*, 108.

3. Ogata Shuma (later Jiraiya) raising his

sword to kill a python attacking a large toad. Cens. Tanaka.

MFA.

4. Ōmori Hikoshichi carrying the demon-woman, and drawing his dirk as he sees the shadow below. Cens. Tanaka.

MFA.

5. O-Kane of Ōmi holding the horse under control. Cens. Tanaka.

MFA.

6. (Takeda) Shingen of Kai seated, armoured and robed, holding out his hand in a Buddhist gesture. Cens. Tanaka.

MFA.

7. Takagi Oriyemon.

PC.

S24.8

8. Hakamadare no Yasusuke standing in a rising mass of waves, his hands in a magical gesture. Cens. Watari.

PC.

S25

Jikken onna ōgi ('Ten wise women's fans'). *Chūban*.

Title on oblong red cartouche; text, by Ryūkatei Tanekazu, on shaded rectangular panel. Single figures of historical women, with or without accessories. Pub. Fujioka-ya Hiko-tarō; cens. Muramatsu; *c.* 1843.

1. Kaji of Gion seated on a bench above water, holding a fan (*uchiwa*) and watching the smoke issuing from a fumigator.

PC.

2. Tora of Ōiso nursing her baby, the son of Soga Jurō Sukenari; toys on the ground.

PC.

3. (Pl.22) Shidzuka-gozen in the robes and

S25.1

S26.5/6

cap of a *shirabyōshi* dancer, carrying a hand-drum (*tsudzumi*).

PC.

S26

Oguri jū-yūshi no ichi-nin ('The ten brave retainers of Oguri, one by one'). *Chūban*, forming diptychs.

Title on small oblong yellow cartouche; character's name on larger adjoining red cartouche; text on shaded rectangular panel. Single figures and accessories. Pub. Yawata-ya Sakujirō; cens. Fu; *c.*1843. (See J. S. de Benneville, *Oguri Hangwan.*)

1 and 2. (title panel omitted) Oguri Hangwan Sukeshige standing, with a closed fan, and Terute-hime seated in a wooden trolley with rope attached.

PC.

3 and 4. Gotō Hyōsuke Suketaka holding his horse and a *naginata* (he was an expert horseman and archer), and his brother Gotō Daihachirō Takatsugu cooking over a fire of burning arrows.

VAM (no.4); PC.

5 and 6. Tanabe Heirokurō Nagahide, with three arrows sticking in his back, drinking *sake* with a dipper from a cask labelled *kirokumo* ('demon-stag's fur'), and his brother Tanabe Heihachirō Nagatame wiping his sword.

VAM; MFA; PC.

7 and 8. Mitono Kotarō Tamehisa and Kazama Hachirō Masakuni both shining dark-lanterns upwards, the former in a fur jacket with a weighted chain, and the latter in what appears to be a Restoration wig, his hand on his sword-hilt.

VAM; PC.

9 and 10. Ike-no-shōji Sukenaga and Kazama Jirō Masasada, both wearing *hakama*, the former leaning on his sword, and the latter

grasping his in both hands; a smashed *bonsai* and ceremonial dipper on the ground.

VAM (no.10); PC.

11 and 12. Night-scene with Katayama Kajirō Harutaka in armour, raising his hat, confronted by Katayama Katarō Harunori holding his sword with both hands behind his back; a *komusō* hat on the ground.

VAM; MFA; PC.

S27

Sumi-ire hyaku-nin isshu ('The Hundred Poets of the Inkstand'). *Koban*.

Title on oblong red cartouche, with poet's name and references to *Manyōshū* and other anthologies adjoining on a similar yellow cartouche; square panel of descriptive text, and poem printed without frame. The style and designs closely resemble those of S19. Pub. Sa-Ichi of Ichigaya; cens. Hama; *c.*1843.

1. Tenchi Tennō. The Emperor on a palace balcony overlooking a misty landscape.
PC.

2. Jitō Tennō. The Empress and a maid looking back at a garden pavilion.
PC.

3. Kakinomoto no Hitomaro. The poet at his writing-desk, chin in hand, watching a pheasant in a tree.
PC.

4. Yamabe no Akahito. The poet(?) on the rocky sea-shore with Mount Fuji in the background.
PC.

5. (not seen)

6. Chūnagon Yakamochi. The poet on a

veranda contemplating a building through the mist.

PC.

7. Abe no Nakamaro. The poet seated on the foreign shore with two Chinamen, one of whom points across the sea towards Japan.
PC.

8. Kisen-hōshi. Two girls seated tea-picking; one of them rebukes a wandering child.
PC.

9. Ono no Komachi. The poetess seated on a palace veranda.
PC.

10. Semimaru. The blind poet seated at the window of his hut listens to the sound of passing travellers on the road.
PC.

11 and 12. (not seen)

13. Yōzei-in. The Emperor, bareheaded, seated on a veranda; background of mist and distant mountains.
PC.

14. Kawara no Sadaijin. The poet seated, dozing, with folded arms; background of river and drying clothes.
PC.

15. Kōkō Tennō. Two court ladies and three pages searching for young greens (*wakana*) in the snow.
PC.

16. Chūnagon Yukihira. Attendants carrying a palanquin, under the eye of a supervisor; wooded hill behind.
PC.

17. Ariwara no Narihira. The poet with a

page beside the Tatsuta river, viewing the autumn maples.
PC.

18. Fujiwara no Toshiyuki Ason. The poet dozing at his writing-table by lamplight, a screen behind him.
PC.

19. Ise. The poetess, fan in hand, walking by the sea-shore; distant sailing-boats.
PC.

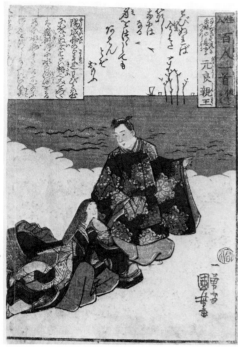

S27.20

20. Motoyoshi-shinnō. The Prince and his lady by the sea; distant sailing-boats.
PC.

(No further numbers of this series have been seen.)

S28

Buyū nazoraye Genji ('Heroic comparisons for the Chapters of Genji'). *Ō-tanzaku*.

Title in plain red cartouche adjoining oblong panel containing *Genji-mon*, an allusive design, and the name of the chapter; descriptive text in a third oblong panel. Historical and legendary scenes. Pub. Iba-ya Sensaburō; cens. Mura; *c*.1843.

1. *Kiritsubo*. Takeshiuchi-no-sukune and the infant Emperor Ōjin.
PC.

2 and 3. (not seen)

4. *Yugao*. Moonlight on Gojō bridge, Kyoto: Ushiwaka playing his flute; Benkei behind.
B; PC. *UT*, 173; *Riccar 1978*, 82; *Bidwell 1980*, 126; *Falteri*, 1981.139.

5 and 6. (not seen)

7. *Momiji no ga*. (Pl.18) Taira no Koremochi awakening from a drunken sleep; a lady behind

him, whose face is reflected as that of a demon in his *sake*-cup; falling maple-leaves. This late tenth-century story formed the subject of the *Nō* play *Momiji-gari*.
B; PC.

8–15. (not seen)

16. *Sekiya*. (Fig.4) Minamoto no Yoshi-iye riding past the barrier guardhouse (*sekiya*) of Nakoso on his way from the subjugation of Mutsu, and admiring the flowering cherries.
B; PC. *Robinson 1961*, Pl.32a; *Riccar 1978*, 79.

17. (not seen)

18. *Matsukaze*. The robber chieftain Kuma-saka Chōhan seated under a pine-tree having a large cup of *sake* poured for him by a henchman.
B; PC.

19–31. (not seen)

S28.32

32. *Umegaye*. Kajiwara Genda Kagesuye, a blossoming plum-branch (*umegaye*) stuck in his armour in honour of his lady-love Umegaye, fighting at Ikuta-no-mori (cf. T153).
B; PC.

33–37. (not seen)

38. *Suzumushi*. Satsuma no Kami Tadanori, in court robes with open fan, outside the house of Kiku-no-maye of the Miyabara family, whom he was courting.
VAM; B; PC.

39–44. (not seen)

45. *Hashi-hime*. Watanabe no Tsuna, on horseback, encounters the demon-woman Ibaraki at the Modori bridge, Ichijō, Kyoto.
VAM; B; PC.

46. *Yadorigi*. The wife of Sano Tsuneyo entertaining the regent Hōjō Tokiyori, disguised as the monk Saimyōji, and cutting up a valuable *bonsai* tree for firewood. Under its title of *Hachinoki*, 'The Potted Trees', this story formed the subject of a *Nō* play.
VAM; B; PC.

47–50. (not seen)

51. *Ukifune*. The death of Nitta Yoshioki at the Yaguchi ferry in 1358, where he was shot down by the Ashikaga in ambush.
B; PC.

52–54. (not seen)

S29

Kenyū fujo kagami ('Mirror of women of wisdom and courage'). *Ōban*.

Title on rectangular coloured cartouche, with text, by Ryūkatei Tanekazu, adjoining on lightly shaded rectangular panel. Each shows the head and shoulders of a historical woman on a circular 'mirror' surrounded by appropriate flowers; plain background. Pub. Arita-ya and Takahashi-ya; cens. Tanaka; *c*.1843.

1. Chiyo-jo.
B; PC.

2. Chūjō-hime holding the two ends of a string-game or puzzle against a background of brocade with a water-wheel design. Lotus.
MFA; B; PC. *Düsseldorf 1961*, 18.

3. Hanjo-gozen with a bamboo branch over her shoulder, to which a fan is attached. Cherry-blossom.
B; PC.

4. Kaji of Gion holding a fan (*uchiwa*) to her mouth. Convolvulus.
MFA; B; PC.

5. Kane-jo of Ōmi carrying a tub of washing. Pinks.
MFA; B; PC. *Bidwell 1968*, Pl.90.

6. Matsushima no Tsubone, a writing-brush in her mouth, examining a roll of stuff bearing a diaper pattern. Tiger-lilies.
B; PC.

7. Ōiko striking a light, a pipe in her mouth. Irises.
B; PC.

8. Ono no Komachi peeping under an umbrella and holding a poem on her fan. Peonies.
B.

9. Tokiwa-gozen in the snow, sheltering her children under her hat. Poppies.

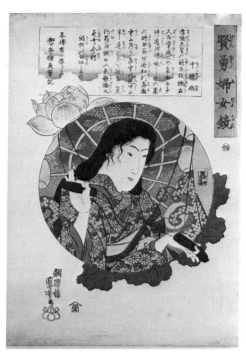

S29.2

S30.4

MFA; B; PC. *Düsseldorf 1961*, 19; *FH*, 6; *Speiser*, p.69.

10. Tomoye-jo.
B.

S30
Kokon honchō meijo hyaku den ('A hundred stories of famous women of our country, ancient and modern'). *Ōban*.

Title on yellow-bordered red oblong cartouche, surmounted by a crown of European type; text above, by Ryūkatei Tanekazu. Single figures of women, with accessories, on plain background shaded at the base. Pub. Kawaguchi-ya Uhei; cens. Tanaka; *c*.1843.

1. Giō and Ginyo (cf. S20.3).
PC.

2. Gion no Nyōgo (cf. S46.26).
PC.

3. Kasane, a farmer's daughter of Haniū, Okada, in the province of Shimosa, seated smoking.
VAM; MFA.

4. The dutiful woman (*kōjo*) of Kawada village in the province of Yamashiro, seated reading a scroll, and surrounded by crabs.
VAM; MFA.

5. Tomoye-gozen, here shown as the wife of Wada Yoshimori, clasping a pillar in the palace.
MFA; PC.

S31
Meikō hyaku yū den ('Stories of a hundred heroes of high renown'). *Ōban*.

Title on rectangular red cartouche, the upper end convex and the lower concave in outline. Single figures on plain background, with biographical text above. Pub. Idzumi-ya Ichibei; various cens. singly; *c*.1843–4. This was the first series in which Kuniyoshi worked out what became his favourite format for series of historical portrait-biographies: single figures on relatively plain ground with text above. It is found in numerous series between 1845 and 1850, e.g. S32, S36, S37, S43, S50–S59, S62, S63, etc.

1. Mukwan-no-tayū Atsumori in armour playing the flute. Cens. Watari.
PC.

2. Musashi-bō Benkei seated, wearing court robes over armour, having just written an inscription dated Juyei 3 (1184) on a notice-board. Cens. Muramatsu.
VAM; MFA; PC.

3. The Empress Jingō Kōgō, robed, seated on a rock, on the summit of which are two jewels in a bowl. Cens. Muramatsu.
RSM. An original sketch for this print is in the Schack collection (see G. Schack, *Japanischen Handzeichnungen*, Hamburg, 1976, Pl.74a).

4. Kadzusa no Shichibyōye Kagekiyo wielding a broken beam as he resists arrest. Cens. Watari.
MFA; PC. *Falteri*, 1981.145.

5. Kajiwara Kagesuye seated, looking at a notebook, his brush in his hand; his body-armour stands behind him. Cens. Mura.
PC.

6. Uyesugi Kenshin, armoured, seated on a stool and holding a general's baton (*saihai*). Cens. Muramatsu.
VAM; RSM; PC. *Falteri*, 1981.143.

7. Sakata no Kintoki breaking two millstones with his bare hands. Cens. Fu.
RSM; MFA; PC.

8. Taira no Kiyomori in later life, seated on a mat with a potted tree beside him. Cens. Fu.
VAM; PC.

9. Suruga Jirō Kiyoshige in armour with a huge anchor. Cens. Mura.
VAM.

10. Kusunoki Masashige in court robes seated beside a celestial globe. Cens. Muramatsu.
VAM; PC.

11. Kamei Rokurō Shigekiyo on one knee, in armour, examining his sword; arrows on the ground. Cens. Mura.
MFA; PC. *Falteri*, 1981.152.

12. Taira no Shigemori, standing, in cap and full court robes of black brocade (blind printing). Cens. Fu.
VAM; PC. *Robinson 1961*, Pl.33.

13. Hatakeyama Shigetada seated on a chest, a notebook on his knee and a brush in his hand, in full armour with helmet-crest of rabbit's ears. Cens. Mura.
VAM; PC.

14. Takeda Shingen, front view, seated on a stool, rosary and war-fan in hand, fully armoured, his helmet having horns and a white mane. Cens. Muramatsu.
VAM; RSM; PC. *Falteri*, 1981.141.

15. Satō Tadanobu on one knee, in armour, tying on one of his greaves, his helmet beside him. Cens. Mura.
MFA; PC. *Falteri*, 1981.151.

16. Sasaki Takatsuna in armour with surcoat and court cap, fan in hand, standing in a respectful posture. Cens. Mura.
MFA; PC. *Falteri*, 1981.149.

17. Takechi- (so read in *kana*, but characters for Takeuchi or Takeshiuchi) no-sukune, an old man in court robes and a Chinese collar, seated on a fur rug, his war-fan on a stand beside him. Cens. Watari.
PC.

18. Kataoka Hachirō Tameharu on one knee, a straw cloak over his armour, holding his sword and a weighted chain. Cens. Mura.
MFA; PC. *Falteri*, 1981.146.

19. (Fig.10) Chinzei Hachirō Tametomo with a huge rough bow, seated on a rock and shading his eyes. Cens. Muramatsu.
RSM; PC.

20. (Soga) Gorō Tokimune, feet planted wide apart, glares ahead while grasping a very long sheathed sword. Cens. Mura.
RSM; MFA; PC.

21. Taira no Tomomori, in cap and court robes over armour, seated on a tiger-skin, a coral sword-rack beside him. Cens. Mura.
VAM; PC.

22. Tomoye-jo (Tomoye is written here with two characters that mean '[archer's] wrist-

S31.20

shield' and 'picture') wearing full armour and a tall black cap, adjusting her hair before a large mirror. Cens. Watari.

PC.

23. Watanabe no Tsuna seated in full court robes, a pile of offerings with *gohei* behind him. Cens. Mura.

PC. *Falteri*, 1981.148.

24. Minamoto no Yorimasa standing in court robes and holding his bow. Cens. Mura.

VAM; MFA; PC.

25. Minamoto no Yorimitsu (Raikō) dancing bareheaded in wide court trousers, fan in hand; a lacquered stool behind him. Cens. Fu.

PC.

26. Minamoto no Yoritomo seated on a fur-covered stool, fan in hand, wearing a court cap and wide trousers. Cens. Muramatsu.

VAM; PC.

27. Asahina Yoshihide in armour, a long sword (*nodachi*) slung on his back, holding a large iron club and the piece of armour he tore from Soga Gorō. Cens. Mura.

VAM; MFA; PC. *Falteri*, 1981.147.

28. Genda Yoshihira in armour, bareheaded, gesturing with his left hand, and with a sword in his right. Cens. Mura.

VAM; PC. *Falteri*, 1981.150.

29. Minamoto no Yoshi-iye, bareheaded in court robes, holding a bow and a fan, and looking at an arrow stuck in the ground. Cens. Muramatsu.

VAM; PC.

30. Ise Saburō Yoshimori seated on a rock with a huge axe. Cens. Mura.

VAM. *Falteri*, 1981.153.

31. Minamoto no Yoshinaka seated on a tiger-skin, in full armour with surcoat, holding a general's baton; his helmet on a stand behind. Cens. Fu.

VAM; PC.

32. Nitta Yoshisada seated on a tiger-skin playing a hand-drum; his sword on a stand behind him. Cens. Fu.

VAM; RSM; MFA; PC.

33. Sanada Yoichi Yoshitada in hunting dress, holding his bow and raising his hat. Cens. Watari.

PC. *Falteri*, 1981.144.

34. Minamoto no Yoshitomo in full armour, seated on a stool with a cup of *sake* in his hand. Cens. Mura.

PC. *Falteri*, 1981.142.

35. Minamoto no Yoshitsune in full armour and surcoat, seated on a tiger-skin, his hand on an arm-rest. Cens. Muramatsu.

VAM; PC.

S32

Honchō buyū kagami ('Mirror of our country's military elegance'). *Ōban*.

Title in red oblong cartouche with rounded wavy frame of yellow; text adjoining in large oblong shaded panel. Single figures of heroes on plain background. Pub. Sano-ya Kihei; cens. Mura; *c*.1845.

1. Asahina Saburō Yoshihide holding the piece of armour he tore from Soga Gorō.

VAM.

2. Musashi-bō Benkei seated, about to write (may form diptych with no.11 below).

VAM.

3. Kwanrei Uyesugi Danjō-no-daihitsu Teru-tora Nyūdō Kenshin Fushiki-in Daisōdzu seated, wearing warrior-monk's robes over armour, and holding a club.

PC.

4. Kumagaye Jirō Naozane in armour, but bareheaded, making a sword-stroke.

PC.

5. Komatsu Naidaijin Shigemori standing in cap and full court robes of black brocade.

BM; VAM; RSM.

6. Takeda Daizendayū-ken Shinano no Kami Minamoto no Ason Harunobu Nyūdō Toku-yeiken Hōshō-in Daisōjō Gizan (Shingen) seated, in monk's robes with hood, holding a war-fan; his helmet, with horns, mask, and white mane, on a stand beside him.

PC.

7. Minamoto no Tametomo shooting.

VAM.

8. Taira no Tomomori, wearing court robes over armour, holding his *naginata*.

VAM; RSM.

9. Tomoye-gozen wearing a *kimono* over armour and holding up a dirk, a tray and *sake*-dipper before her.

VAM; PC.

S32.6

10. Minamoto no Yoritomo seated, bare-headed, in armour, holding a notebook and writing-brush.

VAM; PC.

11. Minamoto no Yoshitsune seated, wearing a court cap and a transparent green robe over his armour, holding a fan.

VAM; PC.

S33

Honchō taoyame soroi ('Set of delicate ladies of our country'). *Ōban*.

Title on red oblong cartouche with narrow frame, the lady's name on a much smaller panel adjoining. Single figures on lightly shaded background of clouds, with poems by various hands. Pub. Wakasa-ya Yoichi; cens. Mura; *c*.1845.

1. Chiyo of Kaga standing with a fan, a blue pot of morning glory standing beside her.

VAM; PC. *Robinson 1963*, Pl.14.

2. Hotoke-gozen in travelling dress by moon-light.

VAM; PC.

3. Kesa-gozen in a *kimono* with wistaria pattern, her sleeves and skirt caught by the breeze.

PC.

4. Shidzuka-gozen standing, wearing a big black sash.

VAM.

5. Muro no Ukareme ('courtesan of Muro'—a busy port) with a long letter blowing about her head like the scarf of a Buddhist statue.

VAM; PC.

S33.2

S34.3

S34

(Shinshū) Kawanakajima hyaku yūshō sen ('A hundred generals, brave in battle, at Kawanakajima (in the province of Shinano)'). *Ōban.*

Title on red oblong cartouche, with the character's name on a similar coloured panel adjoining. Large heads in bold style, and background of river and silhouetted warriors fighting. Various pub.; cens. Fu; *c.*1845.

Takeda

1. Takeda Harunobu Nyūdō Shingen, in his usual horned and maned helmet, raising his war-fan above his head. Pub. Kiyomidzu-ya Naojirō.
    MFA; B.

2. Takeda Inashirō Katsuyori in youth, robed over his armour, holding a fan and with his hand on his dirk-hilt. Pub. Kadzusa-ya Iwazō.
    RSM; B.

3. Takeda Sama-no-suke (Nobushige), 'the loyal general', in armour, grasping a general's baton. Pub. Kojima or Manju.
    MFA; B; PC.

4. (Fig.8) Yamamoto Kansuke Nyūdō Haruyuki, 'the tactician', wounded to death with arrows, grasping a spear. Pub. Kadzusa-ya Iwazō.
    MFA; B; PC.

5. Hara Hayato-no-shō, 'the brave general', bareheaded, in armour, grasping his spear. Pub. Kiyomidzu-ya Naojirō.
    MFA; B; PC.

6. Naitō Shuri Masatoyo, 'the brave general', grasping the shaft of a *naginata*, with helmet-crest of Raijin amid clouds and lightning. Pub. Kadzusa-ya Iwazō.
    RSM.

7. Sanada Kihei Masayuki, bareheaded, with a spear of *hoko* type over his shoulder. Pub. Yamashiro-ya Heisuke.
    MFA; B.

Uyesugi

8. This must be Uyesugi Kenshin, though not seen.

9. (Pl.30) Amakasu Ōmi no Kami, 'the rear-guard', bareheaded in profile, making a stroke with his *naginata*. Pub. Yamashiro-ya Heisuke.
    B; PC. *Bidwell 1968*, Pl.108; *Kennedy, 1980.77.*

10. Arakawa Idzu no Kami, 'the brave general', bareheaded in armour, under the streamers of a standard. Pub. Kadzusa-ya Iwazō.
    RSM; MFA.

11. Nagao Echizen no Kami Masakage, 'the brave general', wearing a helmet with cape attached. Pub. Kadzusa-ya Iwazō.
    RSM; MFA; B; PC.

12. Naoye Yamashiro no Kami Kanetsugu, 'the intelligent general', in a horned helmet, carrying a spear. Pub. Kojima or Manju.
    MFA; PC.

S35

Chūkō meiyo kijin den ('Stories of remarkable persons of loyalty and high reputation'). *Ōban.*

Title in large formal script on colour-flecked oblong cartouche with narrow yellow border, adjoining a coloured and patterned rectangular panel of text. Mostly single figures with full background. Pub. Ise-Ichi or Yenshū-ya Matabei; various cens., singly; *c.*1845.

1. Hatchō-tsubote ('eight *chō* pebble') Kiheiji, so called because he could bring down game at

long range (a *chō* is more than 100 yards) by throwing stones, and his wife Yatsushiro at the attack on the Aso family in Higo. Cens. Kinugasa.
    MFA; PC.

2. Hidari Jingorō the sculptor, the dragon and two 'lions' he has carved coming to life to chase the pursuers of his lord's daughter. Cens. Muramatsu.
    MFA; PC.

3. (Fig.6) Jigoku ('hell') the courtesan, under the patronage of the priest Ikkyū, enthroned, holding a Buddhist fly-whisk, and with a table of incense utensils beside her. Cens. Kinugasa.
    PC.

4. Kaji-jo, the poetess of Gion, Kyoto.
    MFA.

5. Kane-jo, carrying her washing-tub, and the runaway horse. Cens. Kinugasa.
    MFA; PC. *Inouye*, Pl.74; *Riccar 1978*, 207.

6. The poetess Kikaku in a boat under a bridge during a shower of rain. Cens. Muramatsu.
    MFA; PC. *Inouye*, Pl.75.

7. Koshikibu-no-naishi with her servant at the Kitano temple, Kyoto, looking back at a celebrated painting of a cuckoo; when she extemporized a poem the bird responded. Cens. Kinugasa.
    MFA; PC.

8. Miyamoto Musashi, armed with two wooden swords, fencing with the old master Tsukaharà Bokuden, who uses two wooden pot-lids. Cens. Kinugasa.
    RSM; MFA.

9. Oguri Hangwan Ujishige, attended by Terute-hime, holding the vicious horse Oni-kage. Cens. Kinugasa.
    VAM; MFA; PC.

10. Ono no Tōfū (Michikaze), in court robes with an umbrella under a willow-tree, learns perseverance from the efforts of a frog to climb one of the branches. Cens. Kinugasa.
    VAM; MFA; PC.

11. Settsu no Zenji (Hirai) Yasumasa playing the flute on a moonlit windy night, and the robber Hakamadare Yasusuke stealing up behind him. Cens. Kinugasa.
    PC.

12. Shidzuka-gozen.
    MFA.

13. Shūshiki the poetess wearing her father's overcoat in a shower of rain. Cens. Kinugasa.
    MFA; PC. *Robinson 1963*, Pl.12.

14. Sugimoto Sakubei, retainer of Kusunoki Masashige, weeping before the latter's son Masatsura (cf. T352).
    MFA.

15. Chinzei Hachirō Tametomo, with a huge improvised bow, talking to a fisher-girl in his

S35.10

exile on Ōshima, a large anchor behind them. Cens. Kinugasa.
MFA; PC.

16. Yamamoto Kansuke in early life overcoming a giant boar in the snow. Cens. Kinugasa.
MFA; PC.

S36

Dai Nippon rokujūyo-shū ('The sixty-odd provinces of Japan'). *Ōban*.

Title and name of province on oblong red cartouche; text, by Shōtei Kinsui, on upper part of print. One or two figures and accessories on plain background. Adjoining the title is a small inset picture, signed by a pupil and relevant to the main subject, in a rectangular panel. Twenty-one of the forty-seven recorded prints of this series are by Kunisada. Various pub.; cens. Watari; c.1845.

1. Yamashiro. Ono no Komachi, *by Kunisada*. PC.

2. Yamato. 'Kitsune' ('fox') Tadanobu, *by Kunisada*.
VAM; PC.

3. Kawachi (not seen).

4. Idzumi. Kuzunoha, the fox-woman, and her child. Inset by Yoshimune: her husband finds her farewell poem written on the *shōji*. Pub. Fujioka-ya Hikotarō.
VAM; PC.

5. Settsu (not seen).

6. Iga. Karaki Masayemon, *by Kunisada*.
VAM.

7. Ise. Fukuoka Mitsugi, *by Kunisada*.
VAM.

8. Shima. O-Kon by a table on which are a *gohei*, a jingle of bells, and an inscribed tablet. Inset by Yoshikatsu: the 'Husband and Wife'

rocks off the coast of Ise. Pub. Jōshū-ya Kinzō.
VAM; PC.

9. Owari. The lady Akoya, *by Kunisada*.
VAM.

10. Mikawa. Jōruri-hime and her maid. Inset by Yoshiume: Ushiwaka Maru outside her house. Pub. Jōshū-ya Kinzō.
VAM.

11. Tōtōmi (not seen).

12. Suruga (not seen).

13. Kai. Yayegaki-hime, *by Kunisada*.
VAM; PC.

14. Idzu. Tatsu-hime, *by Kunisada*.
VAM; PC.

15. Sagami. Shiragiku Maru, *by Kunisada*.
VAM; PC.

16. Musashi. Banzui Chōbei wielding a kitchen-knife above a captive trussed like a fish. Inset by Yoshitsuna: man with a sword in a *sake*-shop. Pub. Wakasa-ya Yoichi.
VAM; PC. *Robinson 1963*, Pl.13.

17. Awa. Fuse-hime and the dog, *by Kunisada*.
VAM; PC.

18. Kadzusa. Shirafuji Genda and a *kappa*, *by Kunisada*.
VAM; PC.

19. Shimosa (not seen).

20. Hitachi. Oguri Hangwandai Sukeshige, *by Kunisada*.
VAM; PC.

21. Ōmi. Shimidzu no Kwanja Yoshitaka and the giant rat. Inset by Yoshimaru: the daughter of Yoritomo. Pub. Yawata-ya Sakujirō.
VAM; PC.

22. Mino. Ushiwaka Maru at the inn, sword in hand, his *kimono* on a rack behind. Inset by Yoshihisa-jo: Kumasaka Chōhan. Pub. Jōshū-ya Jūzō; eng. Teppō.
VAM; PC.

23. Hida. Koman defending herself against the Taira. Inset by Yoshikono: Munemori on the barge. Pub. Jōshū-ya Kinzō.
VAM.

24. Shinano (not seen).

25. Kōdzuke. Tamamo-no-maye, *by Kunisada*.
VAM.

26. Shimotsuke (not seen).

27. Mutsu (not seen).

28. Dewa. Tamatsukuri, who was compared to Ono no Komachi, looking at an old rotting helmet resembling a skull, just as Narihira is said to have seen the skull of Komachi. Inset by Yoshitsuna: Narihira in the snow by his carriage. Pub. Maru-ya Jimpachi.
PC.

29. Wakasa (not seen).

30. Echizen. Shinodzuka Iga no Kami, *by Kunisada*.
VAM; PC.

31. Kaga (not seen).

32. Noto. Noto no Kami Noritsune, *by Kunisada*.

33. Etchū. Takiyasha-hime, *by Kunisada*.
VAM; PC.

34. Echigo. Naoye Yamashiro no Kami, *by Kunisada*.
VAM; PC.

35. Sado. Hino Kumawaka Maru with his foot on the neck of a vanquished opponent. Inset by Yoshiharu: Kumawaka's father on a balcony in the snow, holding up a lantern. Pub. Yawata-ya Sakujirō.
VAM; PC.

36. Tamba (not seen).

37. Tango. Anju-hime and Tsushiō Maru, *by Kunisada*.
VAM; PC.

38. Tajima. Seijurō in travelling dress with a bearer. Inset by Yoshitada: O-Natsu at a window (from the play *O-Natsu-Seijurō*). Pub. Koga-ya Katsugorō.
VAM.

39. Inaba. Shirai Gompachi, *by Kunisada*.
VAM; PC.

40. Hōki (not seen).

41. Idzumo. O-Kuni in her dressing-room. Inset by Yoshitoyo: Nagoya Sanzayemon at a window. Pub. Jōshū-ya Jūzō.
VAM.

42. Iwami (not seen).

43. Oki. Kojima Bingo no Saburō Takanori holding his *biwa*, and at the same time kneeling on a fallen assailant. Inset by Yoshikazu: court noble on a balcony by a screen. Pub. Wakasa-ya Uhei.
PC.

44. Harima. The murder of the maid O-Kiku by her master Ōkumo Tessan. Inset by Yoshitsuru: retainer by a stream looking at the maid's departing spirit. Pub. Koga-ya Katsugorō.
PC.

45. Mimasaka (not seen).

46. Bizen. The *shirabyōshi* dancer Kamegiku holding up a sword. Inset by Yoshifusa-jo: the young Emperor Go-Toba(?). Pub. Arita-ya Seiyemon.
VAM.

47. Bitchū (not seen).

48. Bingo. Takagi Umanosuke standing by a fire, hand on his sword-hilt, and his hat blowing away. Inset by Yoshisato: Nagoya Sanzaburō in the guise of a *komusō* at the window of a hut. Pub. Fujioka-ya Hikotarō.
VAM; PC.

49. Aki. Heishōkoku Kiyomori, *by Kunisada*.
VAM; PC.

50. Suō. Ōuchi Yoshitaka knocking off the court cap of Suye Harukata with his fan. Inset

by Yoshimasa: Yoshitaka drinking behind a screen with a girl-attendant. Pub. Koga-ya Katsugorō.
VAM; PC.

51. Nagato. Kezori Kuyemon, *by Kunisada*.
VAM; PC.

52. Kii. Ishikawa Goyemon, *by Kunisada*.
VAM; PC.

53. Awaji. Shinchūnagon Taira no Tomo-mori, symbolically represented by a seaman in a *kimono* with a rope pattern, and carrying a large anchor, knocking down an assailant.

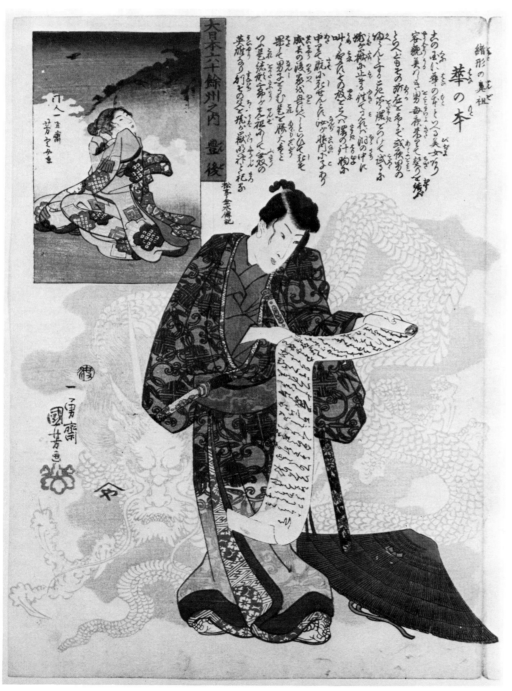

S36.61

Inset by Yoshiteru: his wife and child at home. Pub. Koga-ya Katsugorō.
PC.

54. Awa. Awa no Jurobei resisting arrest by two policemen. Inset by Yoshitama-jo: his wife by a stream. Pub. Maru-ya Jimpachi.
PC.

55. Sanuki. Kajiwara Kagetoki in full armour with a lantern. Inset by Yoshifuji: man and woman in a shop. Pub. Koga-ya Katsugorō.
VAM.

56. Iyo (not seen).

57. Tosa. Tosa no Matabei (who is shown in the inset, by Yoshitsuya) looking down at his

wife, in the main part of the print, playing a hand-drum by a stone water-tank. Pub. Wakasa-ya Uhei.
VAM; PC.

58. Chikuzen (not seen).

59. Chikugo (not seen).

60. Buzen (not seen).

61. Bungo. Akagari Daidō, son of Hana-no-moto and the divinity of Ubagadake, the latter here shown as a ghostly dragon. Inset by Yoshitori-jo: Hana-no-moto looking up at the mountain (see *Heike*, p.469). Pub. Fujioka-ya Hikotarō.
VAM; PC.

62. Hizen (not seen).

63. Higo. Chinzei Hachirō Tametomo with a page carrying his sword. Inset by Yoshifuji: Shiranui-hime in the palace with the crane's cage (cf. S64.5). Pub. Arita-ya Seiyemon.
VAM; PC.

64. Hyūga. Hito Maru, *by Kunisada*.
VAM; PC.

65. Ōsumi. Katō Sayemon Shigeuji looking at a cherry-blossom in a *sake*-cup. Inset by Yoshifusa(?)-jo: garden, and strange shadows in the window of the house. Pub. Jōshū-ya Jūzō; eng. Teppō.
VAM.

66. Satsuma. Satsuma Gengobei, *by Kunisada*.
VAM; PC.

67. Iki (not seen).

68. Tsushima. Shinchūnagon Tomomori, wounded with arrows at the battle of Dan-no-ura, carrying his broken *naginata*. Inset by Yoshifuji: man (Shunkwan?) on a rock hailing offshore ships by waving his hat. Pub. Yawata-ya Sakujirō.
VAM; PC.

S37

Honchō kendō ryaku den ('Abridged stories of our country's swordsmanship'). *Ōban*.

Title on oblong red or shaded cartouche with narrow yellow border; character's name on adjoining blue panel; text above. Single figures with accessories; yellow ground shading into brick-red at the top. Pub. Kadzusa-ya Iwazō; various cens., singly; *c.*1845–6.

1. Araki Matayemon standing, examining his sword. Cens. Kinugasa.
MFA; PC.

2. Banzui Chōbei holding up a lantern, his other hand on the hilt of his sword (may form diptych with no.19). Cens. Mera.
VAM; PC.

3. Fuwa Bansaku, having just struck off the head of a stone 'lion' with his bare fist. Cens. Hama.
MFA; PC.

4. Inuda Kobungo examining a sword mounted in *shirazaya*. Cens. Watari.
PC.

5. Inudzuka Shino wielding his sword, his foot on a fallen follower of Kempachi (no.6), during the fight on the Hōryūkaku roof. Cens. Mera.
PC.

6. (Pl.23) Inukai Kempachi wielding an iron truncheon in his fight with Shino (no.5). Cens. Mera.
PC.

7. Inukawa Sōsuke Yoshitō on one knee grasping his sword; behind him a kettle hangs over a wood fire (forms diptych with no.9). Cens. Watari.
PC.

8. Inumura Kakutarō seated on a rock reading a scroll, paper-wrapped pine-sprigs in his mouth. Cens. Watari.
PC.

9. Inuyama Dōsetsu Tadatomo, smoke from a wood fire swirling round him, standing, hand on sword-hilt, looking back at Sōsuke (no.7, with which this forms a diptych). Cens. Watari.
PC.

10. Inuye Shimbyōye, hand on sword-hilt and wearing a *kimono* patterned with toy dogs, watches falling banana-leaves. Cens. Watari.
PC.

11. Inudzuka (incorrectly for Inuzaka) Keno Tanetomo standing, holding the hilt of one of his swords, a wide straw hat on the ground behind him. Cens. Watari.
PC.

12. Keyamura no Rokusuke, stripped to the waist and drying his back, is addressed by a young *kappa*; a bundle of rushes and carrying-pole behind. Cens. Hama.
MFA; PC.

13. Matsui Tomijirō Shigenaka, standing, looks down at three wriggling snakes; basket and bundle behind him. Cens. Hama.
MFA; PC.

14. Minamoto no Ushiwaka Maru knocking over a *tengu* during a fencing-bout with wooden swords. Cens. Hama.
MFA; PC.

15. Minamoto no Yoshinaka.
PC.

16. Miyamoto Musashi dressed for travelling (probably forms diptych with no.18). Cens. Kinugasa.
MFA; PC.

17. Nagoya Sanzaburō Motoharu, sword in hand, holds up the severed head of a young woman still holding a scroll of paper in her mouth. Cens. Mera.
MFA.

18. Sasaki Ganryū standing, in profile, with clenched fist (probably forms diptych with no.16). Cens. Kinugasa.
MFA; PC.

19. Shirai Gompachi, with drawn sword,

looking down at a dog which looks up at him (may form diptych with no.2). Cens. Mera.
VAM; PC.

20. Sono-jo, daughter of Yoshioka Ichimisai, in nun's robes, puts the arm on an attacking rough. Cens. Hama.
PC.

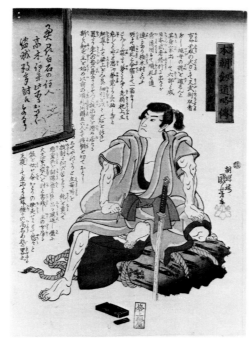

S37.21

21. Takagi Oriyemon seated on a large rock with rope attached, having written on a wall a record of his destruction of a robber-gang; his sword sticking in the ground. Cens. Hama.
VAM; MFA; PC.

22. Yoshioka Kanefusa defending himself in an attack by police. Cens. Hama.
MFA; PC.

S38

Mitate jūnishi ('Selection for the Twelve Signs'—the first word is written with two characters that mean, literally, 'beautiful shields'). *Ōban.*

Title on large coloured oblong cartouche with narrow yellow border incorporating a small representation of the Sign in question. Single figures with strong theatrical overtones. Text by Ryūkatei Tanekazu (except no.2) in decorative panels of various forms. Various pub.; cens. Mura; *c.*1845.

1. The Rat. Yuki-hime clasping a sword, a white-blossomed cherry-tree behind her, with falling petals. Pub. Yebi-ya Rinnosuke.
MFA; PC.

2. The Ox. Sakura Maru holding the rope of the Imperial ox-cart (in the play *Sugawara*); poem by Umeya. Pub. Iba-ya Sensaburō.
VAM; MFA; PC.

3. The Tiger. Soga Jurō Sukenari, fan in

S38.1

hand, leaning on a palanquin under a willow-tree. Pub. Ise-ya Ichibei.
MFA; PC.

4. The Hare. Yama-uba on Mount Ashigara with a rattle, and a white hare playing a toy drum. Pub. Yenshū-ya Matabei.
MFA; PC.

5. The Dragon. Tatsuyasha-hime in a pine-forest, sword in hand, and a mirror suspended on her bosom, planning to avenge her father by witchcraft. Pub. Kojima.
MFA; PC.

6. The Snake. O-Roku standing near a domestic shrine, looking over her shoulder at a basket of wooden tallies; even snakes were afraid of her. Pub. Iba-ya Kyūbei.
MFA; PC.

7. The Horse. O-Miwa dancing on a bridge at the Ataka Barrier in order to secure a passage. Pub. Ise-ya Sōyemon.
MFA; PC.

8. The Goat. O-Koma of Shiroki-ya looking through a curtain as she stands by her dressing-table. Pub. Kojima.
MFA; PC.

9. The Monkey. Yojirō, brother of the courtesan Otoshi, seated fan in hand by a smoking fire with refreshments before him. Pub. Iba-ya Sensaburō; eng. Fusajirō.
MFA; PC.

10. The Cock. Sukune Tarō seated on a chest beneath a blossoming cherry-tree. Pub. Yenshū-ya Matabei.
MFA; PC.

11. The Dog. Inuda Kobungo the wrestler umpiring a match between two crabs on the

S39.T178

sea-shore; drying nets behind him. Pub. Iba-ya Sensaburō; eng. Fusajirō.

MFA; PC.

12. The Boar. Yamamoto Kansuke striding through the snow in straw cloak and cap, carrying a bamboo pole (cf. S35.16). Pub. Iba-ya Kyūbei.

MFA; PC.

S39

Mitate hakkei ('Selection for the Eight Views', using the same punning characters as the preceding series). Triptychs. See T176–T182.

S40

Kuniyoshi moyō shōfuda tsuketari genkin otoko ('Men of ready money with true labels attached, Kuniyoshi fashion'). *Ōban.*

Title on red or blue oblong cartouche with narrow yellow border, adjoining a smaller blue or red panel bearing the character's name. Large boldly drawn half-length figures of *otokodate* dramatic characters on grey ground with poems above. The title of this series probably echoes that of a play, *Shōfuda tsuki kongen kusazuri*, staged at the Kawarazaki theatre in the first month of the second year of the period Kōkwa (February 1845). Pub. Iba-ya Kyūbei; cens. Hama or Watari; 1845.

1. Banzui Chōbei, his blue *kimono* patterned with floral butterflies; poem by Harunoya Kōichi. Eng. Renkichi.

MFA; B; PC.

2. Danshichi Kurobei emptying a bucket of

water over himself; poem by Hōshitei. Eng. Renkichi.

BM; VAM; RSM; MFA; PC. *Illing 1978*, 24.

3. Goshaku Somegorō playing a bamboo flute (*shakuhachi*), his *kimono* patterned with melon-plants; poem by Umeya. Eng. Renkichi.

VAM; RSM; MFA; B; PC.

4. Nozarashi Gosuke carrying a large sword over his shoulder, from which is suspended a wooden sandal with skull-like markings; his *kimono* is patterned with skulls made up of cats; poem by Ryūkatei Tanekazu.

VAM; RSM; MFA; B; PC. *Illing 1980*, 117.

5. Nuregami Chōgorō the wrestler holding his tobacco-pipe; poem by Rōshō. Eng. Renkichi.

VAM; MFA; B; PC.

6. Shirai Gompachi holding a spotted scarf over his shoulders and with a *shakuhachi* stuck in the back of his girdle; poem by Ryūkatei Tanekazu.

VAM; MFA; B; PC.

7. Teranishi Kanshin with an open fan, his *kimono* patterned with paulownia leaves and sprays; poem by Gosōnoya of Ise. Eng. Renkichi.

VAM; RSM; MFA; B; PC. *Bidwell 1968*, Pl.96.

8. Tōken Gombei, three-quarter back view, looking at himself in a mirror, his *kimono* patterned with scenes in hell; poem by Takara-ya Masuo.

VAM; B; PC. *Riccar 1978*, 177; *Bidwell 1980*, 133.

S40.6

9. Ude Kisaburō with folded arms, looking grim; poem by Kunoya Umeki.

RSM; MFA; B; PC. *Bidwell 1968*, Pl.97; *Riccar 1978*, 178; *Bidwell 1980*, 134.

10. Ume no Yoshibei glaring, his hand on his sword-hilt; poem by Umeya. Eng. Renkichi.

VAM; MFA; B; PC. *Kruml*, 9.45.

S41

Chūkō tenarai-zōshi ('Copy-book of loyalty'). *Ōban.*

Title in large script on oblong red cartouche

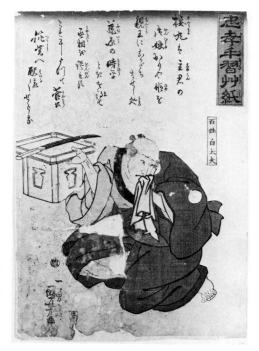

S41.1

S42.6

with narrow yellow border; text above. Single figure and accessories on plain ground. Pub. Kadzusa-ya Iwazō; cens. Watari; *c*.1845.

1. The farmer Shiradayū weeping as he holds up a tray bearing an unsheathed dirk.
MFA; PC.

S42
Date moyō kekki kurabe ('Comparisons of physical energy, Date style'). *Ōban.*

Title on coloured cartouche; character's name on adjoining panel with flowers. Single figures, several repeating those in S40, with text above. Pub. Murata-ya Ichibei; cens. Hama; *c*.1845–6.

1. Danshichi Kurobei drinking from a well-bucket, his sword stuck in the ground. Eng. Fusajirō.
RSM; MFA.

2. Hokke Chōbei, seated on a *sake*-barrel, shading his eyes with one hand and holding a large axe in the other. Eng. Fusajirō.
RSM; MFA.

3. Kakurega no Mohei, an umbrella on his shoulder, extends a lantern towards a small *kappa*. Eng. Fusajirō.
RSM; MFA.

4. Konjin Chōgorō wrestling with a green demon, watched by two other demonic figures.
MFA.

5. Nozarashi Gosuke seated, with an apparition of a fox-divinity descending on a cloud. Eng. Fusajirō.
RSM; MFA.

6. Shibori no Somegorō holding his hand under a small waterfall. Eng. Fusajirō.
RSM; MFA; PC.

7. Ude no Kisaburō, seated half-naked, about

to cut off his arm at the elbow with a saw.
RSM; MFA.

8. Yume no Ichirobei, in a wide hat and voluminous clothes, in a truculent attitude.
RSM; MFA.

S43
Hodomoyoshi toki ni (ryūkō) Ōtsu-ye ('Hodomoyoshi's [i.e. Kuniyoshi's] fashionable Ōtsu pictures'). *Ōban.*

Title on oblong red cartouche adjoining an inset *Ōtsu-ye*, the traditional folk-painting sold to travellers at Ōtsu on Lake Biwa near Kyoto. Figures of dramatic characters on plain background, with poem by Umeya above, and a shaded band of Kuniyoshi's *kiri* (paulownia) device repeated. Pub. Iba-ya Sensaburō; cens. Hama or Watari; *c*.1845–6.

1. Chidori and Kiri-ishi Tange, she standing behind him with closed fan, he on one knee holding a tub over his head. *Ōtsu-ye* of Daikoku shaving the head of Fukurokuju.
VAM; PC.

2. Ihei the servant, back view, standing on one leg. *Ōtsu-ye* of retainer carrying sheathed spear.
PC.

3. Kamada Matahachi, half-naked, carrying a huge bell. *Ōtsu-ye* of Benkei carrying the bell of Miidera.
PC.

4. Katō Shigeuji seated on a bench holding out a *sake*-cup. *Ōtsu-ye* of Asahina Saburō swallowing a huge bowl of *sake*.
VAM; PC.

5. Kichizō, a young aristocrat, carrying a box. *Ōtsu-ye* of a falconer. Eng. Fusajirō.
VAM; PC.

6. Miyamoto Musashi outside a doorway. *Ōtsu-ye* of a demon and a hanging cloth. Eng. Fusajirō.
PC.

7. O-Shun standing, carrying a bundle. *Ōtsu-ye* of the Wistaria Maiden. Eng. Fusajirō.
VAM; PC.

8. O-Yumi, wife of Awa no Jurobei, and her little daughter O-Tsuru holding a wide straw hat. *Ōtsu-ye* of a cat and rat feasting together. Eng. Fusajirō.
PC.

9. Seigen-biku the nun, in travelling dress, with a stick, looking over her shoulder. *Ōtsu-ye* of the demon-priest (*oni-nembutsu*).
VAM; PC.

S43.10

10. Shimidzu Kwanja Yoshitaka raising his sword at a giant rat which gnaws the end of the scroll he carries (cf. S36.21). *Ōtsu-ye* of a blind man raising his stick at a dog.
VAM; PC.

S44
Tōkaidō gojūsan tsui ('Fifty-three parallels for the Tōkaidō Road'). *Ōban.*

The upper part of each print, which is divided off, contains, on the right, the title of the series in large formal characters reserved in a black rectangle; on the left, a decorative panel with the name of the post-station and short text. Form and content are very similar to those of S45 and S46, the main design fluctuating between straightforward historical illustration and local legends and customs; in the present series, however, the *kabuki* element is very small. Complete set of fifty-three stations, three of them (Mitsuke, Ishiyakushi, and Ōtsu) represented by two prints each, plus the start (Nihombashi) and the finish (Kyoto), making fifty-eight in all. Nineteen of the designs were contributed by Hiroshige, and eight by Kunisada. Various pub.; cens. Mura; c.1845–6.

1. Nihombashi. *Geisha* on the bridge with a little girl and her toy figure; Fuji in the background. Pub. Iba-ya Sensaburō; eng. Fusajirō.
VAM; B; PC.

2. Shinagawa. Shore-scene at night: Shirai Gompachi wiping his sword as a rough creeps up on him with a club; boundary-pillar (r.) inscribed with the invocation *namu myōhō renge kyō*. Pub. Iba-ya Kyūbei.
VAM; B; PC.

3. Kawasaki. Nitta Sahyōye-no-suke Yoshioki with his two comrades I Danjō and Ōshima Suō no Kami on a sinking boat in mid-stream. He was thus trapped and killed by the Ashikaga at the Yaguchi ferry in 1358 (cf. S28.51). Pub. Kojima.
VAM; B; PC.

4. Kanagawa. Girl fishing. *By Kunisada.*
VAM.

5. Hodogaya. Scene in camp: Yura Hyōgo, armed, seated on a stool and attended by his wife Minato, watching a dance executed by Shinodzuka Hachirō; both were retainers of the Nitta. (This incident occurred immediately after that depicted in no.3 above.) Pub. Yebi-ya Rinnosuke.
VAM; B; PC.

6. Totsuka. A *daimyō*'s maid. *By Hiroshige.*
VAM.

7. Fujisawa. Scene at the waterfall by which Oguri Kojirō Sukeshige was cured of his injuries after being dragged there on a beggar's cart (seen on the l.) by the faithful Terute-hime. He is shown demonstrating his cure by lifting a large rock, much to Terute's astonishment. Pub. Ise-Ichi.
VAM; B; PC.

8. Hiratsuka. Inage Saburō Shigenari. *By Hiroshige.*
VAM.

9. Ōiso. Night-scene: Soga Jurō and his mistress Tora-gozen with her little maid, by a tall wattle-fence; lantern behind. Pub. Yebi-ya Rinnosuke.
VAM; B; PC.

10. Odawara. Yoritomo admitted to the house of Masako, daughter of Hōjō Tokimasa, who is seen on the right awaiting him. Pub. Yenshū-ya Matabei.
VAM; B; PC.

11. Hakone. Hako-ō Maru (Soga Gorō in boyhood), with background of mountainous landscape and waterfall. Pub. Iba-ya Kyūbei.
VAM; B.

S44.7

12. Mishima. A local festival. *By Hiroshige.*
VAM.

13. Numadzu. Travellers on the road: a young man and a young woman exchanging glances, and an old porter between them. Pub. Kojima.
VAM; B; PC. *Düsseldorf 1961*, 21.

14. Hara. The old bamboo-gatherer Sanugi no Miyakko at the garden gate; his daughter Kaguya-hime seated within (*Edmunds*, p.611). *By Hiroshige.*
VAM; PC.

15. Yoshiwara. Panic among the Taira troops caused by a flight of wild geese at the battle of Fujikawa, 9 November 1180 (*Edmunds*, p.674, s.v. Yoshinobu). Pub. Iba-ya Sensaburō.
VAM; B; PC.

16. Kambara. Girl reading by a window through which Mount Fuji can be seen; her *samisen* rests behind her. Pub. Yenshū-ya Matabei.
VAM; B; PC. *Robinson 1963*, Pl.10; *Riccar 1978*, 296; *Kruml*, 9.50.

17. Yui. Fisher-girl mending her net, through which Fuji is seen. Pub. Yebi-ya Rinnosuke.
VAM; B. *Kruml*, 9.52.

18. Okitsu. The poet Yamabe no Akahito. *By Hiroshige.*
VAM.

19. Yejiri. The fairy flying away with the robe of feathers (*hagoromo*) (*Edmunds*, p.370). *By Hiroshige.*
VAM; PC.

20. Fuchū. Local girls picking tea, for which Fuchū was famous. *By Hiroshige.*
VAM; PC.

21. Mariko. Taira no Shigehira and the lady Senjū-no-maye. *By Hiroshige.*
VAM.

22. Okabe. The cat-witch of Okabe and a girl-victim; she was later turned into the Cat Rock, a local landmark. Pub. Iba-ya Kyūbei; eng. Renkichi.
VAM; B; PC. *Graf*, Pl.40; *Riccar 1978*, 295; *Bidwell 1980*, 124.

23. Fujiyeda. Renshō-hōshi (formerly Kumagaya Naozane; *Edmunds*, p.515) seeks lodging after being robbed on the way to Kyoto; a girl receives him at the gate. Pub. Iba-ya Sensaburō.
VAM; B; PC.

24. Shimada. A wrestler crossing the Ōigawa. *By Kunisada.*
VAM.

25. Kanaya. A lady carried across the Ōigawa by coolies. *By Hiroshige.*
VAM; PC.

26. Nissaka. (Fig.11) Moonlight scene of a travelling *rōnin* receiving his child from the ghost of his wife. While he was away, she was raped and murdered by a robber, and her ghost haunted the 'Night-crying Stone' (*yonaki-ishi*); the child, however, was rescued and fed by a priest of Kwannon, and eventually the husband killed the murderer. Pub. Iba-ya Sensaburō.
VAM; B; PC.

27. Kakegawa. The swordsmith Shimosaka reading a letter on the shore in Ise. He is generally known as Yasutsugu, and worked for the Shōgun Iyeyasu, by whom he was permitted to engrave the Tokugawa *mon* of three conventional hollyhock leaves on the tangs of his blades. Pub. Iba-ya Sensaburō; eng. Takejirō.
VAM; B.

28. Fukuroi. Hōnan Shōnin and an apparition. *By Kunisada.*
VAM.

29. Mitsuke (i). Peasants attacked by tortoises. *By Hiroshige.*
VAM; B.

30. Mitsuke (ii). Yoritomo releasing cranes (a pious Buddhist practice) on the shore at the village of Iwai. Pub. Iba-ya Kyūbei.
VAM; PC.

31. Hamamatsu. Taira no Shigemori in captivity at Kamakura, watched by a girl in the foreground. Pub. Yenshū-ya Matabei.
VAM; B; PC.

32. Maizaka. A pirate ship's captain on board, with his pipe and compass. Pub. Yenshū-ya Matabei.
VAM; B; PC. *Lewis*, 1975.7.

33. Arai. Girl in a boat holding her travel-diary (*tabi no nikki*) and with a writing-brush in her mouth. *By Kunisada.*
VAM; PC.

34. Shirasuka. *Geisha* on a terrace. *By Hiroshige.*
VAM.

35. Futagawa. Incident from the comic novel *Hizakurige. By Hiroshige.*
VAM.

36. Yoshida. *Geisha* inviting a *samurai* into a tea-house. *By Kunisada.*
VAM; PC.

37. Goyū. Yamamoto Kansuke and his mother in their hut, approached through the snow by Takeda Harunobu (Shingen). Shingen persuaded him to join the Takeda, to whom he gave distinguished service, being finally killed at Kawanakajima (12 October 1561). Pub. Iba-ya Sensaburō.
VAM; B; PC.

38. Akasaka. Fujiwara no Moronaga and an apparition. *By Hiroshige.*
VAM.

39. Fujikawa. Shore-scene: Isogai Hyōdayū foiling an attack by Fujikawa Midzuyemon by stepping on his sword—a stolen one, made by Nagamitsu of Bizen. Pub. Kojima.
VAM; B; PC.

40. Okazaki. Jōruri-hime (beloved of Yoshitsune) and her maid entering a garden gate. *By Hiroshige.*
VAM; PC.

41. Chiriū. The poet Ariwara no Narihira, his young sword-bearer, and an old gardener on a crazy bridge (*yatsuhashi*) over an iris-pond. Pub. Iba-ya Sensaburō.
VAM; B; PC.

42. Narumi. Woman making local cloth. *By Kunisada.*
VAM.

43. Miya. The lady Fuji no Tsubone appearing to her husband Taira no Tsunemori. *By Kunisada.*
VAM.

44. Kuwana. The pilot Tokuzō, on board ship, confronted by the apparition of the 'Sea Monk' (*Umi Bōzu*). Pub. Kojima.
VAM; B; PC. *Graf*, Pl.84; *Robinson 1961*, Pl.49; *Riccar 1978*, 294; *Kruml*, 9.51; 22.38.

45. Yokkaichi. Girl watching a mirage. *By Kunisada.*
VAM.

46. Ishiyakushi (i). Minamoto no Noriyori, brother of Yoritomo, by whom, after gallant service against the Taira, he was exiled and later put to death. Pub. unidentified.
PC.

46a. Ishiyakushi (ii). Yoshitsune and Benkei among the falling cherry-blossoms at Suma after the battle of Ichi-no-tani. Pub. unidentified.
VAM.

47. Shōno. Sasaki Takatsuna fording the Uji

river to attack Kiso Yoshinaka (1184). Pub. Iba-ya Kyūbei.
VAM; B. *Bidwell 1980*, 125.

48. Kameyama. The dream of O-Matsu. *By Hiroshige.*
VAM.

49. Seki. The priest Ikkyū (1394–1481) and the courtesan Jigoku. *By Hiroshige.*
VAM.

50. Sakanoshita. The brother of the Emperor Tenchi (662–71). *By Hiroshige.*
VAM.

51. Tsuchiyama. Tamura Shōgun (sc. Sakanoye Tamura-maro), directed by Kwannon in the form of a woman, about to kill the demon-deity of Mount Suzuka. This incident took place during a punitive expedition against the rebel Abe no Takamaru. Pub. Ise-Ichi.
VAM; B; PC. *Düsseldorf 1962*, 78.

52. Minakuchi. The strong woman Ōiko, daughter of a farmer of Takashima. In the background are peasants marvelling at the great rock with which she has dammed the river to help irrigate the fields. Pub. Iba-ya Sensaburō.
VAM; B; PC.

53. Ishibe. Half-length figure of a girl cleaning her teeth. Pub. Ise-Ichi; eng. Fusajirō.
VAM; B; PC.

54. Kusatsu. Tawara Tōda Hidesato, on the shore of Lake Biwa with his bow, watches the Dragon Princess rising from the water to implore him to rid the lake of the giant centipede of Seta. This incident is dated in the text to the eighth year of the period Yengi (908). Pub. Yebi-ya Rinnosuke.
VAM; B; PC. *Graf*, Pl.27.

55. Ōtsu (i). Matabei the painter and some of his works. *By Hiroshige.*
VAM; B.

56. Ōtsu (ii). The painter Matabei and his wife before a cylindrical stone tank in the garden. He was popularly supposed to have been the originator of *Ōtsu-ye* (cf. S43). Pub. Iba-ya Sensaburō.
VAM. *Düsseldorf 1962*, 81.

57. Kyoto. Woman and child on a bridge. *By Hiroshige.*
VAM; B.

NOTE. MFA has about twenty-five of this series.

S45
Genji kumo ukiyoye awase ('Ukiyoye comparison of the cloudy Chapters of Genji'). *Ōban.*

Form and content are very similar to those of S44 and S46; the upper part of each print is designed as an open scroll, with the title in ornamental script on the scroll-cover, right; the l.h. portion bears the chapter-title and appropriate *Genji-mon*, together with an allusive design and a poem. Explanatory text on

the main design, by Hanagasa (Kwaritsu). Complete set of fifty-four, plus six supplementary, all numbered correctly in the l.h. margin. Pub. Ise-ya Ichibei; various cens., all singly; *c.*1845–6.

1. *Kiritsubo.* Hatakeyama Shōji Shigetada, fan in hand, seated by a *go*-board, the pieces spilled on the floor; cherry-blossom above. Cens. Watari.
VAM; B; PC.

2. *Hahakigi.* The fox-woman Kuzunoha looking over a screen, on which appears her shadow as a fox, at her sleeping child. Cens. Watari.
VAM; B; PC.

3. *Utsusemi.* Soga Gorō Tokimune, with drawn sword, lifts the mosquito-net preparatory to killing his father's murderer, Kudō Suketsune. Cens. Watari.
VAM; B; PC.

4. *Yugao.* O-Riye, wife of Yazama (cf. S46.92), in the snow with a large dog, carrying a bundle of matting. Cens. Watari.
VAM; B; PC.

5. *Wakamurasaki.* Tegoshi no Shōshō, mistress of Soga Gorō, tying her *obi* on a windy night; flying sheets of paper, and sharpened bamboos on the ground. Cens. Watari.
VAM; B; PC.

6. *Suyetsumu-hana.* Ichikawa Danjurō VII as Kumagaya Jirō Naozane standing over Anewa Heita, who falls backwards holding a large straw hat. Danjurō was in exile at this time (cf. S46.56); the last time he had taken this part was at the Kawarazaki theatre at the beginning of 1838. Cens. Watari.
VAM; B; PC.

7. *Momiji no ga.* On a flight of stone steps amid falling maple-leaves Moritō holds up the severed head of Kesa-gozen. This is probably Ichikawa Danjurō VIII in *Sakigake Genji* at the Kawarazaki theatre at the beginning of 1845. Cens. Watari.
VAM; B; PC. *Bidwell 1980*, 135; *Falteri*, 1981.140.

8. *Hana no yen.* Hinadori and her maid under a blossoming cherry-tree. This is probably Iwai Kumesaburō in *Imoseyama* at the Nakamura theatre in the early summer of 1845. Cens. Kinugasa.
VAM; B; PC.

9. *Aoi.* Kon-ō Maru of Yedo in his boat plying his fishing-net; the fish he brought up became a *tai*, a New Year speciality. Cens. Kinugasa.
VAM; B; PC. *Robinson 1961*, Pl.48.

10. *Sakaki.* O-Miwa holding a ceremonial *sake*-ladle and attended by two ugly court ladies, from the play *Onna Narukami.* Cens. Kinugasa.
VAM; B; PC.

11. *Hanachirusato.* Katō Shigeuji seated with a *sake*-cup in which is a cherry-blossom, attended by his wife. Cens. Mura.
VAM; B; PC.

12. *Suma*. Tamaori-hime, wife of Atsumori, on the sea-shore carrying a *naginata*. Cens. Mura.

VAM; B; PC.

13. *Akashi*. Bandō Shuka as O-Hatsu, by moonlight, holding a sandal beside a lantern; a scene from *Onoye Iwafuji* (Ichimura theatre, spring 1847). Cens. Mura.

VAM; B; PC.

14. *Myodzukushi*. Shimobe Yodohei, a large box on his back, by a garden gate in the snow. Cens. Mura.

VAM; B; PC.

15. *Yomogiū*. Hisamatsu (cf. S43.89) standing holding a napkin, the old man Yamazaki no Kyūsaku seated before him; a bundle behind. Cens. Mura.

VAM; B; PC.

16. *Sekiya*. Shirai Gompachi tying his girdle by a netted palanquin, his foot on the neck of a prostrate bearer. Cens. Watari.

VAM; B; PC.

17. *Ye-awase*. Yayegaki-hime, her chin in her hands, gazing at a portrait of her dead lover Katsuyori, before which incense is burning. Cens. Mura.

VAM; B; PC.

18. *Matsukaze*. Ichikawa Danjurō VII as Kezori Kuyemon the pirate, by moonlight, grasping a huge axe. The last time he took this part before going into exile (cf. no.6 above) was in *Hakata Kojorō* at the Ichimura theatre at the beginning of 1837. Cens. Watari.

VAM; B; PC.

19. *Usugumo*. Sōma Yoshikado reading a scroll, Utou Yasukata seated before him with a drawn sword, and the Earth-Spider in its web behind. This may have been inspired by the play *Sōma dairi* at the Ichimura theatre in the winter of 1844. Cens. Mura.

VAM; B; PC.

20. *Asagao*. Ichikawa Danjurō VIII as Fuwa Banzayemon in *Hiyoku no inadzuma* (Kawarazaki theatre, beginning of 1846) emerging from a palanquin and drawing his sword; a fight is in progress in the background. Cens. Watari.

VAM; B; PC.

21. *Otome*. The girl O-Shichi reclining under the eaves of a temple in the attitude of a *tennin*, or Buddhist angel. Cens. Mura.

VAM; B; PC.

22. *Tamakadzura*. Tamatori, the diving-girl, grasping the sacred jewel and brandishing a dirk, being attacked by an octopus; a vision of Hōrai in the background. Cens. Mura.

VAM; B; PC. *Bidwell 1980*, 136; *Kruml*, 9.49; 13.38.

23. *Hatsune*. Nakamura Utayemon IV as Satō Tadanobu, having overthrown an adversary, wiping his sword behind his back. Cens. Watari.

VAM; B; PC.

24. *Kochō*. Abe Yasuna in court robes waving his fan at two fluttering butterflies, an attendant in red make-up behind him. This is Ichimura Uzayemon XII in *Kwaikei Shinoda* at the Ichimura theatre in the winter of 1845. Cens. Watari.

VAM; B; PC.

25. *Hotaru*. Tamiya Iyemon and his servant Akiyama Chōbei, with the ghost of his murdered wife O-Iwa. This is Ichikawa Danjurō VIII in *O-Iwa kwaidan* at the Nakamura theatre in the summer of 1844. Cens. Mura.

VAM; B; PC.

26. *Tokonatsu*. Danshichi Kurobei, the fishmonger hero of the play *Natsu matsuri*, putting a handgrip on Ōtori Sagayemon. This is probably Nakamura Utayemon IV in the production at the Nakamura theatre in the summer of 1845. Cens. Mura.

VAM; B; PC.

27. *Kagaribi*. The nun Seigen-ni in a boat in a shower of rain; a scene from *Onoye Iwafuji* (Ichimura theatre, spring 1847) with Bandō Shuka in the part. Cens. Mura.

VAM; RSM; B; PC.

28. *Nowaki*. The noble poet Ariwara no Narihira eloping with the lady Takako-hime at night on Musashi moor; pursuers with torches appear in the background. This was perhaps inspired by the play *Rokkasen* ('The Six Poets') at the Ichimura theatre in the autumn of 1846, in which Ichimura Kakitsu played Narihira. Cens. Mura.

VAM; B; PC.

29. *Miyuki*. O-Yasu shaking petals from a sprig of plum-blossom into a bowl. Cens. Mura.

VAM; B; PC.

30. *Fujibakama*. The lady Iwafuji and a servant by a garden fence at night. This seems to be Sawamura Sōjurō V in *Onoye Iwafuji* at the Ichimura theatre in the spring of 1847. Cens. Mura.

VAM; RSM; B; PC.

31. *Makibashira*. Kurō Hangwan Yoshitsune clinging to a pillar on the balcony of the Horikawa palace, watching the approach of Tosa-bō Shōshun and his men through the night mist; arrows are flying. Cens. Mura.

VAM; B; PC.

32. *Umegaye*. Hayakawa Takakage in court robes holding a sprig of plum-blossom; Yadahei crouched before him. Takakage resembles Ichikawa Danjurō VIII, but there seems to be no record of his acting the part. Cens. Murata.

VAM; B; PC.

33. *Fuji no Uraba*. Dembei at night outside a Yoshiwara house, with a woman silhouetted in the window and people passing below. This may represent Onoye Kikugorō III, who took the part of Idzutsu-ya Dembei in *Hanakawado*

at the Kawarazaki theatre in the autumn of 1845. Cens. Murata.

VAM; B; PC.

34. *Wakana no jō*. Soga Jurō Sukenari standing over the seated Kobayashi Asahina (in full stage make-up); *shimenawa* and ferns hanging in the background. Cens. Murata.

VAM; B; PC.

35. *Wakana no ge*. Yaye, the wife of Sakura Maru, under a blossoming cherry-tree holding a sort of truncheon; from the play *Sugawara*. Cens. Murata.

VAM; RSM; B; PC.

36. *Kashiwagi*. The girl Sankatsu, with broom and duster, looks back at the little child O-Tsū, who plays the *samisen* while the cat gets at her food. Cens. Mura.

VAM; RSM; B; PC.

37. *Yokobuye*. Ichikawa Danjurō VII as Tombei the ferryman glares down at his daughter O-Fune who kneels before him in entreaty. Before his exile (see S46.56) Danjurō took this part in *Yaguchi no watashi* at the Kawarazaki theatre in the early summer of 1841; O-Fune was acted by Iwai Tojaku. Cens. Murata.

VAM; B; PC.

38. *Suzumushi*. Fukuoka Mitsugi defending himself against three roughs, slicing a lantern in two with his sword. This may be Nakamura Utayemon IV, who took the part in *Ise ondo* at the Nakamura theatre in the winter of 1844. Cens. Murata.

VAM; B; PC.

39. *Yūgiri*. The wrestler Kinugawa Tanizō dealing with two assailants. The main character seems to be Ichikawa Danjurō VIII. Cens. Murata.

VAM; B; PC.

40. *Minori*. Taira no Tomomori, with the huge anchor, in his death-throes at the battle of Dan-no-ura (1185). Cens. Murata.

VAM; B; PC.

41. *Maboroshi*. Nikki Danjō Naonori in court robes standing in front of a cloud of smoke. This part was acted by Nakamura Utayemon IV in *Kinkwazan* at the Kawarazaki theatre in the spring of 1844, and by Arashi Kichisaburō in *Hana no Yedo-gata*, which was running simultaneously at the Ichimura theatre; it is uncertain which performance is here represented. Cens. Mura.

VAM; B; PC.

42. *Niou-miya*. Outside a chrysanthemum fence, Torazō (really Ushiwaka Maru) holding a document-box, the other hand on his sword; behind him is Minadzuru-hime, daughter of Ki-ichi Hōgen. Cens. Murata.

VAM; B; PC.

43. *Kōbai*. Keyamura Rokusuke in an aggressive attitude, with O-Sono behind him holding a spray of plum-blossom. Cens. Murata.

VAM; B; PC.

44. *Takegawa*. Sakingo Ashikaga Yorikane by moonlight, with a drawn dirk and two hanks of hair, having murdered the courtesan Takao. Cens. Murata.

VAM; B; PC.

45. *Hashi-hime*. The servant-maid Chidori escaping from a castle by night with a pair of swords; her pursuers are crossing the moat bridge. This was a subsidiary part in *Sembon-zakura*. Cens. Mura.

VAM; B; PC.

46. *Shii-ga-moto*. Gonta, a pipe in his mouth, stooping to pick up petals which he is putting into his hat; behind him are Wakaba-no-naishi and her son Rokudai-gozen. This is another incident from *Sembonzakura*. Cens. Murata.

VAM; B; PC.

47. *Agemaki*. Sukeroku, a drawn sword in his hand, tossing an opponent (Sempei) in the air. This is probably Ichikawa Danjurō VIII's first appearance as Sukeroku in the popular play of the same name at the Nakamura theatre in the spring of 1844. Cens. Murata.

VAM; B; PC.

48. *Sawarabi*. The lady Masaoka seated on a balcony whilst her son Chimatsu helps himself from a box of sweetmeats. Cens. Murata.

VAM; B; PC.

49. *Yadorigi*. Kwanshōjō (Sugawara no Michizane) with a fan, turning away from Kariya-hime, who crouches behind him. This is probably Onoye Kikugorō III and Iwai Kumesaburō in *Sugawara* at the Nakamura theatre in the early summer of 1844. Cens. Murata.

VAM; B; PC.

50. *Adzuma-ya*. The inferior retainer (*ashi-garu*) Kichiyemon in a garden, the house behind, holding a pair of sandals; two other pairs on the ground before him. He was a minor character in the Ichimisai–Kyōgoku revenge story. Cens. Murata.

VAM; B; PC.

51. *Ukifune*. O-Matsu attacking Akabori Midzuyemon on a boat; the latter falls back, defending himself with one foot. Cens. Murata.

VAM; B; PC.

52. *Kagerō*. The wrestler Akitsushima seated by a brazier, a writing-brush in his mouth, holding a long inscribed scroll of paper. This is clearly Ichikawa Danjurō VIII, who took the part in *Shōbudzuke* at the Nakamura theatre early in 1847. Cens. Murata.

VAM; B; PC.

53. *Tenarai*. Matsuō Maru with his sword (undrawn) under the chin of a kneeling boy; Gemba behind, in red make-up. This is a scene from *Sugawara*. Cens. Murata.

VAM; B; PC.

54. *Yume no ukihashi*. Aoto Fujitsuna, seated on a stool before a fire, his sword-bearer squatting behind him, looks out on a distant

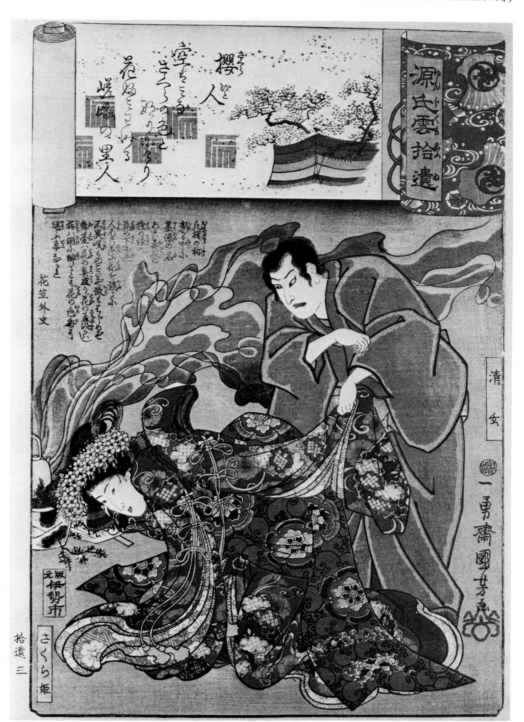

S45.57

mountain beyond a misty valley. This is Nakamura Utayemon IV in the production of *Aoto-zōshi* at the Ichimura theatre in the summer of 1846. Cens. Murata.

VAM; B; PC.

55. (Supplement 1) *Kumokakure*. Ichikawa Danjurō VIII in red make-up as Matsugaye Sekinosuke, grasping a small knife; tea-house and lake behind. Cens. Murata.

B; PC.

56. (Supplement 2) *Sumori*. Kakugawa Monzō (sc. Kakogawa Honzō, a prominent character in the *Chūshingura*), wearing a black *kesa* and

carrying a *shakuhachi*, turns to his daughter Namiko (Konami in the *Chūshingura*) who kneels behind him. Cens. Murata.

VAM; B; PC.

57. (Supplement 3) *Sakurabito*. Seigen plucks at the sleeve of Sakura-hime, who cringes away from him; a smoking brazier behind. Cens. Murata.

B; PC.

58. (Supplement 4) *Norinoshi*. Ichikawa Danjurō VIII as Oniwaka Maru (Benkei in boyhood), armed with a *naginata*-blade, overthrows a man who was trying to secure him

with cords; guardhouse and two guards in the background. Cens. Murata.

VAM; B; PC.

59. (Supplement 5) *Hibariko*. Udaijin Toyonari, in hunting dress, chucking Chūjō-hime under the chin; river and hut behind. Toyonari has the appearance of Nakamura Utayemon IV. Cens. Murata.

B; PC.

60. (Supplement 6) *Yatsuhashi*. Ichikawa Danjurō VIII as Teranishi Kanshin, with an open fan and wearing a *kimono* patterned with skulls, walking on a crazy bridge (*yatsuhashi*) across an iris-pond. He took this part in *Hiyoku no inadzuma* at the Kawarazaki theatre at the beginning of 1846. Cens. Murata.

VAM; B; PC.

NOTE. MFA has thirty-nine of this series.

S46
Ogura nazoraye hyaku-nin isshu ('Ogura imitation of the Hundred Poets'). *Ōban.*

As in S44 and S45 the upper part of each print is divided off and contains, on the right, the title in large formal script; on the left, the name and poem of the poet concerned. From no.51 to the end these latter are enclosed, together with a small portrait of the poet, in a bean-shaped panel, to the left of which is the descriptive text for the main design (in nos. 1–50 this appears on the main design itself), written by Ryūkatei Tanekazu. The main subjects are mostly from history and legend, but as the series proceeds the dramatic (*kabuki*) element becomes increasingly prominent. The set is numbered correctly throughout in the l.h. margin. Of the 100 designs, 51 are by Kuniyoshi, 35 by Hiroshige, and 14 by Kunisada, whose contributions are confined to the second half of the set. Pub. Iba-ya Sensaburō; various cens. (singly and in pairs) and eng.; *c.* 1845–8.

1. Poem by Tenchi Tennō. Onzōshi Ushiwaka Maru (the young Yoshitsune) in the evening outside the house of Jōruri-hime. Cens. Muramatsu; eng. Fusajirō.

VAM; RSM; PC.

2. Poem by Jitō Tennō. Saimyōji (Hōjō) Tokiyori, during his incognito travels in the provinces, is entertained by the Sano family, whose daughter Shirataye cuts up a valuable *bonsai* tree to provide firewood for him. Cens. Kinugasa; eng. Fusajirō.

VAM; RSM; PC.

3. Poem by Kakinomoto Hitomaro. Kaga no Chiyo fanning a smoking brazier. Cens. Muramatsu; eng. Fusajirō.

VAM; RSM; PC.

4. Poem by Yamabe Akahito. A married woman seated before a porcelain bowl and a lacquer box piled with snow to represent Fuji; this was a custom connected with the temple at Yushima. Cens. Muramatsu.

VAM; RSM; PC.

5. Poem by Sarumaru-dayū. Soga Hako-ō Maru (Gorō, the younger of the two brothers) holding out a robe, and with a Buddhist scroll over his shoulder; reading-table and book behind. No cens.; eng. Take.

VAM; RSM; PC.

6. Poem by Chūnagon Iyemochi. Meeting of Watanabe Genji Tsuna with the demon-woman Ibaraki. *By Hiroshige.* Cens. Muramatsu.

VAM; RSM; PC.

7. Poem by Abe Nakamaro. (Fig.7) Nagoya Sanzaburō wiping his sword with a sandal under a willow in the moonlight. Cens. Kinugasa; eng. Take.

VAM; RSM; PC. *Düsseldorf 1961*, 24.

8. Poem by Kisen-hōshi. Nyūdō (Gen Sammi) Yorimasa, having written a farewell poem on his fan, prepares to perform *seppuku* after his defeat by the Taira at the Uji river (1180). Cens. Muramatsu; eng. Fusajirō.

VAM; RSM; PC. *Robinson 1961*, Pl.50; *Düsseldorf 1961*, 25.

9. Poem by Ono no Komachi. Sonobe Sayemon (apparently acted by Ichikawa Danjurō VIII) with an open fan and a poem-card under a blossoming cherry-tree. *By Hiroshige.* Cens. Kinugasa.

VAM; RSM; PC.

10. Poem by Semimaru. The wrestler Nuregami Chōgorō seated on a rice-bale with his pipe and tobacco-pouch, watching two butterflies. His rival was Hanaregoma Chōkichi, and they were the subject of a play, *Futatsu Chōchō* ('The Two Butterflies'). Cens. Kinugasa; eng. Take.

VAM; RSM; PC.

11. Poem by Sangi. Minamoto no Yoshitsune seated on the shore with a diving-girl, whom he ordered to recover the Sword of the regalia from the sea-bottom at Yashima in the province of Sanuki (so the text on the print; actually the Sword was lost at Dan-no-ura). Cens. Muramatsu.

VAM; RSM; PC. *Düsseldorf 1961*, 26.

12. Poem by Sōjō Henjō. Hotoke-gozen, mistress of Taira no Kiyomori in succession to Giō, in the dress of a *shirabyōshi* dancer, making a respectful bow. *By Hiroshige.* Cens. Kinugasa; eng. Fusajirō.

VAM; RSM; PC.

13. Poem by Yōzei-in. Oniwaka Maru (Benkei in boyhood) about to kill the giant carp near Shōshazan in the province of Harima. Cens. Muramatsu.

VAM; RSM; PC.

14. Poem by Kawara Sadaijin. O-Tsū, the madwoman of Fumi-hiroge, who had studied literature, but lost her senses when forced to give it up. The book held by the boy accompanying her is inscribed 'Kōkwa . . . ninth month'. Cens. Muramatsu; eng. Take.

VAM; RSM; PC.

15. Poem by Kōkō Tennō. Tomoye-gozen, mistress of Yoshinaka, riding through the snow to tend him when he was sick. Her horse threw up such quantities of snow that the Taira outposts were alarmed and thrown into confusion. *By Hiroshige.* Cens. Kinugasa; eng. Take.

VAM; RSM; PC.

16. Poem by Chūnagon Yukihira. The wife of Matsuō Maru, with an attendant servant, taking her son Kotarō to school at the house of Takebe Genzō (from the play *Sugawara*). Cens. Kinugasa; eng. Take.

VAM; RSM; PC.

17. Poem by Ariwara no Narihira Ason. Kwaoshō Rochishin, one of the heroes of the *Suikoden*, breaking up the image of Kongōjin at Godaizan. Cens. Kinugasa.

VAM; RSM; PC.

18. Poem by Fujiwara no Toshiyuki Ason. The lady Akoya with a little maid bringing her umbrella. *By Hiroshige.* Cens. Kinugasa; eng. Fusajirō.

VAM; RSM; PC.

19. Poem by Ise. O-Tani, wife of Masayemon, carrying her child through the snow. After much wandering she was eventually reunited with her husband. Cens. Kinugasa.

VAM; RSM; PC.

20. Poem by Motoyoshi Shinnō. Yojō (Yü Jang) of Chin, by a bridge, drawing a sword from a bamboo scabbard. He is disguised as a beggar, attempting to revenge the death of his lord Chihaku (Che Pêh) on Cho-bujutsu (Chao Wu-su). Cens. Kinugasa; eng. Take.

VAM; RSM; PC.

21. Poem by Kisen-hōshi. Umewaka Maru caught by the slave-dealer Shinobu Sōda. *By Hiroshige.* Cens. Kinugasa; eng. Fusajirō.

VAM; RSM; PC.

22. Poem by Fumiya (Bunya) Yasuhide. The Taira court lady Tenji no Tsubone with the boy-Emperor Antoku watching the banners of an army among the mountains above a band of mist. Cens. Kinugasa; eng. Take.

VAM; RSM; PC.

23. Poem by Ōye Chisato. The *shirabyōshi* dancer Giō, mistress of Taira no Kiyomori (cf. no.12 above), on Saga moor on a breezy moonlit evening in autumn. Cens. Kinugasa; eng. Fusajirō.

VAM; RSM; PC. *Riccar 1978*, 297.

24. Poem by Kanke. The courtesan Takao arranging her hair before a mirror. *By Hiroshige.* Cens. Kinugasa; eng. Take.

VAM; RSM; PC.

25. Poem by Sanjō Udaijin. Urabe Suyetake, one of Raikō's Four Retainers (*Shitennō*), in hunting dress, with the young prodigy Kwaidō Maru (later Sakata Kintoki) carrying a large axe. Cens. Kinugasa.

VAM; RSM; PC.

26. Poem by Teishin-kō. Gion-nyōgo seated before a low screen holding a sword. She was a

girl of humble origin, but outstanding beauty. Cens. Kinugasa; eng. Take.

VAM; RSM; PC.

27. Poem by Chūnagon Kanesuke. The ghostly fox-woman Kuzunoha and her child by Abe no Yasuna. *By Hiroshige.* Cens. Kinugasa.

VAM; RSM; PC.

28. Poem by Minamoto no Muneyuki Ason. Kanawa Gorō Imakuni pouring *sake* on to the ground from a ladle; he took part in the slaying of Soga no Iruka in 645, an episode that forms the background to the popular play *Imoseyama*. Cens. Kinugasa; eng. Fusajirō.

VAM; RSM; PC.

29. Poem by Ōshikōchi no Mitsune. Shiragiku Maru, a skull held in his mouth, carrying a large inscribed stone slab through the whirlpool of Chigo-ga-fuchi at Yenoshima by night. Cens. Kinugasa; eng. Take.

VAM; RSM; PC.

30. Poem by Mibu no Tadamine. The old lady Kakuju and the girl Kariya-hime watching the departure of Kwanshōjō (Sugawara no Michizane) from the Dōmyōji temple (an episode from the play *Sugawara*). *By Hiroshige.* Cens. Mura; eng. Fusajirō.

VAM; RSM; PC.

31. Poem by Sakanouye Korenori. Satō Tadanobu, his foot on the overturned *go*-board, prepares to resist arrest, his treacherous mistress peeping round the sliding door. Cens. Mura; eng. Take.

VAM; RSM; PC.

32. Poem by Harumichi no Tsuraki. Kinugawa Yoyemon under the willow-tree by the river where he murdered his wife Kasane, whose ghost afterwards haunted the spot. Cens. Mura.

VAM; RSM; PC.

33. Poem by Ki no Tomonori. The madwoman of Miidera, with the great bell and cherry-blossom in the background. Her child was stolen by a merchant and she went mad with grief. *By Hiroshige.* Cens. Watari; eng. Take.

VAM; RSM; PC.

34. Poem by Fujiwara no Okikaze. Higuchi Jirō Kanemitsu keeping watch in a pine-tree. Cens. Mura.

VAM; RSM; PC.

35. Poem by Ki no Tsurayuki. The monk Karukaya Dōshin (Katō Shigeuji) and his son Ishidō Maru, characters in a popular play, *Tsukushi no iyedzuto*. Cens. Mura; eng. Fusajirō.

VAM; RSM; PC.

36. Poem by Kiyowara no Fukayabu. Hyōye-no-suke Yoritomo and his bride Tatsu-hime. *By Hiroshige.* Cens. Watari; eng. Fusajirō.

VAM; RSM; PC.

37. Poem by Fumiya Asayasu. The court lady Tamamo-no-maye, the Japanese incarnation of the Nine-tailed Fox in the reign of the

Emperor Konoye (1142–56). The play *Tamamo-no-maye*, with Onoye Kikugorō III in the name part, was produced at the Nakamura theatre in the autumn of 1844. Cens. Mura.

VAM; RSM; PC.

38. Poem by Ukon. Shunkwan on the shore crying after the departing ship. Cens. Kinugasa; eng. Fusajirō.

VAM; RSM; PC.

39. Poem by Sangi Hitoshi. The monk-recluse Sōgen before a portrait of Orikoto-hime, a daughter of the Ōtomo family with whom he was infatuated. *By Hiroshige.* Cens. Mura; eng. Take.

VAM; RSM; PC.

40. Poem by Taira no Kanemori. Iga no Tsubone encounters the spirit of Fujiwara no Nakanari. *By Hiroshige.* Cens. Muramatsu; eng. Fusajirō.

VAM; RSM; PC.

41. Poem by Mibu no Tadami. Hasebe Nobutsura tying his girdle and holding a flute in his mouth as the Taira troops approach to capture him after the defeat of Yorimasa at the Uji river (1180). Cens. Muramatsu; eng. Take.

VAM; RSM; PC.

42. Poem by Kiyowara no Motosuke. The mad poet Wankyū (short for Wanya Kyūyemon) followed by two little girls. *By Hiroshige.* Cens. Watari.

VAM; RSM; PC.

43. Poem by Chūnagon Atsutada. The lady Kenrei-monin seated with a lacquer book-case. *By Hiroshige.* Cens. Muramatsu; eng. Take.

VAM; RSM; PC.

44. Poem by Chūnagon Asatada. Yendō Musha Moritō reading a letter, which lies before him together with the head of Kesa-gozen in a bag. Cens. Kinugasa; eng. Take.

VAM; RSM; PC. *Stewart*, Pl.52.4.

45. Poem by Kentoku-kō. Yaoya O-Shichi standing by a low screen behind which are a sword and a fan on the floor. *By Hiroshige.* Cens. Watari; eng. Take.

VAM; RSM; PC.

46. Poem by Sone no Yoshitada. Usuyuki-hime, dressed for travel, standing by a moored boat from which the ferryman grimaces at her. *By Hiroshige.* Cens. Hama.

VAM; RSM; PC.

47. Poem by Yekyō-hōshi. Heishōkoku (Taira no) Kiyomori, acted by Nakamura Utayemon IV, looking at a poem, written on the window, urging him to give up women and lead the life of a religious hermit. This is probably from the play *Gempei Soga*, staged at the Nakamura theatre at the beginning of 1845. Cens. Watari; eng. Take.

VAM; RSM; PC.

48. Poem by Minamoto no Shigeyuki. The maid O-Kiku weeping over the plate she has broken, while a little maid expresses conster-

nation. *By Hiroshige.* Cens. Watari; eng. Take.

VAM; RSM; PC.

49. Poem by Ōnakatomi no Yoshinobu Ason. Kamiya Niyemon (real name Tamiya Iyemon) terrified by a fire, lantern, ropes, etc., that combine to form the ghost of his murdered wife O-Iwa. Cens. Kinugasa; eng. Take.

VAM; RSM; PC.

50. Poem by Fujiwara no Yoshitaka. The Chinese hero Kwanu (Kuan Yü) seated under a blossoming tree, stroking his beard. Cens. Muramatsu; eng. Fusajirō.

VAM; RSM; PC.

51. Poem and portrait of Fujiwara no Sanekata Ason. The wife of Katō Shigeuji and his concubine Chidori-no-maye playing at chequers. *By Hiroshige.* Cens. Hama; eng. Take.

VAM; RSM; PC.

52. Poem and portrait of Fujiwara no Michinobu Ason. Taheiji, acted by Matsumoto Kinshō, grasping a kitchen-knife, while the terrified O-Yone cowers before him; background of a smoking fire. *By Kunisada.* Cens. Murata; eng. Fusajirō.

VAM; RSM; PC.

53. Poem and portrait of the mother of Udaishō Michitsuna. Nakamura Utayemon IV as Fujiya Izayemon dancing with a small drum; from the play *Kuruwa Bunsho*, staged at the Kawarazaki theatre in the winter of 1846. Cens. Murata; eng. Fusajirō.

VAM; RSM; PC.

54. Poem and portrait of the mother of Gidō Sanshi. O-Towa dressing the hair of the wrestler Inagawa Jirokichi. *By Hiroshige.* Cens. Hama; eng. Fusajirō.

VAM; RSM; PC.

55. Poem and portrait of Dainagon Kintō. Yuki-hime, seated under an overhanging rock with her hand on the hilt of her dirk, turns to look at a small golden dragon in a waterfall. Cens. Mura.

VAM; RSM; PC.

56. Poem and portrait of Idzumi no Shikibu. Ichikawa Danjurō VII as Akushichibyōye Kagekiyo at Tōdaiji, a black robe over his armour, glaring defiance and grasping a large *naginata*. Danjurō VII was in exile from Yedo 1842–50, but played Kagekiyo at Osaka in the winter of 1843. Cens. Mura; eng. Take.

VAM; RSM; PC. *Düsseldorf 1962*, 43.

57. Poem and portrait of Murasaki Shikibu. Isami Tomokichirō, a purse in his mouth, prepares to fight Rokuya Ongundayū. Probably a scene from *Jiraiya*, staged at the Kawarazaki theatre in the early summer of 1844. *By Hiroshige.* Cens. Hama.

VAM; RSM; PC.

58. Poem and portrait of Daini-no-sammi. Yokoyama Tarō, acted by Ichikawa Danjurō VIII, seated in formal attire; his wife Asaka behind him with a bucket of autumn maple.

By Kunisada. Cens. Murata; eng. Takejirō.
VAM; RSM; PC.

59. Poem and portrait of Akazome-yemon. Nakamura Utayemon IV as Yaoya Hambei in a street by moonlight. The last time he took this role was in *Yoigoshin* at the Kawarazaki theatre in the summer of 1844. Cens. Mera–Murata; eng. Fusajirō.
VAM; RSM; PC. *Apollo,* January 1950, p.14.

60. Poem and portrait of Koshikibu Naishi. Hatsu-jo looks back at a flight of crows as she passes a house at night. A scene from the play *Kagamiyama.* By *Hiroshige.* Cens. Hama; eng. Fusajirō.
VAM; RSM; PC.

61. Poem and portrait of Ise no Ōsuke. Yadahei, acted by Ichikawa Danjurō VIII, seated with Kokonohe-tayū under a blossoming cherry-tree. Cens. Murata.
VAM; RSM; PC.

62. Poem and portrait of Seishōnagon. Kwanshōjō (Sugawara Michizane), probably acted by Onoye Kikugorō III, in court robes; Hangwandai Terukuni behind him. *By Kunisada.* Cens. Murata; eng. Fusajirō.
VAM; RSM; PC.

63. Poem and portrait of Sakyō-no-tayū Michimasa. Koman seated in an attitude of distress before a scroll on which she has been writing; a *samisen* behind her, inscribed *Godairiki* (the name of a popular play). *By Hiroshige.* Cens. Fu; eng. Fusajirō.
VAM; RSM; PC.

64. Poem and portrait of Gonchūnagon Sadayori. The maid Chidori dancing with a fan before an armour-box. Cens. Mura; eng. Take.
VAM; RSM; PC.

65. Poem and portrait of Sagami. The villain Kyōgoku Takumi seated on a chest holding up a lantern, and at the same time treading on the sword of O-Kiku, who attacks him to avenge her father Yoshioka Ichimisai. Cens. Murata.
VAM; RSM; PC.

66. Poem and portrait of Daisōjō Gyōson. Kuganosuke in contemplation outside a pavilion on a river-bank. *By Hiroshige.* Cens. Murata; eng. Take.
VAM; RSM; PC.

67. Poem and portrait of Suō no Naishi. Shirai Gompachi, acted by Ichikawa Danjurō VIII, reading a letter by moonlight, while a lap-dog brings him another paper; a scene from the play *Hiyoku no inadzuma,* staged at the Kawarazaki theatre at the beginning of 1846. *By Kunisada.* Cens. Murata; eng. Take.
VAM; RSM; PC.

68. Poem and portrait of Sanjō-in. Hōkai-bō, a character in the play *Sumidagawa,* on a flight of temple steps by moonlight, holding a half-opened scroll-painting of a carp in a waterfall. Cens. Hama; eng. Fusajirō.
VAM; RSM; PC.

69. Poem and portrait of Nōin-hōshi. Sukune Tarō, with arms folded, and wearing red make-up, standing under a pine-tree by a stream, while Tatsuta-no-maye plucks at his sleeve. *By Hiroshige.* Cens. Murata; eng. Take.
VAM; RSM; PC.

70. Poem and portrait of Ryōzen-hōshi. Nakamura Utayemon IV as Ishidome Busuke drawing a sword, restrained by his younger sister O-Hana. *By Kunisada.* Cens. Murata.
VAM; RSM; PC.

71. Poem and portrait of Dainagon Tsunenobu. Akogi Heiji raising his hat and looking into a stream, while Hiragawara Jirozō glares at him among the reeds behind. Probably a scene from *Samezaya,* produced at the Kawarazaki theatre in the early summer of 1846. Cens. Hama.
VAM; RSM; PC.

72. Poem and portrait of Yūshi-naishinnō-ke Kii. Yayegaki-hime burning incense before a portrait of her betrothed, Takeda Katsuyori. *By Hiroshige.* Cens. Mera–Murata.
VAM; RSM; PC.

73. Poem and portrait of Saki-no-chūnagon Kunifusa. The farewell between Mukwan-no-tayū Atsumori and Tamaori-hime before the battle of Ichi-no-tani (1184) in which the former was killed by Naozane. Cens. Muramatsu–Yoshimura.
VAM; RSM; PC.

74. Poem and portrait of Minamoto no Toshiyori Ason. Ichikawa Danjurō VIII as Narukami Shōnin and Onoye Yeisaburō as Kumo no Tayema seated by a waterfall. *By Kunisada.* Cens. Mera–Murata.
VAM; RSM; PC.

75. Poem and portrait of Fujiwara no Mototoshi. The girl Umegawa, under a willow-tree, observes the approach of old Magoyemon on a dyke across the paddy-fields, while Kameya Chūbei hides behind a rice-stook. *By Hiroshige.* Cens. Fu; eng. Fusajirō.
VAM; RSM; PC.

76. Poem and portrait of Hōshōji Nyūdō Saki-no-kwampaku Daijō-Daijin. The robber Hakamadare Yasusuke in court robes with a large box of loot on his back; he had robbed the palace at Kyoto, but was captured by the night-watch. The figure has the unmistakable features of Nakamura Utayemon IV, but there seems to be no record of his having acted this part. Cens. Hama; eng. Take.
VAM; RSM; PC. *Robinson 1963,* Pl.15.

77. Poem and portrait of Sutoku-in. Miyagi Asojirō and Miyuki in a boat, with a large ship behind. This is a scene from the play *Asagao monogatari,* produced at the Ichimura theatre in the late summer of 1848, with Ichikawa Danjurō VIII as Asojirō and Bandō Shuka as Miyuki. *By Kunisada.* Cens. Mera–Murata; eng. Fusajirō.
VAM; RSM; PC.

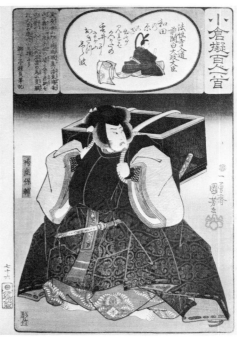

S46.76

78. Poem and portrait of Minamoto no Kanemasa. Kumagaye Jirō Naozane with his horse on the shore at Ichi-no-tani. This clearly represents Nakamura Utayemon IV in *Ichi-no-tani yukimi no takadono* at the Kawarazaki theatre in the winter of 1846. *By Hiroshige.* Cens. Murata; eng. Take.
VAM; RSM; PC.

79. Poem and portrait of Sakyō-no-tayū Akisuke. Ume no Yoshibei reading a letter by moonlight on the river-bank; young Chōkichi squats behind him, and further off is Gembeibori Gembei. This is a scene from *Megumi no Kagekiyo,* produced at the Nakamura theatre at the beginning of 1848, with Nakamura Utayemon IV as Yoshibei, Iwai Kumesaburō as Chōkichi, and Ichikawa Kuzō as Gembei. Cens. Murata.
VAM; RSM; PC.

80. Poem and portrait of Taiken-monin Horikawa. Yamazakiya Yogorō holding a fan and a robe, and watching a couple of butterflies, while Fujiya Adzuma squats behind him. Yogorō is clearly acted by Ichimura Uzayemon XII, and the play is probably *Kakizome Soga* (Ichimura theatre, beginning of 1848). *By Kunisada.* Cens. Mera–Murata.
VAM; RSM; PC. *Düsseldorf 1962,* 48.

81. Poem and portrait of Go-tokudaiji Sadaijin. Takahashi Yajurō and his wife Satsuki on either side of a gate in an iris-garden. Yajurō appears to be represented by Ichikawa Danjurō VIII. *By Hiroshige.* Cens. Murata; eng. Fusajirō.
VAM; RSM; PC.

82. Poem and portrait of Dōin-hoshi. Act IV of the *Chūshingura:* Sawamura Sōjurō V as Ōboshi Yuranosuke outside the castle, holding the fatal dirk, and accompanied by his son

Rikiya, acted by Iwai Kumesaburō, with a lantern. Cens. Muramatsu–Yoshimura.

VAM; RSM; PC. *Stewart*, Pl.52.3.

83. Poem and portrait of Kōtaikōgū-no-tayū Toshinari. Ōtonai and Akazawa Jūnai, armed with swords, by a bamboo hedge. This may well be a scene from *Soga no hatsuyume* (Nakamura theatre, beginning of 1847). *By Kunisada.* Cens. Murata; eng. Take.

VAM; RSM; PC.

84. Poem and portrait of Fujiwara no Kiyo-suke Ason. Sakura Maru, grasping a sword, stands over his wife Yaye. This is a scene from *Sugawara* (Kawarazaki theatre, winter 1847). *By Hiroshige.* Cens. Mera–Murata.

VAM; RSM; PC.

85. Poem and portrait of Shunye-hōshi. Matano Gorō (Kagehisa) holding a lantern above the spirit of the mandarin duck; the former is Ichikawa Danjurō VIII in red make-up, and the latter (probably) Bandō Shuka, but it has not been possible to identify the production. Cens. Murata; eng. Take.

VAM; RSM; PC.

86. Poem and portrait of Saigyō-hōshi. Benkei, in elaborate stage costume and make-up, seated, a finger to his lips. Behind him are Shidzuka-gozen and a huge pair of swords. *By Kunisada.* Cens. Murata.

VAM; RSM; PC.

87. Poem and portrait of Jakuren-hōshi. Yayegiri with her hat and stick by a hedge outside a garden gate. *By Hiroshige.* Cens. Mera–Murata; eng. Fusajirō.

VAM; RSM; PC.

88. Poem and portrait of Kōka-monin-no-bettō. The *ashigaru* Ichiyemon watching a wasps' nest in a pine-tree; peasants and paddy-fields behind. Cens. Murata.

VAM; RSM; PC.

89. Poem and portrait of Shikishi-naishinnō. Hisamatsu looking out of a window, outside which is O-Some with a rolled paper in her hand. Probably a scene from *Soga no hatsuyume* (Nakamura theatre, beginning of 1847) with Ichikawa Danjurō VIII and Iwai Kumesaburō. *By Kunisada.* Cens. Mera–Murata.

VAM; RSM; PC.

90. Poem and portrait of Impu-monin-no-ōsuke. Act I of the *Chūshingura*: Kō no Moronao holding his love-letter, and Kaoyo-gozen seated coyly behind him by a clothes-rack. This might be Seki Sanjurō and Iwai Kumesaburō in *Chūshin meimei* (Nakamura theatre, summer 1847). *By Hiroshige.* Cens. Mera–Murata; eng. Fusajirō.

VAM; RSM; PC.

91. Poem and portrait of Go-kyōgoku-sessho Saki-no-dajōdaijin. Matsuwaka Maru plucking the sleeve of Seigen-ni; two conventional butterflies. Scene from *Onna Seigen* (Nakamura theatre, early 1847) with Ichikawa Danjurō

VIII and Iwai Kumesaburō. Cens. Mera–Murata.

VAM; RSM; PC. *Düsseldorf 1962*, 49; *Riccar 1978*, 298.

92. Poem and portrait of Nijō-in Sanuki. Yazama Jūtarō, with two swords in a bundle, turns fiercely on his wife O-Riye, who kneels in the snow. *By Kunisada.* Cens. Mera–Murata; eng. Fusajirō.

VAM; RSM; PC.

93. Poem and portrait of Kamakura Udaijin. (Nitta) Yoshitaka seated, with O-Fune standing behind him. Possibly a scene from *Yaguchi no watashi* (Nakamura theatre, early summer 1848). *By Hiroshige.* Cens. Mera–Murata; eng. Fusajirō.

VAM; RSM; PC.

94. Poem and portrait of Sangi Masatsune. Fox-man and fox-woman in the snow, the former rolling on his back, and the latter dancing. Probably a scene from *Tabi suzume Yoshino no irogoto* (Kawarazaki theatre, autumn 1847) with Nakamura Utayemon IV as Tadanobu and Onoye Baikō as Shidzuka. Cens. Murata; eng. Takejirō.

VAM; RSM; PC.

95. Poem and portrait of Saki-no-daisōjō Jiyen. Ōtomo no Kuronushi with a large axe, and Komachi, the spirit of the cherry-tree, with a spray of cherry-blossom. This may be a scene from *Rokkasen* (Ichimura theatre, autumn 1846). *By Kunisada.* Cens. Mura.

VAM; RSM; PC. *Düsseldorf 1962*, 38.

96. Poem and portrait of Nyūdō Saki-no-dajōdaijin. The villain Fuwa Banzayemon in a wide hat by a fenced cherry-tree at night. Ichikawa Danjurō VIII, who took the part in *Inadzuma-zōshi* at the Ichimura theatre in the spring of 1848, is here represented. *By Hiroshige.* Cens. Mera–Murata.

VAM; RSM; PC. *Düsseldorf 1962*, 39.

97. Poem and portrait of Gonchūnagon Sada-iye. The 'Blind Man of Hyūga' (sc. Kagekiyo), with a drawn sword, on the shore with his daughter Hito Maru. A scene from *Megumi no Kagekiyo* (Nakamura theatre, beginning of 1848) with Nakamura Utayemon IV and Onoye Kikujirō. Cens. Muramatsu–Yoshimura; eng. Takejirō.

VAM; RSM; PC.

98. Poem and portrait of Shōsammi Iyetaka. Ichikawa Danjurō VIII standing, holding a sword, and Matsumoto Kinshō (Kōshirō VI) seated holding a box. They are taking the parts of Danshichi Kurobei and Issun Tokubei respectively, both characters in the play *Natsu matsuri*, but so far it has not been possible to trace a production of it in which these two actors appeared together. *By Kunisada.* Cens. Muramatsu–Yoshimura.

VAM; RSM; PC.

99. Poem and portrait of Go-Toba-in. Sammi Chūjō Koremori standing with his back to O-

Sato, who peeps coyly over her shoulder. A scene from the play *Goban Tadanobu* (Ichimura theatre, winter 1848) with Ichimura Uza-yemon XII and Bandō Shuka. *By Hiroshige.* Cens. Muramatsu–Yoshimura; eng. Take.

VAM; RSM; PC.

100. Poem and portrait of Juntoku-in. Performance of the Shakkyō dance in lion-mask and long red mane. It was performed by Ichikawa Danjurō VIII at the Kawarazaki theatre in the summer of 1846, which is probably the occasion represented. Cens. Muramatsu–Yoshimura; eng. Fusajirō.

VAM; RSM; PC.

NOTE. MFA has about thirty of this series.

S47
Tsūzoku Suikoden gōketsu hyakuhachi-nin ('The hundred and eight heroes of the popular *Suikoden*'). *Chūban.*

Title (occasionally omitted) and hero's name on oblong red cartouche of irregular outline framed with flowers, an open scroll, etc. Single figures on fully coloured backgrounds. Pub. Yamamoto-ya Heikichi; various cens., singly and in pairs; *c.* 1845–53.

1. Botaichū Kotaisō, the amazon, on a river-bank, poising a huge metal-shod beam. Cens. Muramatsu–Yoshimura.

MFA; PC. *Riccar 1979*, 23.

2. Byōkwansaku Yōyū (i) on a rock above water, gazing at a woman's severed head which he holds, a sword in his other hand. Cens. Fuku–Muramatsu.

MFA; PC. *Riccar 1979*, 12; *Kennedy*, 1980.85.

3. Byōkwansaku Yōyū (ii) by a waterfall defending himself with a shield against flying arrows. Cens. Hama–Magome, black *aratame*.

MFA; PC. *Riccar 1979*, 13; *Kennedy*, 1980.83.

4. Chūsenko Teitokuson on a rock overhang-ing a river, threatening with his spear a huge snake drinking from the stream. Cens. Fuku–Muramatsu.

MFA; PC. *Riccar 1979*, 20.

5. Gōtenrai Ryōshin on the sea-shore loading a cannon; he wears a head-dress like a military shako. Cens. Tanaka.

MFA; PC. *Riccar 1979*, 16; *Kruml*, 9.53.

6. Gyōja Bushō seated under a tree with a long iron club; wind in the long grass behind. Cens. Fuku–Muramatsu.

PC. *Riccar 1979*, 5.

7. Hakkwaja Yōshun grasping his sword with both hands, a waterfall and peonies behind him. Cens. Muramatsu–Yoshimura.

MFA. *Riccar 1979*, 19.

8. Hyōshitō Rinchū, spear in hand, looking out from a house on to snow. Cens. Fuku–Muramatsu.

MFA; PC. *Riccar 1979*, 3.

9. Ichijōsei Kosanro facing a flight of arrows,

holding two swords crossed above her head. Cens. Hama–Magome.

MFA; PC. *Riccar 1979*, 17.

10. Ju-unryō Kōsonshō, his hair and garments blown by the wind, seated on a rock above a torrent, holding his sword upright before his face. Cens. Muramatsu–Yoshimura.

MFA; B; PC. *Riccar 1979*, 1.

11. Kikenji Tokyō, half-naked under an overhanging rock and peony, on the shore watching fish in the water. Cens. Fuku–Muramatsu.

PC. *Riccar 1979*, 21; *Kennedy*, 1980.84.

12. Kontenmaō (for Konseimaō) Hanzui, grasping his spear, falls back before an apparition of demons. Cens. Fuku–Muramatsu.

MFA; PC. *Riccar 1979*, 18.

13. Kwaoshō Rochishin, half-naked and tattooed, stamps on a fallen *Niō* figure amid the smashed railings. Cens. Tanaka.

B; PC. *Riccar 1979*, 4; *Kruml*, 9.54.

14. Kwatsuyenra Genshōshichi climbing out of the water on to a rock, his sword between his teeth, leaving his vanquished opponent at the bottom. Cens. Muramatsu–Yoshimura.

MFA; B; PC. *Riccar 1979*, 11; *Bidwell 1980*, 160.

15. Kyumonryō Shishin, half-naked and tattooed under a tree, grasps an armoured foeman by the neck, a long pole in his other hand. Cens. Tanaka.

B; PC. *Riccar 1979*, 7; *Kruml*, 9.58.

16. Rōrihakuchō Chōjun, half-naked and tattooed, with a sword between his teeth, wrenching apart the bars of a water-gate. Cens. Tanaka.

MFA; PC.

17. Ryūchitaisai Genshōji, in a boat, and wearing a straw cloak, defends himself against flying arrows with a long rudder. Cens. Tanaka.

MFA; PC. *Riccar 1979*, 8; *Kruml*, 9.56.

18. Sekibakki Ryūtō, half-naked, seated on a dais beneath a brocade curtain. Cens. Fuku–Muramatsu.

VAM; MFA; PC. *Robinson 1961*, Pl.14; *Riccar 1979*, 6.

19. Sekishōgun Sekiyū, half-naked on a rock by a waterfall, throwing the two halves of a cangue at a foeman whose hand appears in the water. Cens. Fuku–Muramatsu.

PC. *Riccar 1979*, 22.

20. Senkwaji Chō-ō, half-naked and tattooed on a river-bank, wringing out his loincloth, a cloth bag held in his mouth, and his sword stuck in the ground beside him. Cens. Muramatsu–Yoshimura.

PC. *Riccar 1979*, 9.

21. Shameisaburō Sekishū in a wide hat and carrying a *mokugyo* and stick, standing at the base of a castle wall. Cens. Hama–Magome, black *aratame*.

MFA; PC. *Riccar 1979*, 14.

22. Shūgumba Sensan, in a wind by a torrent,

S47.17

makes a stroke with his sword while his hat blows away. Cens. Tanaka.

MFA; B; PC. *Riccar 1979*, 15; *Kruml*, 9.57.

23. Taitō Kwanshō on the sea-shore swinging his huge glaive. Cens. Muramatsu–Yoshimura.

MFA; PC. *Riccar 1979*, 2.

24. Tammeijirō Genshōgo under water grasping a rope, and with a sword in his other hand. Cens. Hama–Magome.

MFA; B; PC. *Bidwell 1980*, 161.

S48

Retsu mō den ('Stories of strength, in order'). *Chōban*.

Title on oblong coloured cartouche, with

name of character on similar panel adjoining. Heroes in action. Pub. Mikawa-ya Tetsugorō; cens. Muramatsu, or *aratame*; Dragon 9–10, *c*.1845 and 1856 (probably all designed *c*.1845). Cf. S49.

1. Hako-ō Maru (Soga Gorō in boyhood) by a waterfall writing *bonji* characters on a rock, and holding up a large image of Fudō with his other hand. 1856.

PC.

2. The low-class retainer (*ashigaru*) Kintarō. PC.

3. Miyamoto Musashi warming his hands before a smoking fire of brushwood. *c*.1845.

PC. *Inouye*, Pl.100.

S48.1

S49.4

on plain ground; single figures, with the horse (and sometimes its name) inset in a rectangular blue panel, upper right, between title and text. Pub. Yamaguchi-ya Tōbei; cens. Muramatsu–Yoshimura; 1847–8.

1. Kumagaye Jirō Naozane with the head of Atsumori; his horse unnamed.
    MFA.

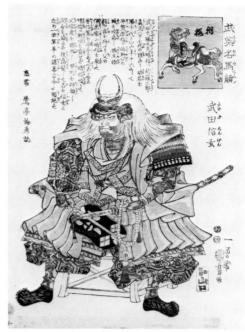

S50.2

2. Takeda Shingen seated in full armour, holding a rosary and a short staff; his horse named Dōyō (or Kanazakura).
    PC.

3. Sasaki Shirō Takatsuna seated on a rock, in armour, holding an open fan; his horse named Ikedzuki.
    PC.

S51
Sayetate no uchi kitai no wazamono ('Skilfully tempered sharp blades'). *Ōban*.

Title and character's name in shaded oblong cartouche with rounded corners and frame of *shimenawa* (the rope with strips of cut paper always suspended in the forges of swordsmiths). Protagonists of stories in which swords figure prominently, in action (mostly of theatrical origin); text above, by Ippitsu-an. Pub. Ise-ya Ichibei; various cens., in pairs; 1847–8. The series is notable for extremely fine engraving.

1. Awa no Jurobei dragging along his terrified daughter (in pilgrim's dress), whom he slew, not recognizing her; his blade was by (Rai?) Kunitsugu. Cens. Mera–Murata.
    RSM; MFA; PC.

2. Fukuoka Mitsugi, bloodstained and with a drawn sword, leaning against a stone watertank; in the background a woman crawling on

4. The strong woman O-Kane.
    PC.

5. Shōbutsu Maru (the child Benkei) holding a thick bamboo pole surmounted by a bale of straw from which project *gohei* and miscellaneous weapons. 1856.
    PC.

6. (Pl.17) Gen Sammi Yorimasa shooting at the *Nuye* (not shown). *c*.1845.
    PC. *Robinson 1961*, Pl.60b; *Johnes*, 48.

S49
Shin-yū kurabe ('Comparisons of true courage'). *Chōban*. Particulars exactly as for S48.

1. Benkei, a rope hitched round his shoulders, drags the bell of Miidera up a mountain-slope. *c*.1845.
    B; PC. *Riccar 1978*, 83; *Bidwell 1980*, 146.

2. Kiyo-hime, below, already beginning her transformation into a dragon, to envelop the bell of Dōjōji, above; cherry-blossom. 1856.
    PC. *Inouye*, Pl.101.

3. (Pl.19) Hachirō Tametomo, in exile, on the rocky shore of Ōshima at sunrise, holding a large stick; his crane and 'wave-birds' (*chidori*) flying above. *c*.1845.
    PC.

4. Taira no Tomomori at the bottom of the sea with a dragon, holding his *naginata*; the great anchor behind him. 1856.
    B; PC. *Bidwell 1968*, Pl.126; *Riccar 1978*, 84; *Bidwell 1980*, 197.

S50
Buyei meiba kurabe ('Comparison of the famous horses of brilliant soldiers'). *Ōban*.

Title, subtitle, and text (by Ōtei Umehiko)

S51.2

the ground. His sword was by Aoi Shimosaka Yasutsugu. Cens. Muramatsu–Yoshimura.
PC.

3. Kamiya Jihei about to perform *seppuku* by a memorial stone, while a dog carries off the severed head of his beloved Koharu. Cens. Mera–Murata.
VAM; RSM; PC.

4. Katsuma Gengobei seated on a stone block looking at a woman's severed head which he holds in his hands; his blade, which sticks in the ground in front of him, was by Morimitsu of Bizen. Cens. Muramatsu–Yoshimura.
VAM; RSM; PC.

5. Ōkumo Hikoroku Tessan, having thrown down a well the body of the maid O-Kiku, whom he had murdered for breaking one of a set of ten valuable plates, looks down the well while wiping his sword; the blade was by Gorō Masamune of Sagami. Cens. Mera–Murata.
PC. *Robinson 1961*, Pl.63.

6. Sano Jirozayemon, bloodstained and with a drawn sword, holds up a lamp to see the feet of a prospective victim projecting from under the bed. His blade was by 'Two-character' Kuni-yuki. Cens. Muramatsu–Yoshimura.
RSM; PC.

7. Sasaki Ganryū by a stone figure of Jizō in a shower of rain, holding a straw hat above his head, and a drawn sword; his blade was by Shinsoku, stolen from the Yoshioka family. Cens. Muramatsu–Yoshimura.
RSM; PC.

8. Shirai Gompachi crouching to wash his hands, while two dogs bark at him from behind; his blade was by Sengo Muramasa of Ise. Cens. Muramatsu–Yoshimura.
RSM; MFA; PC.

9. (Pl.27) Shundō Jiroyemon, covered in blood and his face grey with approaching

death, plunges his sword, carried in a bamboo sheath, into a heap of straw; the blade was by Shimosaka Yasutsugu. Cens. Mera–Murata.
RSM; PC.

10. Yodoya Shinshichi, covered with bloody hand-prints, holds up a long written scroll, his sword in his other hand; the blade was by 'Two-character' Kunitoshi. Cens. Mera–Murata.
RSM; PC.

S52

Gōketsu hakkei ('Heroes for the Eight Views'). *Ōban*.

Title and subtitle, the former in large characters, reserved on rounded oblong black cartouche with decorative coloured frame. Single figures in action, with accessories, and biographical text above, by Ippitsu-an. Pub. Tsuji-Kawa; cens. Mera–Murata; 1847–8.

1. 'Autumn Moon at Toba.' Yendō Musha Moritō standing with drawn sword (Toba was where Kesa-gozen was brought up).
PC.

2. 'Lingering Snow at the Hermit's Cell.' Miyamoto Musashi in the snow on his way to visit the old ascetic Bokuden, who taught him the secrets of swordsmanship.
PC.

3. 'Evening Glow at Hyōgo.' Heishōkoku Kiyomori Nyūdō Jōkai waving his fan with incantations to arrest the sunset (cf. T83).
PC.

4. 'Vesper Bell at Nara.' Kadzusa Shichibei Kagekiyo, wearing monk's robes over armour, preparing to resist arrest at Tōdaiji temple.
PC.

5. 'Returning Boats at Hakata.' Kezori Ku-

S52.4

yemon the pirate, in clothes of European type, seated on a chest with a long tobacco-pipe.
PC.

6. 'Clearing Weather at Mount Shimahiro.' (Pl.26) Musashi Gorō Sadayo defending himself against a hail of arrows at the battle of Mount Shimahiro, in which Masakado was defeated by the Imperial forces.
PC.

7. 'Night Rain at Kurama.' Onzōshi Ushiwaka Maru holding his straw hat under a stream of water; this was a magical operation to deprive Ki-ichi Hōgen of sleep, so that when he finally slept deeply Ushiwaka could steal the strategic scrolls.
PC.

8. 'Homing Geese at Ōkawa.' The archer Ōkawa Kumoyemon carrying a bow over his shoulder, wrapped in a pierced target.
PC.

S53

Kataki- (or ***Ada-***) ***uchi chūkō den*** ('Stories of dutifulness and loyalty in revenge'). *Ōban*.

Title on red cartouche with decorative black border and shaped top; descriptive text, by Ippitsu-an, above. Single figures with or without accessories. Pub. Hachi; cens. Mera–Murata, or Hama–Kinugasa; eng. Takichi; *c*.1847–8.

1. Hatsu-jo 'the loyal' (*chūsetsu*), standing, opening her umbrella; tied round her waist is a cloth bag containing the severed head of Tsubone Iwafuji. The story forms the plot of the popular play *Kagamiyama*.
RSM; PC.

2. Iinuma Katsugorō 'the dutiful' (*kōshi*) leaning back on his cripple's trolley and making a stroke with his sword.
RSM; PC.

3. Ishii Hanzō 'the dutiful' (*kōshi*), on one knee, grasping his sword, a petition in the bosom of his *kimono*, and his sleeves tied up ready for action.
RSM; PC.

4. Keyamura Kida Rokusuke, his sleeves tied up, raising his sword with both hands for a blow. A man of great strength but gentle nature, he helped the daughters of Yoshioka Ichimisai to avenge their father's death, and later fought tigers under Katō Kiyomasa in Korea.
VAM; RSM; MFA; PC.

5. Miyagino 'the dutiful' (*kōshi*) on one knee, a *naginata* in one hand and the other stretched out holding a *sake*-cup. She and her younger sister Shinobu avenged the death of their father Yomosaku on the official who had him unjustly killed.
PC.

6. Miyamoto Musashi practising his *nitō-ryū*, or two-sworded style of fencing, using two sticks.
RSM; PC.

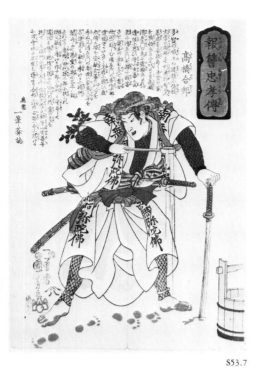

S53.7

7. Takahashi Gappō, his feet bloodstained, and resting one hand on his sword, drinking from a dipper. He avenged his elder brother Seizayemon, who had been unjustly accused of the murder of his lord and killed at the instigation of the real culprit.

VAM; RSM; MFA; PC.

8. Watanabe Shidzuma in a black *kimono*, wiping his sword with a straw sandal. His story is told in *Mitford*, 'Kazuma's revenge' (Kazuma became Shidzuma when the story was staged).

VAM; MFA; PC. *Falteri*, 1981.177.

S54

Seichū gishi den ('Stories of the true loyalty of the faithful *samurai*', sc. the Forty-Seven *Rōnin*). *Ōban*.

Title on red oblong cartouche, the upper outline convex and the lower concave; biographical text (by Ippitsu-an) above. Single figures in action, on plain background; most impressions numbered 1–50. Pub. Yebi-ya Rinnosuke; various cens.; August 1847–January 1848 (see S54.50). This is the earliest, and seems to have been the most popular, of Kuniyoshi's series on the Forty-Seven *Rōnin* (though three drawings for an earlier unpublished set, *Chūshingura gishi soroi*, c.1836, are in the Leyden Museum; see *Lieftinck*, Nos.103, 319(4) and (11)).

1. Ōboshi Yuranosuke Yoshio seated on a camp-stool holding a drum and stick, and a spear over his shoulder. Cens. Hama–Kinugasa.

BM; VAM; MFA; B; PC. *Bidwell 1980*, 143; *Falteri*, 1981.156.

2. Ōboshi Rikiya Yoshikane seated, his helmet attached to the head of his spear, which is over his shoulder. Cens. Muramatsu–Yoshimura.

BM; VAM; MFA; B; PC.

3. Yatō Yomoshichi Norikane holding his spear and drinking from a porcelain cup. Cens. Muramatsu–Yoshimura.

BM (unnumbered); MFA; B; PC. *Bidwell 1980*, 144; *Falteri*, 1981.157.

4. Fuwa Katsuyemon Masatane examining the edge of his sword. Cens. Muramatsu–Yoshimura.

BM (unnumbered); VAM; MFA; B; PC. *Falteri*, 1981.158.

5. Shikamatsu Kanroku Yukishige with his spear, wringing out his sleeves. Cens. Muramatsu–Yoshimura.

BM (unnumbered); MFA; B; PC. *Düsseldorf 1962*, 71.

6. Yoshida Sadayemon Kanesada cutting arrows in flight. Cens. Muramatsu–Yoshimura.

BM (unnumbered); MFA; B; PC. *Falteri*, 1981.159.

7. Sakagaki Genzō Masakata seated on a broken stone garden plinth, grasping his spear. Cens. Muramatsu–Yoshimura.

BM (unnumbered); MFA; B; PC. *Falteri*, 1981.160.

8. Yukugawa Sampei Munenori cutting at a flying hand-lamp. Cens. Muramatsu–Yoshimura.

BM (unnumbered); MFA; B; PC. *Falteri*, 1981.161.

9. Onodera Jūnai Hidetomo crouching with drawn sword, shading his eyes. Cens. Mera–Murata.

BM; MFA; B; PC. *Falteri*, 1981.162.

10. Isoai Juroyemon Masahisa making a stroke with his *naginata*. Cens. Hama–Kinugasa.

BM; MFA; B; PC.

11. Okano Ginyemon Kanehide holding out a lantern, a drawn sword in his other hand. Cens. Muramatsu–Yoshimura.

BM (unnumbered); MFA; B; PC.

12. Senzaki Yagorō Noriyasu running, spear in hand. Cens. Hama–Kinugasa.

BM (unnumbered); MFA; B; PC. *Falteri*, 1981.163.

13. Yazama Jūjirō Moto-oki blowing a signal-whistle, a drawn sword in his other hand. Cens. Hama–Kinugasa.

BM; MFA; B; PC.

14. Ōtaka Gengo Tadao making a thrust with his spear. Cens. Mera–Murata.

BM; MFA; B; PC. *Düsseldorf 1962*, 70.

15. Kataoka Dengoyemon Takafusa resting on his bloodstained spear, a bloodstained band round his forehead. Cens. Mera–Murata.

BM (unnumbered); MFA; B; PC. *Falteri*, 1981.164.

16. Nakamura Kansuke Tadatoki amid a hail

S54.16

of flying firewood, his foot on a bale of charcoal. Cens. Mera–Murata.

BM; MFA; B; PC. *Falteri*, 1981.165.

17. Okajima Yasōyemon Tsunetatsu guarding himself with a brazier-cover marked with hand-prints. Cens. Mera–Murata.

BM; VAM; MFA; B; PC.

18. Teraoka Heiyemon Nobuyuki pouring water with a dipper from a bucket on to a burning brazier. Cens. Mera–Murata.

BM; MFA; B; PC. *Düsseldorf 1962*, 69.

19. Uramatsu Handayū Takanao making a sword-stroke as he falls backwards into the snow. Cens. Muramatsu–Yoshimura.

BM; MFA; B; PC. *Düsseldorf 1961*, 40; *Düsseldorf 1962*, 72; *Ronin*, 88; *Falteri*, 1981.166.

20. Tokuda Sadayemon Yukitaka in a straw rain-cloak tying the chin-strap of his wide straw hat. Cens. Mera–Murata.

BM; MFA; B; PC.

21. Oribe Yahei Kanamaru, an old man, holding his helmet and spear, and leaning forward slightly. Cens. Mera–Murata.

BM; MFA; B; PC.

22. Kiura Okayemon Sadayuki, back view, making a two-handed sword-stroke. Cens. Mera–Murata.

BM; MFA; B; PC. *Bidwell 1980*, 142.

23. Katsuta Shinyemon Taketaka, sword in hand, holds up a lantern to reveal a lap-dog with frilled collar following him. Cens. Mera–Murata.

BM; MFA; B; PC.

24. Takebayashi Sadashichi Takashige tying his girdle. Cens. Mera–Murata.

BM; MFA; B; PC.

25. Kurahashi Zensuke Takeyuki glaring, and lifting a scroll-painting on the blade of his sword. Cens. Mera–Murata.
BM; MFA; B; PC. *Falteri*, 1981.167.

26. Aihara Yesuke Munefusa, his sword raised with both hands, running over a fallen screen, two ladies' pipes and other objects flying. Cens. Muramatsu–Yoshimura.
BM; VAM; RSM; MFA; B; PC.

27. Tomimori Sukeyemon Masakata, his sword raised with both hands as a brazier and burning charcoal are thrown at him. Cens. Mera–Murata.
BM; VAM; MFA; B; PC. *Falteri*, 1981.168.

28. Ushioda Masanojō Takanori tying the cuff of his armour-sleeve. Cens. Mera–Murata.
BM (unnumbered); MFA; B; PC.

29. Hayami Sōzayemon Mitsutaka drinking from a metal kettle. Cens. Muramatsu–Yoshimura.
BM; MFA; B; PC.

30. Onodera Tōyemon Hidetome resting his foot on an upturned *go*-board to tie the lace of his sandal. Cens. Muramatsu–Yoshimura.
BM; MFA; B; PC.

31. Chiba Saburohei Mitsutada standing, holding his helmet and spear. Cens. Muramatsu–Yoshimura.
BM; MFA; B; PC. *Falteri*, 1981.169.

32. Ōboshi Seizayemon Nobukiyo making a sword-stroke as he runs; a knotted cloth flying through the air. Cens. Muramatsu–Yoshimura.
BM; MFA; B; PC. *Ronin*, 89.

33. Sugenoya Sannojō Masatoshi leaning back on one hand, trying to cut loose from the streamers of a *kusudama* in which he has become entangled. Cens. Muramatsu–Yoshimura.
BM; MFA; B; PC.

34. Oribe Yasubei Taketsune holding his sword and a night-robe of Moronao's. Cens. Hama–Kinugasa.
BM; MFA; B; PC.

35. Hayano Wasuke Tsunenari plunging his spear into a black wickerwork chest. Cens. Mera–Murata.
BM (unnumbered); MFA; B; PC.

36. Yata Goroyemon Suketake running among pieces of a broken *shōji* and scattered flowers, his sword raised with both hands. Cens. Hama–Kinugasa.
BM; MFA; B; PC. *Falteri*, 1981.170.

37. Tokuda Magodayū Shigemori making a two-handed sword-stroke by a tall screen. Cens. Hama–Kinugasa.
BM; MFA; B; PC. *Falteri*, 1981.171.

38. (*no okori*, 'origin of', added to title) Kō no Musashi no Kami Moronao in full court robes, starting back in alarm. Forms diptych with the following. Cens. Hama–Kinugasa.
BM; MFA; B; PC.

39. (*no okori*, 'origin of', added to title) Yenya Hangwan Takasada in full court robes, but bareheaded, in a menacing posture. Forms diptych with the preceding. Cens. Hama–Kinugasa.
BM; MFA; B; PC.

40. Yazama Shinroku Mitsukaze, on one knee, holding his sword upright; he has a banner bearing a posthumous name, Sekisōtei-shinshi. Cens. Hama–Kinugasa.
BM; MFA; B; PC. *Falteri*, 1981.172.

41. Mase Magoshirō Masatatsu breaking a fire-pot with a long-handled mallet. Cens. Hama–Kinugasa.
BM; MFA; B; PC. *Falteri*, 1981.173.

42. Uramatsu Kihei Hidenao Nyūdō Ryūyen crouching, sword in hand, behind a clothes-rack. Cens. Mera–Murata.
BM; MFA; B; PC.

43. Yazama Kihei Mitsunobu with a helmet held out on the butt of his *naginata*; jar and cups on the ground. Cens. Mera–Murata.
BM; MFA; B; PC.

44. Mase Chūdayū Masa-aki, full face, aiming an arrow. Cens. Mera–Murata.
BM; MFA; B; PC.

45. Sumino Chūheiji Tsugifusa, sword in hand, on a bed, feeling under the coverlet. Cens. Mera–Murata.
BM; MFA; B; PC.

46. Hara Gōyemon Mototoki on one knee, raising his sword, and with a spear in the other hand. Cens. Mera–Murata.
BM; MFA; B; PC. *Takagi*, 5.

47. Hayano Kampei Tsuneyo, a ghostly figure, making a thrust with his spear. Cens. Muramatsu–Yoshimura.
BM; MFA; B; PC.

48. Kaida Yadayemon Tomonobu, sword in hand, shielding himself from flying arrows with a *koto* in its bag. Cens. Muramatsu–Yoshimura.
BM; VAM; MFA; B; PC.

49. Miura Jiroyemon Kanetsune, sword extended, falling backwards on a basket of charcoal. Cens. Muramatsu–Yoshimura.
BM; VAM; MFA; B; PC. *Kruml*, 9.59; *Falteri*, 1981.175.

50. Yoshida Chūzayemon Kanesuke, back view, seated on a camp-stool and holding out a closed fan. Cens. Muramatsu–Yoshimura. A note to the left of the figure, and another added by Kuniyoshi to his signature, record that the series was begun in the seventh month of the Goat year (August 1847) and completed on the fourteenth day of the twelfth month of the same year (20 January 1848).
BM; VAM; PC.

51. (numbered *taibi*, the end) Jinzaburō, retainer of Shikamatsu Kanroku (no.5 above), offering a basket of cakes from two hampers; a large dog behind. Cens. Mera–Murata.
BM; MFA; B; PC.

S55
Seichū gishi hottan ('Origin of the true loyalty of the faithful *samurai*'). *Ōban*.

Exactly similar in all respects to the preceding, except for the wording of the title; the one print so far noted seems to be an alternative design for S54.38.

S55.1

1. Kō no Musashi no Kami Moronao standing, in full court robes. Text above, by Shōtei Kinsui. Pub. Kame-ya Iwakichi; cens. Muramatsu–Yoshimura.
PC. *Robinson 1961*, Pl.64.

S56
Seichū gishin den ('Stories of faithful hearts and true loyalty'). *Ōban*.

Exactly similar in all respects (except for one character in the title) to S54, to which it was clearly designed as a sequel, covering subsidiary personalities in the *Chūshingura* drama. Text by Ippitsu-an; each print numbered. Pub. Yebi-ya Rinnosuke; various cens. in pairs; 1848.

1. Ishi-jo, wife of Ōboshi (Yuranosuke) Yoshio, making a stroke with a *naginata*; baggage behind her, and a pair of swords with hilt-covers. Cens. Hama–Kinugasa.
VAM; B; PC.

2. Take-jo, wife of Yamaoka Kakubei, crouched weeping, while her child plays with toys in the foreground. Cens. Hama–Kinugasa.
B; PC.

3. Hana-jo, daughter of Oribe Kanamaru,

tying her sash. Cens. Hama–Kinugasa. VAM; PC.

4. The wife of Onodera Jūnai Hidekazu seated, concealing a dirk under her sleeve. Cens. Hama–Kinugasa.
VAM; B.

5. Chūtoda no Tsubone seated before a box containing her lord's head; incense burning. Cens. Hama–Kinugasa.
VAM; B.

6. Amagawa-ya Gihei with his child. Cens. Mera–Murata.
VAM; B.

7. Uyeshima Monya, eldest son of Uyeshima Yasuke, seated diffidently by a lacquered kettle and towel-rack. Cens. Muramatsu–Yoshimura.
VAM; RSM; B; PC.

8. Yōshinin-ni, widow of Yenya, standing by a screen on which is an exotic bird. Cens. Muramatsu–Yoshimura.
VAM.

9. The mother of Tominomori Sukeyemon reading a long letter; a caged bird. Cens. Muramatsu–Yoshimura.
VAM.

10. The mother of Takebayashi Sadashichi walking amid falling cherry-blossoms. Cens. Muramatsu–Yoshimura.
VAM; B.

11. The sister of Aibara Yesuke Munefusa watching a flight of sparrows. Cens. Muramatsu–Yoshimura.
VAM; B.

12. Kashiwagi-dayū, the courtesan who entertained Yuranosuke, standing, holding a roll of

paper. Cens. Muramatsu–Yoshimura.
VAM; B; PC.

13. The wife of Uramatsu Handayū.
B.

14. The wife of Okano Ginyemon seated by a chest of drawers, a cloth in her mouth, clasping a *kimono*. Cens. Mera–Murata.
VAM; MFA; PC.

15. Togishi Tozayemon seated on a mat with his polishing-kit, two swords in boxes labelled 'Munesada' and 'Kunimitsu' behind him. Cens. Mera–Murata.
PC.

16. (not seen)

17. Ōboshi Sampei Nobutomo.
B.

S57

Chūshin gishi kōmei kurabe ('Comparison of the high renown of the loyal retainers and faithful *samurai*', sc. the Forty-Seven *Rōnin*). *Ōban*.

Title on brown cartouche shaped as a *tsuba*. Each print represents one of the *Rōnin* in action, usually against one of Moronao's retainers, and is numbered; text by Ippitsu-an. Pub. Kobayashi-ya Matsugorō; various cens. in pairs; 1848.

1. (not seen)

2. Ōboshi Rikiya Yoshikane strikes a *naginata* out of the hands of Takano Uheinosuke Moroyasu. Cens. Hama–Kinugasa.
B; PC.

3–5. (not seen)

6. Yazama Kihei Mitsunobu making a sword-stroke at a fleeing adversary by a *shōji*, on

which a shadowed figure appears. Cens. Hama–Kinugasa.
PC. *Illing 1978*, 6.

7. Senzaki Yagorō Noriyasu cutting at the fallen Shimmi Yashichirō, who parries the stroke. Cens. Hama–Kinugasa.
PC.

8. Horiye Yasubei Taketsune and Kobayashi Heihachi Kaneyoshi fighting furiously by a fallen screen. Cens. Mera–Murata.
B; PC.

9. Fuwa Katsuyemon Masatane and Toriye Riyemon fighting eyeball to eyeball with crossed swords. Cens. Hama–Kinugasa.
B; PC.

10. Kataoka Dengoyemon Takafusa, sword in hand, running past a cowering woman. Cens. Hama–Kinugasa.
PC.

11. Takebayashi Sadashichi Takashige in combat with Kwandayū Terukage.
B.

12. (not seen)

13. Okajima Yasōyemon Tsuneki in combat with Saitō Jurobei.
B.

14. Sakagaki Shigetaka in combat with Mori Hanyemon.
B.

15. Aihara Yesuke Munefusa in combat with Kempachi.
B.

16. (not seen)

17. Hayami Tōzayemon Mitsutaka, back view, at the end of a sword-stroke, his unnamed opponent stumbling over two broken flower-vases. Cens. Hama–Kinugasa.
B; PC.

18–20. (not seen)

21. Horiye Yahei Kanamaru in combat with Magohachi.
B.

22. Chiba Saburohei Mitsutada, with drawn sword, lifts a coverlet to reveal a cowering adversary, Nakamatsu Kurobei. Cens. Hama–Kinugasa.
B; PC.

22 *bis*. Kadono Jūheiji Tsugifusa in combat with Iwata Yagoyemon.
B.

23–27. (not seen)

28. Ōboshi Seizayemon Nobukiyo in combat with Sutō Senyemon.
B.

29. Katsuta Shinzayemon Taketaka seizing an unnamed opponent by the bosom of his *kimono* and holding a sword at his throat. Cens. Muramatsu–Yoshimura.
B; PC.

30. Ōtaka Dengo Tadao in combat.
B.

S56.12

S57.6

31–33. (not seen)

34. Kiura Okayemon Okiyuki in combat with Horibuchi Kanzayemon.
B.

35 and 36. (not seen)

37. Hayano Wasuke Tsunenari, back view, armed with a *naginata*, engaging the swordsman Hamano Tadanoshin. Cens. Muramatsu–Yoshimura.
B. *Bidwell 1980*, 177.

38. Tokuda Tadayemon Yukitaka, on a snow-covered ledge, attacks with his spear Miya-ishi Shozayemon, who parries it as he cringes below. Cens. Mera–Murata.
B; PC.

39 and 40. (not seen)

41. Yatō Yomoshichi Norikane making a two-handed sideways stroke at Masuhara Sachū, who parries it. Cens. Hama–Kinugasa.
B; PC. *Bidwell 1980*, 176.

42. Yata Goroyemon Suketake, sword in hand, hauls out Sansuke from behind a cauldron, his face black with charcoal. Cens. Mera–Murata.
VAM; B.

43. Uramatsu Handayū Takanao falling backwards into a frozen pond, furiously attacked by Koshio Denshirō with his spear. Cens. Hama–Kinugasa.
B; PC.

44. Shikamatsu Kanroku Yukishige and the maid Sumiji.
B.

45–47. (not seen)

S58

Sekijō gishi den ('Stories of the faithful *samurai* of the Red Castle', sc. the Forty-Seven *Rōnin*; the alternative reading for *Sekijō* is *Akashiro*, short for *Akao no shiro*. Akao is the name of Yenya's castle in the *Chūshingura*.) *Ōban*.

Title in formal script on blue oblong cartouche of convex outline at the top and concave at the bottom; subtitle on exactly similar red panel adjoining. Adventures of the *Rōnin* outside the main plot of the *Chūshingura*; single figures and accessories on plain background; text by Ippitsu-an on the upper part of each numbered print. Pub. Yebi-ya Rinnosuke; various cens. in pairs; 1848.

1. 'Killing of the spy Uyesumi.' Teraoka Heiyemon Nobuyuki making a sword-stroke which has disarmed his opponent (not shown) and sent his hat flying. Cens. Hama–Kinugasa.
PC.

2. 'Spying out the enemy's mansion under the guise of a tradesman.' Senzaki Yagorō Noriyasu displaying fan-paintings from a number of lacquer boxes. Cens. Hama–Kinugasa.
PC.

3. 'The revenge-killing at the Takata race-

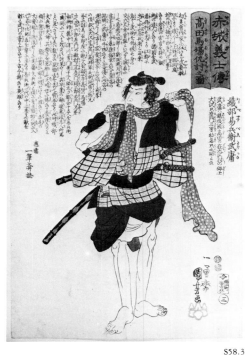

S58.3

course.' Oribe Yasubei Taketsune tying up his sleeves preparatory to his revenge fight (cf. T148, T213). Cens. Hama–Kinugasa.
PC.

4. 'Yoshikane displays his courage in the temple.' Ōboshi Rikiya Yoshikane about to perform *seppuku* in the temple Kwagakuji. Cens. Muramatsu–Yoshimura.
VAM.

S59

Gishi chūshin kagami ('Mirror of the faithful *samurai* and loyal retainers', sc. the Forty-Seven *Rōnin*). *Ōban*.

Title on oblong cartouche with narrow yellow border, black 'dog-tooth' top and bottom, and four Ōboshi *mon* (*futa-tomoye*) round the edge. Subjects and treatment very similar to S58; text by Ippitsu-an. Pub. Shimidzu-ya Naojirō; various cens. in pairs; 1848.

1. Aibara Yesuke Munefusa seizing a half-naked rough by the throat. Cens. Mera–Murata.
RSM; PC.

2. Fuwa Katsuyemon Masatane on one knee, hand on his sword, shielding a child behind him. Cens. Mera–Murata.
VAM; RSM; PC.

3. Hayano Kampei Yoshitoshi seated with his sword drawn, about to perform *seppuku*. Cens. Mera–Murata.
MFA; PC.

4. Ōboshi Rikiya Yoshikane seated, the front of his body exposed, holding his sword near the point preparatory to performing *seppuku*. Cens. Muramatsu–Yoshimura.
PC.

S59.2

5. Sumino Chūheiji Tsugifusa, on one knee, reads a long letter by the light of a lamp. Cens. Muramatsu–Yoshimura.
VAM; RSM; PC.

6. Takebayashi Sadashichi Takashige seated, with clenched fists, looking over his shoulder; a hat and bundles behind him. Cens. Mera–Murata.
VAM; PC.

7. Yata Jiroyemon Suketake leaning back with a smoking gun, having just shot a fox. Cens. Mera–Murata.
VAM; PC.

8. Yatō Yomoshichi Norikane standing by a bucket and wiping his sword on a cloth attached to a bamboo in the hollow of which *sakaki* leaves have been inserted. Cens. Muramatsu–Yoshimura.
VAM; RSM; MFA; PC.

S60

Morokoshi nijūshi-kō ('The twenty-four Chinese Paragons of Filial Piety'). *Chūban*.

Title on red or shaded oblong cartouche with shaped ends, in the r.h. margin; text, by Tanekazu, across the top of each print. This is perhaps the most westernized of all Kuniyoshi's work, and in some copies the surface of the paper has been glazed or polished in imitation of European paper. The complete series includes a title-page in antique seal script, and a preface in seventy-two formal Chinese characters reserved on black, by Musa Dōjin of Kyoto. Pub. Daikwandō (Fushimi-ya Zenroku); cens. Mera–Murata (on nos.7 and 18 only); *c.*1848.

1. Taishun (T'a Shun) and the elephants.
B; PC. *Riccar 1978*, 200.

2. Mōsō (Mêng Tsung) carrying his hoe and bamboo-shoots through the snow.
B; PC. *Bidwell 1980*, 169; *Kruml*, 13.10.

3. Kan no Buntei (Han Wên-ti) kneeling before his mother.
B; PC.

4. Teiran (Ting Lan) derided by his wife as he prostrates himself before the images of his parents.
B; PC.

5. Binshiken (Min-tzu-ch'ien) sweeping for his mother, who reclines in déshabillé with a peacock beside her ('Juno and the Peacock').
B; PC. *Robinson 1961*, Pl.39; *Riccar 1978*, 199; *Ronin*, 87.

6. Sōshin (Tsêng Ts'an), in a tree, senses his mother's distress at home on injuring her finger.
B; PC.

7. Ōshō (Wang Hsiang) catching fish for his mother through a hole in the ice. Cens. Mera–Murata.
B; PC.

8. Rōraishi (Lao Lai Tzu) acting as an infant to please his aged parents.
B; PC.

9. Kyōshi (Chiang Shih) and a carp in the lake, which the gods had caused to appear to save him travelling a long way to procure fish for his mother.
B; PC. *Kruml*, 13.12.

10. Tō-fujin (T'ang Fu-jên) suckling her grandmother.
B; PC. *Riccar 1978*, 198.

11. The tiger approaching Yōkyō (Yang Hsiang) and his father.
B; PC. A preliminary sketch for this is in the VAM (*Robinson 1961*, Pl.94).

12. The Heavenly Weaver flying heavenwards, and Tōyei (Tung Yung) waving her farewell (cf. S13.10).
B; PC. *Bidwell 1980*, 170.

13. Kōkyō (Huang Hsiang) preparing his father's bed, while the latter holds out a wine-cup.
B; PC.

14. Kwakkyo (Kuo Chü) digging for the pot of gold, watched by his wife and child under a tree.
B; PC. For a preliminary sketch see *Robinson 1961*, Pl.94.

15. Shujushō (Chu Shou-ch'ang) resting under a tree on the way to see his mother after a separation of fifty years.
B; PC.

16. Yenshi (Yen Tzu), who wore a deer-skin in order to obtain deer's milk for his mother, encounters a hunter ('Robinson Crusoe').
B; PC. *Robinson 1961*, Pl.38; *Ronin*, 86.

17. Saijun (Ts'ai Shun) attacked by brigands

S60.15

while searching for mulberries to feed his mother during a famine.
B; PC. *Kruml*, 13.13.

18. Yukinrō (Yü Ch'ien-lou) riding to visit his father, of whose illness he had become aware by telepathy. Cens. Mera–Murata.
B; PC. *Robinson 1963*, Pl.17.

19. Rikuseki (Lu Chi) commended by the rich neighbour who had given him oranges, which he took to his mother instead of eating them himself.
B; PC.

20. Chūyū (Chung Yu) carrying bags of ice on his back for the benefit of his parents.
B; PC. *Kruml*, 13.11.

21. Chōkō (Chang Hsiao) and Chōrei (Chang Li), the former offering himself as a substitute for his brother, about to be slain by a bandit.
B; PC.

22. Ōhō (Wang P'ou) amid the lightning on his way to visit his mother's tomb.
B; PC.

23. Gomō (Wu Mêng) keeping the mosquitoes from his aged father by fanning and fumigation.
B; PC.

24. Kōteiken (Huang T'ing-chien), a celebrated poet and official, emptying his mother's chamber-pot.
B; PC.

S61

Meiyo (or *Yeimei*) *sanjūrokkassen* ('Thirty-six famous battles'). *Ōban*.

Title in cartouche framed with gourds and leaves; descriptive text. Historical and legendary scenes. Pub. Ise-ya Ichibei; cens. Murata–Mera, or Hama–Kinugasa; *c*.1848.

1. Fujiwara no Tadabumi, insulted and struck

on the head, leaving the palace amid falling cherry-blossoms.
VAM; RSM.

2. Genji Tsuna in travelling dress watching the child Usui no Sadamitsu, the son of a cooper; impressed by his strength, he presented him to Raikō, whose retainer he became.
VAM.

S61.3

3. Kumawaka Maru encounters his father's murderer, Homma Saburō, in a downpour of rain, a stream of which falls on his hat.
VAM; RSM; PC.

4. Kusunoki Masanori and a retainer charging, the latter with a branch of bamboo to which severed heads are attached.
VAM; RSM; MFA.

5. Heishinnō Masakado with outstretched fan on a dais raging at his brother Rokurō Kintsura, whose cap has been struck off by Sadayo.
VAM; PC.

6. Miyamoto Musashi on his travels, on the banks of the Isagawa in the province of Kawachi, meets a remarkable man who shows him a magnifying glass, and praises his merits.
VAM; RSM; PC.

7. Odai Matarokurō (Yorisada), during his war with Takeda Shingen, breaks the water-storage jar in his castle.
VAM; RSM.

8. Unruly conduct of Oniwaka Maru at Hi-yeizan, where he fought and bullied the other children.
RSM; PC.

9. Soga Jurō Sukenari at Yoshimori's feast

being poured a large cup of *sake* by Furugori Shinzayemon.

VAM; PC.

10. Sōma Kotarō Yoshikado, on the bridge of Fukumi in the province of Harima, encounters Iga Jutarō and his gang of brigands.

VAM; RSM; MFA.

11. Takagawa Katsumasa, after defeating the Hōjō at the battle of Shinagawa, performing the Monkey Dance at the subsequent wine-party.

PC.

NOTE. Later printings of some of the above are found with the publisher's mark of Hayashi-ya Shōgorō.

S62
Taiheiki yeiyū den ('Heroic Stories of the Taiheiki'). Ōban.

The *Taiheiki* ('Chronicle of the Great Peace') is an ironically named history of the wars of the loyalist Nitta and Kusunoki families against the Ashikaga war-lords during the second quarter of the fourteenth century; it was written little more than a generation after the events it describes. In this series, however, all the characters portrayed figured in the civil wars of the sixteenth century, thus providing a striking instance of the Japanese convention of moving back incidents and personalities of comparatively recent date into a more remote period. To complicate matters still further the names of the characters have been changed in almost every case; where it has been possible to identify the actual historical figure, his name has been added in parentheses, and further research by specialists in the complicated history of the *Sengoku* ('country at war') period may well produce further identifications. Some prints of this series are numbered, others not, so it has been thought most convenient to list them in alphabetical order throughout, the numbers on the prints, where they exist, being noted in parentheses.

Title on a red or yellow cartouche of elongated gourd form. Full-length figures and accessories on plain ground, with biographical text above, by Ryūkatei Tanekazu. Pub. Yamamoto-ya Heikichi; cens. Mera–Murata; c.1848–9.

1. (numbered 43) Aigō Kozayemon Hisa-mitsu (perhaps Saigō Masakatsu, d.1561) mounted and armoured (without helmet) in battle, bloodstained and bristling with arrows, levelling his long spear. He was a retainer of the Oda family and served under Shibata Katsuiye.

VAM; B; PC.

2. (numbered 34) Akashi Ridayū Hidemoto, with a peasant's straw rain-cloak over his armour, and armed with a hoe; straw hat and iris-blossom on the ground. On one occasion, together with Shiōren Sajima (no.40 below),

he commanded a force of men dressed as farmers.

VAM; B; PC.

3. Amanaka Shikanosuke Yukimori, fully armoured and carrying a *jūmonji* spear, standing in prayer on the shore by moonlight.

VAM; B; PC.

4. (numbered 27) Aragi Settsu no Kami Murashige (Araki Murashige) in full court dress with a rice-bun (*mochi*) in his mouth; lacquer boxes and a tray of buns behind. On joining Nobunaga he proved his courage by eating rice-buns from the point of the latter's sword.

VAM; PC.

5. (numbered 7) Asai Bizen no Kami Naka-masa (Asai Nagamasa) armoured and seated on a tiger-skin stool, inspecting a severed head held by a squire. He was defeated by Nobunaga after a long struggle.

B; PC.

6. (numbered 8) Asakura Sayemon-no-tayū Yoshikane (Asakura Yoshikage) standing, armoured except for *sode* and helmet, cutting off the end of his waistband with his dirk. A native of Echizen, he fought unsuccessfully against Nobunaga.

B; PC.

7. Chibata Shuri-no-shin Tatsuiye (Shibata Katsuiye) grasping his spear, with which he has just broken the water-jars to induce his men to make a sally while besieged in the castle of Chōkōji in the province of Ōmi (1570) (*Hawley*, 202).

B; PC.

8. (numbered 22) Fujiwara no Masakiyo (Katō Kiyomasa), in full armour, seated on a camp-stool on the shore in Korea, pointing over the sea with his fan to where the summit of Mount Fuji appears; two natives, depicted in western style, attend him.

VAM; B; PC.

9. (numbered 15) Fukishima Masamori (Fukushima Masanori) in armour, struggling with three assailants. He was the son of a cooper in the province of Owari.

B; PC.

10. (numbered 31 and 33) Hamaji Shōgen Mitsukuni, armoured but without helmet, cutting a blossoming branch with his sword, his left arm out-thrown.

B; PC.

11. Hayashi Tanshirō Taketoshi, armoured but without helmet, in his last fight at Uchide-no-hama (1582), where Akechi Mitsuharu was defeated by Hideyoshi; he crushes two opponents, one under each arm. He was a retainer of Sama-no-suke.

VAM; B; PC. *Kruml*, 13.5.

12. (numbered 44) Hida Magobei Masatoshi, in armour but without helmet, in battle against the Chinese in Korea; Chinese weapons and armour on the ground. He was a descend-

ant of Takeshiuchi-no-sukune, minister to the Empress Jingō (170–269), and a relative of Keyamura Rokusuke. (Hida probably for Hotta, cf. *Papinot*, p.187.)

VAM; B; PC.

13. (numbered 17) Hori (Mori) Ran Maru Nagayasu, in court robes, having just knocked off the court cap of Takachi Michihide (Akechi Mitsuhide) with his fan; screen painted with waves behind. He was a retainer of Oda Nobunaga, and fell with him at the Honnōji temple in 1582.

B; PC.

14. (numbered 45) Horimoto Gidayū Taka-toshi (possibly Ikoma Chikamasa, d.1598; *Papinot*, p.201) standing, in full armour, holding his spear.

B; PC.

15. (numbered 2) Inagawa Jibu-no-tayū Minamoto no Yoshimoto (Imagawa Yoshi-moto), in full armour, seated on a camp-stool by a stout fence to which a standard is lashed, giving directions with his *saihai*.

B; PC.

16. (numbered 47) Ina-uye Daikurō Masa-tada, in armour without helmet, his *sashimono* adorned with a skull, discharging a huge gun; peony-blossoms and leaves on the ground.

VAM; B; PC. *Bidwell 1968*, Pl.111; *Riccar 1978*, 57; *Bidwell 1980*, 180.

17. (numbered 27) Ishikawa Sōsuke Sadatomo at the battle of Shidzu-ga-mine (or Shidzu-ga-take, 1583), in which Shibata Katsuiye was defeated by Hideyoshi; armoured but helmet-less and bristling with arrows, he continues, *in extremis*, to wield his long sword, the edge of which is badly chipped.

B; PC. *Bidwell 1968*, Pl.110.

18. (numbered 10) Isono Tamba no Kami Sadamasa seated on a camp-stool, armoured and holding a spear.

B; PC.

19. Kido Takuzayemon Nagachika, in armour but without helmet, on stone steps above a river leading to a water-gate with metal grille; this latter he attacks with a huge metal bar. He was lord of the castle of Uda in the province of Higo.

VAM; B; PC.

20. Kinoshita no Kichirō Hideyoshi.

PC.

21. Ko-ayakawa Sayemon-no-suke Takakane (Kobayakawa Takakage) seated, wearing court dress over his armour. He was favoured by Hideyoshi, after opposing him.

VAM; B.

22. (numbered 18) Matsunaga Daizen Hisahide kneeling on a fur mat, a wrapped dirk before him, about to commit *seppuku*; he dashes to pieces the heirloom tea-kettle called *Hiragumo* to prevent its falling into the hands of Nobunaga at the fall of Shikizan castle.

VAM; B; PC.

23. (numbered 16) Menju Sōsuke Iyeteru retrieves the *gohei* standard of Katsuiye which had been seized by the enemy; he was only sixteen at the time. He was killed later at the battle of Shidzu-ga-mine (1583).
B; PC.

24. (numbered 42) Nagamura Bunkasai Michi-iye, in armour but without helmet or *sode*, standing bald-headed, having just broken a pottery vessel against the wall; miscellaneous objects on the floor.
B; PC. *Kruml*, 13.4.

25. (numbered *taihi*) Naka-ura Sarukichirō Hisayoshi (Toyotomi Hideyoshi).
B.

26. (numbered 26) Negoro no Komidzucha (*Papinot*, p.437, s.v. Negoro-dera) dressed as a warrior-monk, fighting with a long nail-studded club and a broken bloodstained *naginata*, while swords fly about him.
VAM; B; PC.

27. Orio Mosuke Yasuharu (Horio Yoshiharu), in early youth, overcoming a huge wild boar, a feat which caused Hideyoshi to take him into his service.
VAM; B; PC. *Cologne 1963*, 103.

S62.28

28. Ōta Kadzusa no Suke Taira no Harunaga-kyō (Oda Nobunaga), in court robes, but bareheaded and girt with a *tachi* in tiger-skin sheath, ripping a tent-curtain apart.
VAM; B; PC. *Robinson 1963*, Pl.21.

29. (numbered 40) Sada Mutsu no Kami Arimasa in the snow, armoured (without helmet) and mounted, plying his riding-whip, the horse refusing to proceed.
B; PC.

30. (numbered 36) Saitō Kuranoshin Toshikazu, three-quarter back view, wearing a *kimono* over half-armour, and raising his straw hat against the wind. He was lord of the castle of Ikuchiyama in the province of Tamba.
B; PC.

31. (numbered 48) (Pl.21) Saitō Toshimoto Nyūdō Ryūhon, in armour, struggling with a Chinese champion under water; two fish (upper l.).
VAM; B; PC. *FH*, 10.

32. (numbered 6) Saitō Uhyōye-no-tayū Katsuoki (Saitō Tatsuoki) partially armoured (the rest of his armour standing by) cutting flying arrows with his sword. He was the eldest son of Mino no Kami Yoshikatsu (Yoshitatsu).
B; PC.

33. (numbered 4) Saitō Yamashiro no Kami Hidetatsu Nyūdō Jōsan (probably Saitō Yoshitatsu) standing, in court robes with wide-brimmed straw hat and a *tachi* with tiger-skin scabbard.
VAM; B; PC. *Kruml*, 13.3.

34. (numbered 41) Sakurai Takichi Kiyokazu, armoured (without helmet), and with a *sashimono* adorned with black discs containing the *jūnishi* surrounding the character *sakigake* (leader), making a great stroke with his *naginata*.
B; PC.

35. (numbered 24) Sama-no-suke Fujiwara no Yasuakira (perhaps Katō Yoshiaki), in armour with *haori*, carrying a *jūmonji* spear in an aggressive attitude. He was adopted into the Satō family.
VAM; B; PC.

36. (numbered 12) (Fig.9) Sasai Kyūzō Masayasu (Sakai in *Hawley*) enveloped in smoke and disintegrating before a volley of musketry at the battle of the Anegawa (1570).
VAM; B; PC. *Robinson 1961*, Pl.62; *Riccar 1978*, 60; *Bidwell 1980*, 181; *Kruml*, 13.2; 20.72.

37. Sasai Ukon Masanao (perhaps Asai Nagamasa, 1545–73; *Papinot*, p.23), three-quarter back view, in armour with *haori* but no helmet, standing on a huge pine-trunk with drawn sword. He was father of the preceding.
B; PC. *Robinson 1963*, Pl.22.

38. (numbered 32) Shimura Masazō Katsutoyo (possibly Yamanouchi Kazutoyo, 1546–1605; *Papinot*, p.746) seated and stripped to his loincloth, a *kimono* over one shoulder; his swords, a bucket of water, and a bunch of paper towels behind.
VAM; PC. *Kruml*, 13.8.

39. (numbered 25) Shinano Sakon Tomoyuki, bareheaded and in court dress, kneeling and offering a *naginata* with both hands.
VAM; B; PC.

40. (numbered 29) Shiōren Sajima-no-kami Masataka, in armour but without helmet, turning over a scroll of Buddhist scripture with

his spear at Kōtokuji temple. (A very similar incident involving Shirafuji Hikoshichirō is illustrated in T243.)
VAM; B; PC.

41. (numbered 28) Suzuchi Hida no Kami Shigeyuki crouching in half-armour by a bamboo-brake, having just discharged his pistol.
VAM; B; PC. *FH*, 12.

42. (numbered 14) Takuma Gemba-no-jō Morimasu (Sakuma Morimasa) armoured and wielding his sword while two men attempt to secure him, a three-pronged rake-like pole-arm caught in his waistband.
MFA; B; PC.

43. (numbered 39) Tambe Jijū Taira no Harutaka (Kambe Nobutaka) seated on a stool, front view, in full armour including *mempō*, with a banner behind him.
B; PC.

44. (numbered 5) Tatenaka Kwambyōye (Takenaka Hambei) Shigeharu standing, in civilian dress, with a sword; a globe, a fur rug on the floor, and a cupboard behind with scrolls and potted fungus.
B; PC. *Riccar 1978*, 59; *Kruml*, 13.7.

45. (numbered 20) Tatsugawa Sakon Katsumasa (Takigawa Kazumasu) in full court robes, attended by two retainers in armour, pointing emphatically to the right.
B; PC.

46. (numbered 38) Toki Jurozayemon Mitsuchika wounded to death, surrounded by bloodstained corpses; he still grasps his sword, and a banner hangs over his shoulder. He was lord of the castle of Fukuchiyama in the province of Tamba.
VAM; MFA; B; PC. *Illing 1978*, 7; *Kruml*, 13.6.

47. (numbered 9) Tokiuji seated on a cushion with folded arms, a book on a rest in front of him, and his sword on a rack behind.
B; PC.

48. (numbered 21) Tsuchii Yamato no Kami Nyūdō Juntei (Tsutsui Junkei) seated, with bowed head, on a fur rug, and wearing armour under court robes; a *tachi* with tiger-skin scabbard on a stand behind him.
VAM; B; PC. *Kruml*, 9.67.

49. (numbered 30) Yasuda Takubyōye Kunitomo, fully armoured, running with spear levelled downwards; trays of refreshments overturned, and a *biwa* lying on the floor.
VAM; B; PC.

50. Yendō Giyemon Masatada, armoured, in battle, about to hurl a severed head at Nobunaga.
PC.

51. (numbered 31) Yūshi Sama-no-suke Mitsuharu (Akechi Mitsuharu).
PC.

S63

Kōyetsu yūshō den ('Stories of courageous generals of the provinces of Echigo and Kai'). *Ōban.*

Title in red cartouche with convex outline at the top and concave at the bottom; descriptive and biographical text by Ryūkatei Tanekazu or Ippitsu-an. Heroes of the Kawanakajima campaigns between Takeda Shingen (Kai) and Uyesugi Kenshin (Echigo) between 1553 and 1563; each print shows a single figure, with or without accessories, on a plain ground. The series was designed for twenty-four heroes from each side, and prints from it are often found numbered; the presence of a number may perhaps indicate a slightly later printing. Pub. Sumiyoshi-ya Masagorō; various cens. in pairs; *c*.1848–9.

Takeda

1. (numbered 1) Takeda Daizen-no-tayū Jugo-i-geken Shinano no Kami Harunobu Nyūdō Shingen standing, in full armour and robes, shading his eyes with his right hand. He was descended from the Seiwa branch of the Minamoto clan, and fought his first battle in 1536 at the age of thirteen. Cens. Muramatsu–Yoshimura.

MFA; PC.

2. Takeda Sama-no-suke Nobushige, helmetless, leaning on his sword, enveloped in a cloud of battle-smoke, with grey face and blood issuing from the corners of his mouth. Cens. Hama–Kinugasa.

MFA; PC. *Kruml*, 21.54.

3. (numbered 3) Yamamoto Kansuke Nyūdō Dōkisai Haruyuki, the one-eyed Takeda general, leaning on a spear, with one foot on a severed head; he is grey-faced and badly wounded, with arrows sticking in his armour. Cens. Muramatsu–Yoshimura.

VAM; MFA; PC. *Geneva 1965*, 74.

4. (numbered 7) Anayama Idzu no Kami Nobuyoshi in full armour on a breakwater of stones enclosed in basketwork, defying the Uyesugi troops. Cens. Hama–Kinugasa.

VAM; MFA; B; PC.

5. (numbered 10) Yamagata Saburohei Masakage, bareheaded and with grey face, plunging his sword into the neck of a prostrate foeman. Cens. Fuku–Muramatsu.

MFA; B; PC.

6. (numbered 13) Amari Sayemon-no-jō Haruyoshi, helmetless, bestriding his fallen charger, an open black fan in his right hand and a spear in his left. Cens. Hama–Magome.

B; PC.

7. (numbered 17) Oyamada Bitchū no Kami Masatatsu, helmetless, a drawn sword in his hand, shouting defiance as he faces a volley from the Uyesugi musketeers. Cens. Mera–Murata.

VAM; MFA; PC.

8. Ō Hyōbu-shōyū Toramasa, mounted, grasping a spear, and glaring downwards. Cens. Hama–Kinugasa.

B; PC.

9. (numbered 23) (Pl.20) Morozumi Bungo no Kami Masakiyo falling on his sword (the point in his mouth) and at the same time being blown up by a land-mine which killed all his followers. He counts as one of the 'three heroic deaths in battle'. Cens. Mera–Murata.

VAM; MFA; B; PC. *Apollo*, May 1949, p.125; *Bidwell 1968*, Pl.109; *Riccar 1978*, 63; *Bidwell 1980*, 162.

S63.18

10. (numbered 21) Obata Matabei Kuniharu cuts off the head of a spear while grasping a standard in his left hand. Cens. Mera–Murata. MFA.

Uyesugi

(Presumably Uyesugi Kenshin headed the Uyesugi heroes, but the actual print has not so far been seen.)

11. (numbered 13) Kakizaki Idzumi no Kami Kage-iye cutting off the corner of a wooden

shield (*tate*) with a stroke of his sword. Cens. Hama–Kinugasa.

VAM; PC.

12. (numbered 16) Kurogane Kōdzuke no Suke Hidetake holding his horse's bridle and looking over his shoulder. Having taken on a gang of robbers in his native village at the age of thirteen, he joined Uyesugi Kenshin two years later. Cens. Mera–Murata.

MFA; PC.

13. (numbered 18) Uno Sama-no-suke Takamasa, amid flying arrows, grasping a standard whose streamers half cover him. Cens. Mera–Murata.

MFA.

14. (numbered 20) Nagao Tōtōmi no Kami Fujikage, sword in hand, lifting a Takeda tent-curtain. Cens. Hama–Magome.

VAM; MFA; PC.

15. Matsumoto Mokusuke kneeling on one knee, having just discharged a large gun. He was a noted gunner at Kawanakajima. Cens. Hama–Kinugasa.

VAM; MFA; PC.

16. Onikojima Yatarō Torahide trying to pull down a length of fencing or palisade. His family name was originally Kojima, but Oni ('demon') was added after he had dealt with a gang of robbers who had been plaguing the country. Cens. Muramatsu–Yoshimura.

VAM; MFA; PC.

17. Usami Suruga no Kami Sadayuki, mounted on a black horse, deflects a flying sword with the shaft of his spear. Cens. Hama–Kinugasa.

PC.

18. (numbered 24) Saitō Shimotsuke no Kami Tomonobu, one of the 'Three Master-Gunners' of the Uyesugi, in armour, a ramrod in his mouth, loading his musket; a squad of musketeers behind him, taking aim. He shot the horse of Shingen's son, thereby causing the Takeda to retreat. Cens. Mera–Murata.

PC.

NOTE. Sadahide published a pair of triptychs entitled (i) *Kōshū nijūshi-shō no shinzō* ('True portraits of the twenty-four generals of Kai province'), and (ii) *Echigo jūshichi-shō no shinzō* ('True portraits of the seventeen generals of Echigo province'), copies of which are in the Royal Scottish Museum, Edinburgh; it may be of interest to list the names here, in alphabetical order:

(i) Hosshō-in Shingen Daikōji, Akiyama Hōki no Kami, Amari Sayemon, Anayama Baisetsu, Baba Mino no Kami, Hara Hayato-no-shō, Hara Mino no Kami, Kosaka Danjō, Morozumi Bungo no Kami, Mutō Kihei, Naitō Shuri-no-suke, Obata Kadzusa no Kami, Obata Yamashiro Nyūdō, Oyamada Hyōbu-no-jō, Saigusa Kageyu, Sanada Genda Sayemon, Sanada Hyōbu-no-jō, Sone Shimotsuke, Tada Awaji no Kami, Takeda Shirō

Katsuyori, Takeda Shōyōken, Tsuchiya Uyemon, Yamagata Saburohei, Yamamoto Kansuke Nyūdō, Yokota Bitchū no Kami.

(ii) Fushiki-in Daisōdzu Kenshin-kō, Amakazu Ōmi no Kami, Arakawa Idzu no Kami, Honshō Yagorō, Iimori Settsu no Kami, Kakizaki Idzumi no Kami, Karazaki Sama-no-suke, Momonoi Sanuki no Kami, Mori Kadzusa no Suke, Nagai Tamba no Kami, Naoye Nyūdō, Naoye Yamashiro no Kami, Onikojima Yatarō, Saitō Shimotsuke no Kami, Shikiyama Suō no Kami, Shintō Dewa no Kami, Takanashi Gengorō, Usami Suruga no Kami, Uyesugi Kiheiji Kagekatsu.

S64

Tametomo homare no jikketsu ('Ten famous excellencies of Tametomo'). *Ōban.*

Title on a white banner; nos. 2, 4, 5, 6 and 8 have in addition a shaded oblong panel containing narrative text by Ryūkatei Tanekazu. Pub. Arita-ya Seiyemon; various cens.; *c.* 1848–51. For Tametomo's career in general, see *Papinot*, p. 380; *Edmunds*, p. 615; *Ozaki*, pp. 1–24. But the more extravagant legends are contained in Bakin's novel *Yumihari-dzuki*, of which no English translation has been traced.

1. Tametomo at the age of thirteen (1151) catching arrows shot at him by two of the Emperor's guard in a competition with Shōnagon Nyūdō Shinsei. Cens. Hama–Kinugasa.

MFA; PC.

2. (numbered 2) Tametomo separating two fighting wolf-cubs with his bow. He had lost his way on a hunting-expedition; the cubs put him right, and he kept them as pets, naming them Nokaze and Yamao. Cens. Hama–Kinugasa.

VAM; RSM; MFA; B; PC.

3. Tametomo beheads a monkey-like monster (the body is not shown) by a waterfall; the head leaps in the air and bites an overhanging rock. MFA; PC.

4. Tametomo's faithful retainer Kiheiji, left behind by mistake when Tametomo sailed for Japan from the Ryūkyū Islands, throws a weighted rope an immense distance to the ship, by means of which he is hauled in. Cens. Kinugasa–Watanabe.

PC. *Illing 1978*, 22.

5. (numbered 5) Tametomo on the sea-shore with a caged crane on his back. This crane had belonged to Tametomo's ancestor Yoshi-iye, and acted as his guide in the Ryūkyū Islands, where he found it. Cens. Hama–Kinugasa.

MFA; PC.

6. Yatsushiro, the pregnant wife of Kiheiji, aided by the snarling wolf Nokaze, defending herself with a *naginata* against flying arrows (see S35.1). Cens. Kinugasa–Murata; eng. Take.

VAM; RSM; MFA; PC.

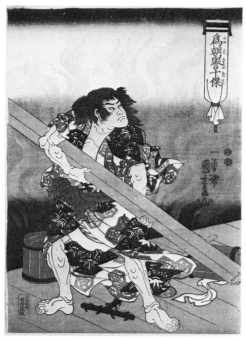

S64.7

7. Tametomo, armed with a broken beam, prepares to resist arrest by the hot spring of Ishiyama, whither he had resorted to cure the wound inflicted by the monster Yamaotoko (no. 3 above). Cens. Kinugasa–Watanabe.

PC. *Illing 1978*, 23.

8. Shiranui, wife of Tametomo, shining a dark lantern and armed with a roped hook, going to rescue him at the post-station of Senkwan. Cens. Hama–Kinugasa.

MFA; PC.

9. Tametomo, about to commit *seppuku* at the tomb of the Emperor Sutoku, for whom he fought unsuccessfully in the war of Hōgen (1156), is prevented by an apparition of the Emperor and Minamoto clan forebears. Cens. Hama–Kinugasa.

VAM; RSM; MFA; PC.

10. Tametomo, in hunting dress and half-armour, holding his bow, sees an apparition of an old man rising from a severed bear's head. Cens. Kinugasa–Murata.

RSM; PC.

S65

Hodo Yoshitsune koi no Minamoto ichidaiki ('Biography of Yoshitsune'). *Ōban.*

Title in oblong cartouche framed in bamboo, the leaves at the lower l.h. corner forming the Minamoto *mon*; descriptive text on an adjoining scroll with the title *Sanryaku-den*, and sometimes the number of the print in the series, on the cover. Pub. Iba-ya Kyūbei or Jōshū-ya Jūzō; various cens. in pairs; 1848–53.

1. The flight of Tokiwa-gozen through the snow with her three children, Imawaka,

S65.1

6. Yoshitsune with Jōruri-hime, the former drying his hands, and the latter with a lacquer jug and basin. Cens. Mera–Murata; eng. Renkichi.

VAM; MFA; B. *Bidwell 1968*, Pl. 105.

7. Yokogawa no Kankai (sc. Tankai) attacks Yoshitsune from behind, the latter ready to draw his sword. Cens. Hama–Kinugasa.

VAM.

8. Yoshitsune displaying his horsemanship before Fujiwara no Hidehira and his suite at the latter's castle in Mutsu. Cens. Hama–Kinugasa.

VAM; MFA; PC.

9. The fight on Gojō bridge (i): Yoshitsune, with open fan, hangs over the rail of the bridge, while Benkei's *naginata* is entangled in his veil; looted swords tied to the bridge-rail. Cens. Mera–Murata.

VAM; RSM; MFA; PC.

10. The fight on Gojō bridge (ii): Yoshitsune and Benkei fighting with swords. Cens. Hama–Kinugasa.

VAM.

11. Yoshitsune discovers Washio Saburō at Hiyodori-goye (just before the battle of Ichi-no-tani) trussing up a wild boar by a waterfall. Cens. Hama–Magome; Ox 1.

VAM; MFA.

12. Yoshitsune with Benkei and other followers under the cherry-blossom at Suma, after Ichi-no-tani. Cens. Hama–Magome; Ox 1.

VAM.

13. Yoshitsune's 'eight boat leap', pursued by Noritsune, at the battle of Dan-no-ura. Cens. Hama–Magome; Ox 1.

VAM; MFA.

14. Yoshitsune and Shidzuka-gozen defending themselves at Horikawa against the treacherous attack of Tosa-bō Shōshun. Cens. Fuku–Muramatsu; Ox 2.

VAM; MFA.

15. Yoshitsune with Benkei and his other retainers in their ship, beset by the ghosts of the Taira, some in the form of crabs, during a storm. Cens. Hama–Magome; Ox 1.

VAM; MFA; PC.

16. Satō Tadanobu, wearing Yoshitsune's armour, leaping down upon the warrior-monk Yokogawa Kakuhan at Yoshino. Cens. Hama–Magome; Ox 1.

VAM; MFA.

Otowaka, and Ushiwaka; her hat blows away. Cens. Mera–Murata.

VAM; RSM; PC.

2. The *tengu* king (here called Kibune no keshin, 'incarnation of Kibune') gives Ushiwaka a fencing lesson, watched by three other *tengu*, one with an axe. Cens. Mera–Murata; eng. Renkichi.

VAM; RSM; PC.

3. Yoshitsune, clinging to the branch of a tree, kicks over Mitsuma no Daita (who later became his retainer Kisanda). Cens. Mera–Murata.

VAM; MFA.

4. Kawachi Kakutei, on the look-out in a pine-tree, sees a party of travellers through the mist; Chōhan and his gang below. Cens. Mera–Murata.

VAM; PC.

5. Kumasaka Chōhan outside Yoshitsune's room at the inn; the latter ready, with drawn sword. Cens. Hama–Kinugasa.

VAM.

S66

Sangoku yōko dzuye ('The Magic Fox of the Three Countries, illustrated'). *Ōban.*

Title in large rectangular cartouche incorporating a brief caption for each print. Scenes from the legend of the Nine-tailed Fox, with some strong western influence. Pub. Ise-ya Chūsuke or Echizen-ya Hachiyemon; various cens. in pairs; c. 1849–50.

S66.1

the old Fox, flies away to the Eastern Heaven.' Hansoku runs helplessly along the palace balcony whilst above him the old Fox, still retaining part of her court lady's costume, flies off. Cens. Hama–Magome.

VAM; PC. *Robinson 1961*, Pl.61.

Japan

5. 'Dōsei, having prayed at the Kiyomidzu temple, finds a child.' Dōsei and his wife on the river-bank find the baby Tamamo-no-maye (the Fox's Japanese incarnation) wrapped in brocade among the rushes. Cens. Hama–Magome.

VAM; PC.

6. 'Genō Ikkatsu destroys the spirit of the wicked Fox.' While two acolytes cower, the aged priest, carrying a fly-whisk and a rosary, strikes with his staff the rock which housed the spirit of the Fox, in the shadow of which are human bones and a dead bird; above the rock appears the ghost of Tamamo-no-maye. This rock, on the moor of Nasu, was called Sesshō-seki, the 'Death Stone'.

PC.

S67

Chiyū rokkasen ('Selection of six men of wisdom and courage'). *Ōban.*

Title on large red oblong cartouche; descriptive text, by Ryūkatei Tanekazu, above. Single figures on shaded background. Pub. Fujioka-ya Keijirō; cens. Fuku–Muramatsu; *c.*1850.

1. Gen Sammi Yorimasa standing, in court robes and half-armour, grasping his bow.

VAM; MFA; PC.

2. Hachimantarō Minamoto no Yoshi-iye seated on a tiger-skin, holding an open fan.

VAM; MFA; PC.

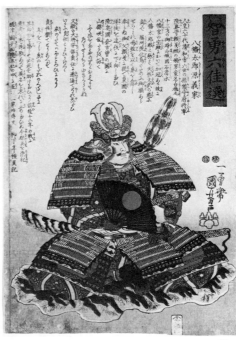

S67.2

China

1. 'The revived Dakki appears by magic in the hall of the post-station.' The old Fox (who appeared in China as the Imperial concubine Dakki) seated on a platform, threatened by a court lady (*jijo*) with a dirk. Cens. Kinugasa–Watanabe.

MFA; PC.

India

2. 'The marvellous strength of Prince Hansoku, King of Southern India.' (Fig.2) On a palace balcony Hansoku places his foot on the

neck of a cowed lion, watched by the fox-woman Kwayō-fujin. Cens. Kinugasa–Watanabe.

B; PC. *Riccar 1978*, 70; *Bidwell 1980*, 182.

3. 'Kwayō-fujin shoots Saiki in the eye; King Hansoku is amused.' Saiki is tied to a tree (rather like St. Sebastian) with an arrow in his eye, watched by the royal couple; Kwayō-fujin, in a towering hat and Louis XIV wig, fits another arrow to her bow. Cens. Fuku–Muramatsu.

VAM; MFA; PC.

4. 'Kwayō-fujin, resuming her true form as

3. Kajiwara Genda Taira no Kagesuye seated, in court dress over armour, holding a fan.
VAM; RSM; MFA.

4. Oda Mochisuke Nyūdō Minamoto no Dōkwan seated, in riding dress, with a fan.
VAM; MFA.

5. Satsuma no Kami Taira no Tadanori, in court dress over armour, seated on a tiger-skin, writing.
VAM; MFA.

6. Udaishō Minamoto no Yoritomo-kyō seated, in court dress, holding a fan.
VAM; RSM; MFA.

S68
Jūroku Musashi-bō Benkei ('Sixteen [stories of] Musashi-bō Benkei'). *Ōban.*

Title on red oblong cartouche with repeating wheel (*rimbō*) pattern reserved, and framed with Benkei's weapons; text above. Pub. Jōshū-ya Kinzō and Daikoku-ya Heikichi; cens. Mera–Murata, or Muramatsu–Yoshimura; *c.*1848–50.

1. Oniwaka beating two young monastery acolytes.
RSM.

2. Oniwaka shaving his head.
RSM.

S68.3

3. Oniwaka and the monster carp; he is shown wringing out his clothes, the carp strung up by the tail.
BM.

4. Oniwaka, razor in hand, looking down a well.
PC.

5. Benkei and a leaping magic fox in the snow.
RSM.

6. Benkei in full robes seizing Tosa-bō Shōshun, dressed in black, by the scruff of the neck.
RSM; PC. *Falteri*, 1981.176.

S69
Yeiyū ippyaku den ('A hundred heroic stories'). *Ōban.*

Title on red cartouche with decorated ends; name of character on adjoining blue oblong panel; descriptive text above. Single figure on plain ground. Pub. Fujioka-ya Keijirō; cens. Kinugasa–Murata; *c.*1851.

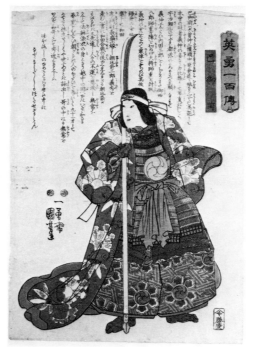

S69.1

1. Tomoye-gozen standing, in armour, and holding a *naginata.*
PC.

(No further prints of this series have been noted.)

S70
Kyōkaku giyū den ('Stories of chivalrous persons of loyalty and courage'). *Ōban.*

Title on oblong red cartouche; single figures and accessories on plain background, with short text above. Pub. Sumiyoshi-ya Masagorō; cens. Kinugasa–Murata; 1851.

1. Goshaku Somegorō eating a live snake, a huge bowl of hot *sake* in his left hand, and a dead cat on a dish before him; this unpleasant meal was offered him by the villain Dairoku, whom he subsequently slew.
PC.

2. Hotei Ichiyemon, half-naked and tattooed, with both arms outflung, in front of a drying fishing-net. He is about to separate fighting roughs.
PC.

S70.2

S71
Seichū gishin kagami ('Mirror of the true loyalty of the faithful retainers', sc. the Forty-Seven *Rōnin*). *Chūban.*

Title in plain oblong cartouche; name of character in similar but smaller panel. Single figures of the *Rōnin* in action. Some numbered in lower l.h. corner. Pub. Kagi-ya Hanjirō; cens. Hama–Magome, with black *aratame*; *c.*1851.

1. (numbered 8) Yatō Yomoshichi Norikane carrying a spear and a lantern.
MFA.

S71.3

2. (numbered 10) Shikamatsu Hanroku Yukishige carrying a large axe.
MFA.

3. (numbered 16) Yoshida Sadayemon Kanesada raising his sword amid falling baskets and charcoal.
MFA.

4. (unnumbered) Uramatsu Kihei Hidenao threatening one of Moronao's retainers.
MFA.

5. (unnumbered) Sugino Jūheiji Tsugifusa seated, in ordinary clothes, looking up from reading a long scroll.
MFA.

6. (numbered *taibi*, the end) Ōboshi Seizayemon Nobukiyo in ordinary clothes and a wide straw hat by moonlight.
MFA.

S72

Chūshingura gojūsan tsugi ('The fifty-three post-stations of the *Chūshingura*'). *Ōban*.

Title in fairly large oblong cartouche incorporating the name of the Tōkaidō station(s), a view of which occupies the upper third of the print in an inset panel. Characters from the *Chūshingura* in pairs. The first six are numbered beginning at Kyoto, not (as normally) Nihombashi. Pub. Yebi-ya Rinnosuke; cens. Kinugasa–Watanabe; *c.* 1851.

1. Kyoto. Ōboshi Rikiya conversing with O-Iri, daughter of Uramatsu Rihei.
MFA.

2. Ōtsu and Kusatsu. Yase Chindayū in travelling dress, and Hara Goyemon tying his sock-ribbon.
MFA.

3. Ishibe and Midzukuchi. Ōboshi Seiza-

yemon kneeling before Ōwashi Bungo, who holds a branch of cherry-blossom.
MFA.

4. Tsuchiyama and Sakanoshita. Satō Yomoshichi on one knee, a basket and sickle beside him, addressed by Miura Shiroyemon.
MFA.

5. (not seen)

6. Shōno and Ishiyakushi. Oribe Yasahei and O-Sono, daughter of Yahei.
MFA.

7. (unnumbered; should be about 13 or 14) Hamamatsu and Mitsuke. Yada Goroyemon with a loaded pack on his back, and Senzaki Yagorō seated, with carpenter's tools.
MFA.

8. (unnumbered; should be about 18 or 19) Fuchū and Yejiri. Hayano Kampei raising his *komusō* hat to the courtesan Karumo; incense burning.
MFA.

9. (unnumbered; should be about 25) Fujisawa and Totsuka. Yazama Jūtarō, holding a black *kimono*, and his wife O-Riye, daughter of Koga Yayemon.
MFA.

S73

Yūkwai sanjūrokkassen ('Courageous leaders in thirty-six battles'). *Ōban yokoye*.

Title in oblong cartouche incorporating number in series. Battles and other historical scenes. Pub. Idzumi-ya Ichibei; various cens. in pairs; 1851–2.

1. (not seen)

2. Encounter of Takeda Shingen and Uyesugi Kenshin in the river at Kawanakajima; Hat-

sukano Denyemon behind. No pub. visible; cens. Hama–Magome.
PC.

3. (not seen)

4. Nitta Yoshisada throwing his sword into the sea as an offering to calm the waves. Cens. Hama–Magome.
B; PC.

5. Sasaki Takatsuna and Kajiwara Kagesuye at the Uji river crossing. Cens. Hama–Magome.
PC.

6 and 7. (not seen)

8. Kiso Yoshinaka attempting to escape across the frozen bog after the battle of Awadzu-ga-hara; the fatal arrow is already on its way, and Kanemitsu fights off pursuers in the background. Cens. Hama–Magome.
PC.

9. Minamoto no Yoritomo and his followers hiding in the hollow tree after the battle of Ishibashiyama; he is urged in by Yūki Shichirō, Shinkai Arajirō, and Adachi Tokurō, while Doi Jirō watches for the approaching enemy. Cens. Fuku–Muramatsu.
PC.

10. Ichirai-hōshi and Tsutsui Jōmyō defending the partly dismantled bridge at the first battle of the Uji river (1180) between Yorimasa and Tomomori. No pub. visible; cens. Hama–Magome.
PC.

11. Satō Tadanobu, in the armour of Yoshitsune, leaping down upon Yokogawa Kakuhan at Yoshino.
B.

12. (not seen)

13. Prince Ōto-no-miya Morinaga-shinnō,

S72.4

S73.14

151

wounded after a battle, drinking *sake* with his followers, while Kodera Sagami-bō dances before him with sword and fan. Cens. Hama–Magome.

MFA; PC.

14. Idzumi Saburō Chikahira in defiance discharges an arrow across the river into the camp of the Hōjō. Cens. Mera–Watanabe.

MFA; PC.

15. (not seen)

16. Asahina Saburō breaking down the gate of the Shōgun's palace in his attack on Hōjō Yoshitoki.

PC.

17–32. (not seen)

33. Kusunoki Masatsura presenting a farewell cup of *sake* to his father Masashige, whilst all present weep. Cens. Fuku–Muramatsu; Rat intercalary.

PC.

34 and 35. (not seen)

36. Shirafuji Hikoshichirō confronting his horse on a dike; in the background, Taka-uji taking refuge in a shrine. Cens. Fuku–Muramatsu; Rat intercalary.

PC.

S74

Kisokaidō rokujūku tsugi ('The sixty-nine Post-Stations of the Kisokaidō Road'). *Ōban*.

Title in red cartouche with border of emblematic design suited to the main subject; subtitle in coloured or shaded rectangular panel with reeded border; inset panel of varying shape with view of Station; the main design devoted to some associated scene of history, legend, or popular fiction. No less than twelve different pub.; various cens. in pairs; date-seals Rat 5–Ox 2, June 1852–March 1853.

1. Title-page with contents in four large rectangular panels on background of pale blue with gourd-creeper. At the top, the court cap of a palace guard, riding-whip, cherry-blossom, and conventional hollyhock leaves; bottom left, a straw-wrapped *sake*-barrel inscribed *Yedo jiman: Nihon ichi* ('The pride of Yedo: unique in Japan'). Pub. Minato-ya Kohei; cens. Fuku–Muramatsu; Rat 10.

MFA; PC.

2. (numbered 1) Nihombashi. Scene on the bridge: Ashikaga Yorikane (l.) watches the wrestlers Nuregami Katsunosuke (r.) and Ukiyo Watabei quarrelling. Inset: street-scene. Pub. Tsujioka-ya Bunsuke; cens. Hama–Magome; Rat 5.

MFA; PC.

3. (numbered 2) Itabashi. Scene from the *Hakkenden* of Bakin: Inudzuka Shino in the water holding on to a tree on the bank, while Sabojirō swims behind; Hikiroku clings to Shino, and Totarō sits in a boat in the background. Inset: river-scene. Pub. Sumi-

yoshi-ya Masagorō; cens. Hama–Magome; eng. Sugawa Sennosuke; Rat 5.

VAM; MFA; PC. *Robinson 1961*, Pl.68.

4. (numbered 3) Warabi. (Fig.29) Inuyama Dōsetsu seated amid flames and smoke, hands clasped, and in his mouth magic pine-sprigs wrapped in paper (*aomatsuba*). Inset: village road. Pub. Idzutsu-ya Shōkichi; cens. Hama–Magome; Rat 5.

MFA; PC.

5. (numbered 4) Urawa. Uoya ('fishmonger') Danshichi, half-naked on the river-bank, emptying a bucket of water over himself to clean off mud, a drawn sword leaning against the adjacent well-head, and a festival procession in the background. Inset: uphill road. Pub. Sumiyoshi-ya Masagorō; cens. Hama–Magome; eng. Sugawa Sennosuke; Rat 5.

MFA; PC. *Lewis*, 1975.21.

6. (numbered 5) Ōmiya. The captive rebel Abe no Munetō kneeling before the minister Fujiwara no Mitsuyori, the latter holding a spray of plum-blossom and attended by two courtiers, palace behind. Inset: roadside tea-house in the rain. Pub. Takeda-ya Takezō(?); cens. Fuku–Muramatsu; eng. Chōryūta; pr. Kozenki; Rat 6.

VAM; MFA; PC.

7. (numbered 6) Ageo. The actor Bandō Shuka as the courtesan Miura no Takao being weighed against money; a man and a woman look on in astonishment; 'greenhouse' interior behind. Inset: village and paddy-fields. Pub. Hayashi-ya Shōgorō; cens. Fuku–Muramatsu; Rat 6.

MFA; PC.

8. (numbered 7) Okegawa. Tamaya Shimbei, imprisoned in a huge tub, is given a drink of water by a girl under the direction of Kojorō; lantern and two watchmen (l.). Inset: landscape with pines. Pub. Sumiyoshi-ya Masagorō; cens. Fuku–Muramatsu; eng. Sugawa Sennosuke; Rat 6.

MFA; PC.

9. (unnumbered) Kōnosu. Musashi no Kami Moronao in the snow being hustled by retainers to his hiding-place among the firewood. Inset: roadside village and distant hills. Pub. Yawata-ya Sakujirō; cens. Hama–Magome; eng. Takichi; Rat 5.

MFA; PC.

10. (numbered 9) Kumagaya. Kojirō Nao-iye, armoured and mounted, at the base of a castle wall on the shore of a lake. Inset: road-scene with coolies carrying a palanquin. Pub. Yawata-ya Sakujirō; cens. Hama–Magome; eng. Takichi; Rat 5.

MFA; PC.

11. (numbered 10) Fukaya. The ancient hero Yuriwaka Daijin shooting with his huge bow before two dumbfounded spectators. Inset: road with rest-house and pine-trees. Pub. Kaga-ya Yasubei; cens. Hama–Magome; Rat 5.

MFA; PC.

12. (numbered 11) Honjō. Night-scene in a downpour of rain: Shirai Gompachi, a purse in his mouth, sheathing his sword; another sword, sandal, and umbrella on the ground. Inset: roadside village and marsh behind. Pub. Minato-ya Kohei; cens. Hama–Magome; eng. Takichi; Rat 5.

MFA; PC.

13. (numbered 12) Shimmachi. Encounter of Gokumon Shōhei and Kurofune Chūyemon on a bridge. Inset: view of a mountain across a lake. Pub. Ise-ya Kanekichi; cens. Fuku–Muramatsu; Rat 6.

MFA; PC.

14. (numbered 13) Kuragano. The robber chief Jiraiya with two followers seated by a fire under a huge pine-tree. Inset: a hilly road among mountains. Pub. Sumiyoshi-ya Masagorō; cens. Hama–Magome; eng. Sugawa Sennosuke; Rat 5.

MFA; PC.

15. (numbered 14) Takazaki. A Chinese interior: Konomura Ōinosuke, an old man in Chinese dress, holding an unrolled *kakemono* of a hawk on a pine-branch; the hawk has come to life and flies off, carrying a white cloth. Inset: village at the foot of a mountain. Pub. Yawata-ya Sakujirō; cens. Fuku–Muramatsu; eng. Takichi; Rat 5.

MFA; PC.

16. (numbered 15) Itahana. Onzōshi Ushiwaka Maru discomfiting two *tengu* at fencing, using wooden swords. Inset: trees and a cloud-shrouded mountain. Pub. Hayashi-ya Shōgorō; cens. Fuku–Muramatsu; Rat 5.

MFA; PC.

17. (numbered 16) Annaka. Seigen the monk, praying to Fudō, sees a vision of his beloved Sakura-hime; mountains and a traveller in the snow are seen through the window. Inset: moonlit village and distant hills. Pub. Kaga-ya Yasubei; cens. Fuku–Muramatsu; Rat 6.

MFA; PC.

18. (numbered 17) Matsuida. Matsui Minjirō watching two snakes in a river; Yama-uba seated on a rock behind, with a monkey. Inset: trees, paddy-fields, and distant mountain. Pub. Tsujioka-ya Bunsuke; cens. Fuku–Muramatsu; Rat 6.

MFA; PC.

19. (numbered 18) Sakamoto. Scene in Gojōzaka, a district of Kyoto: a young *samurai*, preceded by a child, on a sloping road near a tea-house. Inset: man leading a horse along a mountain road. Pub. Minato-ya Kohei; cens. Hama–Magome; Rat 9.

MFA; PC. *Falteri*, 1981.188.

20. (numbered 19) Karuizawa. The strong man Kamada Matahachi at the base of a huge red temple-pillar which he grasps; a flight of pigeons above, and an altar (l.). Inset: road amid hills, with band of mist. Pub. Takada-ya Takezō(?); cens. Mera–Watanabe; Rat 7.

VAM; MFA; PC.

21. (numbered 20) Kutsukake. The Han hero Chōryō (Chang Liang) fitting the shoe he has retrieved from the stream to the foot of Kōsekikō (Huang-shih-kung), the 'yellow stone elder', beneath a pine-tree. Inset: mountain and band of mist, with village roof-tops in the foreground. Pub. Ise-ya Kanekichi; cens. Fuku–Muramatsu; Rat 6.

MFA; PC.

22. (numbered 21) Oiwake. The hideously deformed O-Iwa squeezing blood from a hank of her hair, watched in horror by Iyeyoshi. Inset: travellers on the road amid paddy-fields under a clouded full moon. Pub. Takada-ya Takezō(?); cens. Fuku–Muramatsu; Rat 6.

MFA; PC.

23. (numbered 22) Odai. Teranishi Kanshin, his *kimono* patterned with skeletons, standing with open fan by a trussed-up coolie on a sort of palanquin; *sake*-barrels and posters behind. Inset: road among hills and pine-trees at sunset. Pub. Ise-ya Kanekichi; cens. Mera–Watanabe; Rat 7.

MFA; PC.

24. (numbered 23) Iwamurata. The strong woman Ōiko damming a river with a huge boulder in order to irrigate the rice-fields, watched by three astonished peasants. Inset: paddy-fields, band of mist, and distant mountains. Pub. Kaga-ya Yasubei; cens. Mera–Watanabe; Rat 7.

MFA; PC.

25. (numbered 24) Shionada. Torii Matasuke, holding a severed head in his teeth, wringing out his loincloth after swimming a river; horsemen and attendants on the opposite bank. Inset: evening landscape with mountains, trees, and fields. Pub. Tsujioka-ya Bunsuke; cens. Fuku–Muramatsu; Rat 6.

MFA; PC.

26. (numbered 25) Yawata. Ōmi no Kotōda and Yawata Saburō, in hunting dress, observe the standards of a body of troops moving through a gorge below them; a rainbow in the sky, and a little rain. Inset: paddy-fields, mountain, and mist. Pub. Hayashi-ya Shōgorō; cens. Fuku–Muramatsu; Rat 6.

MFA; PC.

27. (numbered 26) Mochidzuki. Kwaidō Maru (Kintoki), attended by a monkey and a white hare, capturing a small *tengu*, for which a wicker cage has been prepared; waterfall behind. Inset: wooded hill and mountainside. Pub. Hayashi-ya Shōgorō; cens. Fuku–Muramatsu; eng. Take; Rat 6.

MFA; PC. *Kruml*, 9.71.

28. (numbered 27) Ashida. The witch Nyogetsu-ni, carrying a sword and a bell, with a mirror hanging on her breast, and a torch alight at both ends in her teeth, followed up a snowy mountain-slope at night by Arai Maru, who carries a severed head attached to a branch. Inset: village among mountains. Pub.

S74.31

Sumiyoshi-ya Masagorō; cens. Kinugasa–Murata; Rat 8.

MFA; PC.

29. (numbered 28) Nagakubo. Kichizō, seated on a bench, looks round at O-Shichi who holds a framed calligraphy (*shōchikubai*) signed by herself. Inset: tea-houses, paddy-fields, and distant hills. Pub. Tsuji-ya Yasubei; cens. Hama–Magome; eng. Shōji; Rat 9.

MFA; PC.

30. (numbered 29) Wada. Wada Hyōye, in court dress on a bridge, defies four musketeers whose guns point at him; house behind decorated with the Takeda *mon*. Inset: village and paddy-fields among hills. Pub. Sumiyoshi-ya Masagorō; cens. Hama–Magome; Rat 9.

MFA; PC.

31. (numbered 30) Shimo no Suwa. Yayegaki-hime dancing with the helmet of Shingen, while ghost-foxes dance behind her. Inset: conifers above a gorge, with waterfall. Pub. Yawata-ya Sakujirō; cens. Mera–Watanabe; Rat 8.

MFA; PC.

32. (numbered 31) Shiojiri. Takagi Tora-nosuke with his wife and children looking out over the sea, where a number of boats surround a half-submerged whale. Inset: road between pine-trees leading towards a mountain. Pub. Idzutsu-ya Shōkichi; cens. Kinugasa–Murata; eng. Mino; Rat 8.
MFA; PC.

33. (numbered 32) Seba. Musashi-bō Benkei, having captured Tosa-bō Shōshun in the night-attack on the Horikawa palace, carries his captive before him on his horse; two spectators, one leading the horse. Inset: green landscape with wooded hill and band of mist. Pub. Yawata-ya Sakujirō; cens. Kinugasa–Murata; eng. Shōji; Rat 8.
MFA; PC.

34. (numbered 33) Motoyama. Yama-uba descending on a cloud, portrayed as a young court dancer with open fan. Inset: village under a hill, with band of evening mist. Pub. Yawata-ya Sakujirō; cens. Mera–Watanabe; eng. Takichi; Rat 7.
MFA; B; PC.

35. (numbered 34) Niyekawa. Takeshiuchi-no-sukune defeating his treacherous brother Amamiuchi-no-sukune in the ordeal of boiling water. This is said to have occurred in AD 278 (*Nihongi* I, p.258, where the brother's name is given as Umashi-no-sukune). Inset: three travellers approaching a bridge; river and mountain behind. Pub. Kaga-ya Yasubei; cens. Fuku–Muramatsu; Rat 5.
MFA; PC.

36. (numbered 35) Narai. Zenkichi, in travelling dress, taking leave of O-Roku at a comb-shop. Inset: hilly landscape with golden mist. Pub. Minato-ya Kohei; cens. Hama–Magome; Rat 5.
MFA; PC.

37. (numbered 36) Yabuhara. Suye Harukata, armoured and mounted, cuts through a bamboo spear with which he has been attacked at the battle of Itsukushima (1555). Inset: extensive landscape with travellers, hills, and a distant village. Pub. Sumiyoshi-ya Masagorō; cens. Fuku–Muramatsu; eng. Sugawa Sennosuke; pr. Daikyū; Rat 6.
MFA; PC.

38. (numbered 37) Miyanokoshi. Prince Ōtono-miya, with an acolyte, seated at the mouth of a cave reading the scriptures; his murderer, Fuchibe Yoshihiro, approaches in the foreground. Inset: pine-tree on mountain-slope, roof-tops below; mist and distant mountain. Pub. Sumiyoshi-ya Masagorō; cens. Hama–Magome; eng. Sugawa Sennosuke; pr. Daikyū; Rat 5.
MFA; PC.

39. (numbered 37) Fukushima. Urashima Tarō on the shore under a pine-tree with a tortoise, from whose mouth issues a vision of Hōrai. Inset: descending road between steep wooded hills. Pub. Idzutsu-ya Shōkichi; cens. Hama–Magome; Rat 5.
MFA; PC.

40. (numbered 39) Agematsu (read as Uye-matsu on the print). Yeda Genzō, Yoshitsune's retainer, in a pine-tree near the Horikawa palace, watching the lanterns of Shōshun's men approaching through the night mist. Inset: hill with pine-trees overlooking a wide landscape with village and distant mountains. Pub. Takada-ya Takejirō; cens. Mera–Watanabe; Rat 7.
MFA; PC.

41. (numbered 40) Suwara. The poet Ariwara no Narihira eloping with Nijō-no-tsubone, whom he carries on his shoulders through a reed-bed; pursuers with torches in the background. Inset: a mountain pass. Pub. Kadzusa-ya Iwazō; cens. Mera–Watanabe; Rat 7.
MFA; PC.

42. (numbered 41) Nojiri. Hirai Yasumasa playing the flute among rushes; Hakamadare Yasusuke with drawn sword under a pine-tree in the foreground. Inset: mountainous road. Pub. Idzutsu-ya Shōkichi; cens. Hama–Magome; Rat 5.
MFA: PC. *Ronin*, 81.

43. (numbered 41) Mitono (read as Midono on the print). Mitono Kotarō fighting off three roughs on a ruined temple veranda, while an old woman cowers. Inset: village among pine-trees and paddy-fields, with mountain behind. Pub. Minato-ya Kohei; cens. Fuku–Muramatsu; eng. Chōsen; Rat 6.
MFA; PC.

44. (numbered 43) Tsumago (read as Tsumagome on the print). Abe no Yasuna entering through the *shōji* to find his child and an apparition of its mother, the fox-woman Kuzunoha. Inset: roof-tops on wooded hillside and mountain behind. Pub. Minato-ya Kohei; cens. Fuku–Muramatsu; eng. Takichi; Rat 6.
MFA; B; PC. *Düsseldorf 1961*, 42; *Riccar 1978*, 299; *Bidwell 1980*, 189.

45. (numbered 45) Magome. Road-scene: a coolie farting at Takebayashi Sadashichi; loaded pack-horse and river behind. Inset: hilly road with band of pink mist. Pub. Sumiyoshi-ya Masagorō; cens. Fuku–Muramatsu; pr. Daikyū; Rat 6.
MFA; PC.

46. (numbered 44) Ochiai. Kume Sennin falls into the water after staring at a bare-bosomed washerwoman. Inset: road descending to a village through wooded hills. Pub. Sumiyoshi-ya Masagorō; cens. Fuku–Muramatsu; eng. Take; Rat 6.
MFA; PC.

47. (numbered 46) Nakatsugawa. The aunt of Horibe Yasubei and her daughter in a grove of pine-trees watching him execute his revenge on the murderer of his uncle (not shown). Inset: travellers in the plain between mountains and a village among pine-trees. Pub. Yawata-ya Sakujirō; cens. Mera–Watanabe; eng. Takichi; Rat 8.
MFA; PC.
NOTE. On the print the ladies are described as the wife and daughter of Yasubei, but aunt and cousin is the relationship usually given.

48. (numbered 47) Ōi. The robber Ono Sadakurō calling after Yoichibei (Act V of the *Chūshingura*) in the rain. Inset: tea-house, traveller with led horse, and distant mountains. Pub. Kaga-ya Yasubei; cens. Hama–Magome; Rat 5.
MFA; PC.

49. (numbered 48) Ōkute. A young woman grappling with the Hag of the Lonely House at Adachi-ga-hara, who brandishes a kitchen-knife; shadowy figure of the Thousand-armed Kwannon in the background. Inset: wide road at sunset, leading towards a mountain. Pub. Yawata-ya Sakujirō; cens. Mera–Watanabe; eng. Takichi; Rat 7.
VAM; RSM; MFA; PC. *Speiser*, p.115; *Ronin*, 82; *Kruml*, 9.70.

50. (numbered 49) Hosokute. Horikoshi Dairei, the villainous nobleman, drawing his sword against the ghostly manifestations of Asakura Tōgo. Inset: road between pine-trees with green mountain in the background. Pub. Yawata-ya Sakujirō; cens. Mera–Watanabe; eng. Takichi; Rat 7.
MFA; PC.
NOTE. A highly successful new play on this story, *Higashiyama Sakura sōshi*, was produced at the Nakamura theatre in September 1851, with Bandō Hikosaburō IV in the villain's part.

51. (numbered 50) Mitake. Kagekiyo carrying a *naginata* on the colossal Buddha of Tōdaiji, where he was arrested. Inset: mist among the mountains, and huts by a river. Pub. Sumiyoshi-ya Masagorō; cens. Fuku–Muramatsu; eng. Sugawa Sennosuke; Rat 6.
MFA; PC. *Düsseldorf 1961*, 45; *Ronin*, 80.

52. (numbered 51) Fushimi. Tokiwa-gozen sheltering her three children. Inset: road past a tea-house; paddy-fields and distant hills. Pub. Hayashi-ya Shōgorō; cens. Fuku–Muramatsu; Ox 2.
MFA; PC.

53. (numbered 52) Ōta. Amagawa-ya Gihei seizing Yabui Ryōchiku by his coat-collar in a moonlit street (from the *Chūshingura*). Inset: tree-bordered road among hills. Pub. Kobayashi-ya Matsugorō; cens. Kinugasa–Murata; eng. Sennosuke; pr. Daikyū; Rat 8.
MFA; PC.

54. (numbered 53) Unuma. The farmer Yoyemon murdering his deformed wife Kasane with a sickle under a willow-tree on the river-bank, her spirit issuing like a coloured globule; a man on the bridge behind. Inset: rocky landscape with waterfall and distant mountain. Pub. Kadzusa-ya Iwazō; cens.

Mera—Watanabe; Rat 7.

MFA; PC. *Düsseldorf 1961*, 46.

55. (numbered 54) Kanō. The child Hōtarō and his nurse O-Tsuji in a wind by a plantation of lotuses. Inset: hill road ascending from a rest-house between banks and pine-trees. Pub. Yawata-ya Sakujirō; cens. Mera—Watanabe; eng. Sennosuke; Rat 7.

MFA; B; PC.

56. (numbered 55) Gōdo. Girl watching blind men crossing a river. Inset: pine-trees on green hillocks and distant mountain. Pub. Kadzusa-ya Iwazō; cens. Mera—Watanabe; Rat 7.

MFA; PC.

57. (numbered 56) Miyeji. *Momiji-gari*, 'Viewing Autumn Leaves'. Three girls drinking *sake* in the intervals of burning autumn leaves. Inset: very similar to no.55 above. Pub. Kagaya Yasubei; cens. Mera—Watanabe; Rat 7.

MFA; PC. *Ronin*, 83.

58. (numbered 57) Akasaka. The Empress Kōmyō-kōgō, attended by a maid, washing Buddha in the form of a diseased beggar. Inset: road across paddy-fields, with blossoming cherry-trees and distant mountains. Pub. Iseya Kanekichi; cens. Mera—Watanabe; Rat 7.

MFA; PC.

59. (numbered 58) Tarui. The boy Sarunosuke being tied to a well-head by three other boys; river in the background. Inset: wooded hillside, roof-tops, and distant mountain. Pub. Yawata-ya Sakujirō; cens. Mera—Watanabe; eng. Takichi; Rat 7.

MFA; PC.

60. (numbered 59) Sekigahara. The rival wrestlers Hanaregoma Chōkichi and Nuregami Chōgorō throwing a ladder one to another, the ground strewn with debris. Inset: travellers in a mountain landscape. Pub. Idzutsu-ya Shōkichi; cens. Hama—Magome; eng. Mino; Rat 9.

MFA; PC.

61. (numbered 60) Imasu. The Soga brothers, with drawn swords, about to enter the tent of Kudō Suketsune, their father's murderer. Inset: travellers with loaded pack-horse approaching a village; mountains and pine-woods behind. Pub. Tsujioka-ya Bunsuke; cens. Fuku—Muramatsu; eng. Uyemura Yasu; Rat 6.

MFA; PC.

62. (numbered 61) Kashiwabara. The *geisha* Sankatsu of Kasa-ya in the street with a servant carrying her effects (including a pair of swords in brocade bags). Inset: travellers on the road, pine-trees, and distant mountains. Pub. Yawata-ya Sakujirō; cens. Kinugasa—Murata; eng. Shōji; Rat 8.

MFA; PC.

63. (numbered 62) Samegai. Mountain snow-scene: Kanai Tanigorō thrusts a monstrous lizard over a precipice with a bamboo spear,

while a terrified girl cowers behind him. Inset: mountain and mist with wooded hills in front. Pub. Tsujioka-ya Bunsuke; cens. Fuku—Muramatsu; Rat 6.

MFA; PC.

64. (numbered 63) Bamba. The painter Domori ('stammerer') Matabei squatting outside his house, his wife and child behind. Inset: wide road among hills, with conifers. Pub. Ise-ya Kanekichi; cens. Hama—Magome; Rat 9.

MFA; PC.

65. (numbered 64) Toriimoto. The old oil-thief at work, discovered by Taira no Tadamori. Inset: travellers on the road in open country. Pub. Takada-ya Takezō; cens. Fuku—Muramatsu; Rat 6.

MFA; PC.

66. (numbered 65) Takamiya. Kamiya Iyemon, villain of the play *Yotsuya kwaidan* (see no.22 above), fishing; traveller among water-meadows behind. Inset: paddy-fields and distant hills, with large pine-tree in the foreground. Pub. Kobayashi-ya Matsugorō; cens. Kinugasa—Murata; eng. Sugawa Sennosuke; pr. Daikyū; Rat 8.

MFA; PC.

67. (numbered 66) Yechikawa. Sagi-no-ike Heikurō, attended by a squire, washing his axe in a river; three severed heads beside him. Inset: farmhouse and paddy-fields with a mountain behind. Pub. Kadzusa-ya Iwazō; cens. Mera—Watanabe; Rat 7.

MFA; PC.

68. (numbered 48) Musa. The swordsman Miyamoto Musashi, suspended over a chasm in a travelling cradle, strikes at a monstrous bat. Inset: travellers in open country approaching a village. Pub. Sumiyoshi-ya Masagorō; cens. Fuku—Muramatsu; eng. Sugawa Sennosuke; Rat 6.

MFA; PC. *Robinson 1963*, Pl.27; *Kruml*, 22.44.

69. (numbered 67) Kusatsu. Kwanja Yoshitaka, acted by Ichikawa Danjurō VIII, looking down at a coolie tied to a standing horse. Inset: travellers approaching a stone-faced embankment, with the top of a large pine-tree in the foreground. Pub. Minato-ya Kohei; cens. Hama—Magome; Ox 1.

MFA; PC.

70. (numbered 68) Moriyama. Daruma eating an enormous quantity of spaghetti, watched in amazement by the assistants in the spaghetti-shop; embankment and river behind. Inset: travellers on the road between large conifers. Pub. Takada-ya Takezō; cens. Mera—Watanabe; pr. Kozenki; Rat 7.

MFA; PC.

71. (numbered 70) Ōtsu. Koman swimming with the white banner of the Minamoto in her mouth; police on the bank, and Munemori's barge near-by. Inset: wooded mountains and waterfall. Pub. Minato-ya Kohei; cens. Mera—Watanabe; eng. Ryūtarō; Rat 7.

MFA; PC.

72. (numbered *taibi*, the end) The monster *Nuye*, with monkey's head, tiger's body and legs, and snake's tail, descending on the Imperial palace in a black cloud amid lightning. Inset: a wooded mountain. Pub. Minato-ya Kohei; cens. Fuku—Muramatsu; Rat 10.

MFA; PC. *Düsseldorf 1961*, 47.

S75
Tsūzoku Sangokushi ('Popular History of the Three Kingdoms'). Triptychs. See T277, T278, T290, T293–T297, T301, T302, T306–T311, T348.

S76
Yōbu hakkei ('Military brilliance for the Eight Views', cf. S8). *Ōban*.

Title and subtitle on oblong cartouche, with poem on adjoining panel framed with military accoutrements. Large half-length figures of historical characters. Pub. Yenshū-ya Hikobei;

S75.T306

S76.1

cens. Mera–Watanabe; date-seal Rat 7, August–September 1852.

1. 'Autumn Moon at Gojō Bridge.' Ushiwaka Maru, his head covered with a veil, playing his flute on the bridge by moonlight.
    VAM; MFA; PC.

2. 'Lingering Snow at Ishiyama.' Suzuki Shigeyuki with his pistol among snow-covered bushes (cf. S62.41).
    VAM; MFA; B; PC. *Riccar 1978*, 61.

3. 'Evening Glow at Awadzu.' Tomoye-gozen, with arrows sticking in her armour, riding away after the battle of Awadzu-ga-hara.
    VAM; MFA; PC.

4. 'Vesper Bell at Tōdaiji [temple].' Akushichibyōye Kagekiyo, in black and grey monk's habit, *naginata* in hand, ready to resist arrest.
    VAM; MFA; PC.

5. 'Returning Boats at the Ryūkyū Islands.' Minamoto no Tametomo, fan in hand, on board ship; Kiheiji swimming in the background (cf. S64.4).
    VAM; MFA; PC. *FH*, 9; *Speiser*, p.110.

6. 'Clearing Weather at Horikawa.' (Pl.25) Yeda Genzō amid a shower of arrows at the defence of the Horikawa palace.
    VAM; MFA; PC. *Geneva 1978*, 75; *Riccar 1978*, 62.

7. 'Night Rain at Narumi.' Inagawa Yoshioto (sc. Imagawa Yoshimoto) fighting in a downpour of rain at the battle of Okehazama (1560) where he was killed.
    VAM; MFA; PC.

8. 'Homing Geese at the Northern Capital.' Fujiwara no Masakiyo (sc. Katō Kiyomasa) watching geese flying over a Chinese town

S77.3

against a mountain background.
    VAM; MFA; PC.

S77
Yeiyū sanjūrokkasen ('Thirty-six hero-poets'). *Ōban*.

Title in red cartouche with frame of military accoutrements; name of character adjoining; and a large panel with landscape features and a poem composed by the hero in question. Large single figures. Pub. Murata-ya Ichibei; cens. Mera–Watanabe; eng. Nantō; date-seal Rat 11, December 1852–January 1853.

1. Chinzei Hachirō Tametomo, face in profile, seated on a fur rug in armour, his *naginata* resting on a stand of bamboo: sea between mountains.
    PC.

2. Gen Sammi Yorimasa seated on a palace balcony in court robes over armour, shielding his face with his sleeve: irises (*ayame*) behind in allusion to Ayame-no-maye who was given him in marriage by the Emperor after he killed the *Nuye*.
    VAM; PC. *Robinson 1963*, Pl.28.

3. Hachiman-tarō Yoshi-iye in hunting dress,

bareheaded, carrying his bow: green hillside.
PC.

4. Jingō Kōgō ('Empress regent'), in court robes, seated leaning on an arm-rest by a brocade curtain: chrysanthemums behind.
PC.

5. Shinchūnagon Taira no Tomomori in court robes over armour, grasping a *naginata*: behind, green hillside above a band of mist.
PC.

S78

Seichū gishi shōzō ('Portraits of the faithful *samurai* of true loyalty'). *Ōban*.

Title, in formal script, and a short poem on an oval red cartouche with green frame; character's name on adjoining panel. Large half-length figures of the *Rōnin* with bold westernizing effects of characterization, shading, foreshortening, etc. Pub. Sumiyoshi-ya Masagorō; cens. Kinugasa–Murata; eng. Yokogawa 'Horitake' (Takejirō); date-seal Rat 12, January–February 1853. Drawings for unpublished prints in this series are in the Leyden Museum (*Lieftinck*, No.750) and in private possession (*Kruml*, 9.72).

1. Ōboshi Yuranosuke Yoshio with a spear over his shoulder, to which is attached a ticket bearing the name of Hayano Kampei. Pr. Daikyū.
VAM; RSM; MFA; B; PC. *Inouye*, Pl.102; *Robinson 1961*, Pl.69; *Bidwell 1968*, Pl.128; *Riccar 1978*, 66; *Bidwell 1980*, 187 (Pl.8).

2. Yatō Yomoshichi Norikane holding a decorated lantern, his sword in the other hand.
VAM; RSM; B; PC. *Düsseldorf 1962*, 58; *Riccar 1978*, 67; *Bidwell 1980*, 188.

3. Yoshida Sawayemon Kanesada blowing the signal-whistle. Pr. Daikyū.
VAM; B; PC.

4. Yokogawa Kampei Munenori in the snow, with dripping hair, wringing out his clothes. Pr. Daikyū.
VAM; B; PC.

5. Kanzaki Yagorō Noriyasu, by a transparent screen, making a downward thrust with his sword.
B; PC. *Riccar 1978*, 69; *Kruml*, 21.53.

6. Nakamura Kansuke Masatatsu warding off a jar of hot ashes that has been hurled at him. Pr. Daikyū.
RSM; MFA; B; PC. *Düsseldorf 1962*, 57; *Kruml*, 21.52.

7. Muramatsu Sandayū Takanao in the snow, holding his spear and drinking from a dipper.
VAM; MFA; B; PC.

8. Horibe Yahei Kanamaru parrying a spear-thrust with his sword and left hand.
VAM; B; PC. *Illing 1978*, 18.

9. Tominomori Sukeyemon Masakata with his sword drawn, a globular bell suspended above him. Pr. Daikyū.

S78.7

VAM; RSM; MFA; B; PC. *Inouye*, Pl.103; *Riccar 1978*, 68.

10. Ushioda Masanojō Takanori discharging an arrow from his bow.
VAM; B; PC. *Robinson 1963*, Pl.29.

11. Yada Gorozayemon Suketake in the snow, making a two-handed stroke with his sword.
VAM; RSM; B.

12. Sugino Jūheiji Tsugifusa looking through a lifted curtain, his sword drawn.
VAM; MFA; B. *Bidwell 1968*, Pl.127; *Riccar 1978*, 65; *Bidwell 1980*, 186.

S79

Morokoshi nijūshi-kō ('Twenty-four Chinese Paragons of Filial Piety'). *Ōban yokoye*.

Title in red cartouche of varying shape with narrow yellow border; the name of the character is sometimes included, but sometimes appears on a separate small panel adjoining. Pub. Idzumi-ya Ichibei; various cens.; date-seals Ox 1–8, February–September 1853.

1. Teiran (Ting Lan), in a room with the images of his parents in a niche, upbraiding two visitors, who hold up their hands in protest. Cens. Fuku–Muramatsu; Ox 2.
PC.

2. Ōshō (Wang Hsiang), half-naked in a snowy landscape, catching fish through a hole in the ice. Cens. Hama–Magome; Ox 1.
PC. *Illing 1978*, 33.

3. Tōyei (Tung Yung) encounters the Heavenly Weaver on the shore. Cens. Fuku–Muramatsu; Ox 2.
PC.

4. Kwakkyo (Kuo Chü) and his wife discover the pot of gold in the ground outside their house. Cens. Hama–Magome; no date-seal visible.
BM; PC.

5. Kōkaku (Chiang Ko) pleading with three armed robbers for his aged mother who kneels in the roadway. Cens. Fuku–Muramatsu; Ox 2.
PC.

6. Yenshi (Yen Tzu) being shot at from a wooded hill by a man of markedly European appearance. Pub. Wakasa-ya Yoichi; cens. Kinugasa–Murata; Ox 8.
PC.

S79.5

S80

Gishi shinzō ('True portraits of the faithful *samurai*', sc. the Forty-Seven *Rōnin*). *Ōban*.

Title in formal script on oblong red cartouche with narrow yellow border; on adjoining blue panel the name of the *Rōnin* and his age; a poem on a large oblong panel, coloured and patterned. Each 'portrait' is a large full-length figure on plain grey background; the outer *kimono*, though black and white, is not of the usual 'dog-tooth' pattern, and on the helmet of each is one of the *iroha* syllables, often in reverse, several being duplicated. The set is also noteworthy in that Kuniyoshi uses his family name, Igusa, in his signature, which terminates with the expression *kinsha* ('respectfully copied') in place of the usual *gwa* ('drew'); this, together with the unusual style of the figures, may suggest that they were copied from some set of portraits or portrait-figures of the Forty-Seven *Rōnin*, like the figures representing historical and other scenes set up at Okuyama, Asakusa, described by Griffis and Alcock, of which a number of prints were made by Kuniyoshi, his pupils, and contemporaries in the 1850s. Pub. Yamaguchi-ya Tōbei, or Mikawa-ya Kihei; various cens.; date-seals Ox 3–7, April–August 1853.

1. Hara Gōyemon Mototoki, aged fifty-five, eagerly crouching. Cens. Mera–Watanabe; eng. Take; Ox 7.
    PC.

2. Tomimori Sukeyemon Masakata, aged thirty-three, seated with a spear. Cens. Hama–Magome; Ox 5.
    PC.

3. Takebayashi Sadashichi Takashige, aged thirty-one, seated with a spear. Cens. Mera–Watanabe; Ox 3.
    PC.

4. Kataoka Dengoyemon Takafusa, aged thirty-six, feeling the edge of his sword. Cens. Mera–Watanabe; eng. Take; Ox 3.
    PC.

5. Mimura Jiroyemon Kanetsune, aged thirty-six, seated with a spear. Cens. Mera–Watanabe; eng. Take; Ox 7.
    PC.

6. Oribe Yahei Kanamaru, aged seventy-one, seated holding his helmet. Cens. Mera–Watanabe; eng. Take; Ox 3.
    PC.

7. Katsuta Shinyemon Taketaka, aged twenty-three, standing with drawn sword. Cens. Hama–Magome; Ox 5.
    PC.

8. Yada Gorozayemon Suketake, aged twenty-eight, standing with his hand on his sword. Cens. Hama–Magome; eng. Mefuji; Ox 5.
    PC.

9. Onodera Mitsuyemon Hidetomi, aged twenty-seven, seated holding a sheathed sword. Cens. Hama–Magome; Ox 5.
    PC.

10. Okajima Yasuyemon Tsunetatsu, aged twenty-six, standing with drawn sword. Cens. Mera–Watanabe; eng. Take; Ox 3 or 7 (seal cut off only available copy).
    PC.

11. Yatō Yomoshichi Norikane, aged seventeen, standing with a spear. Cens. Mera–Watanabe; eng. Take; Ox 3.
    PC.

12. Kanzaki Yagorō Noriyasu, aged thirty-seven, standing with a bow. Cens. Mera–Watanabe; eng. Take; Ox 3.
    PC.

13. Ōtaka Gengo Tadao, aged thirty-one, seated holding a writing-brush and notebook. Cens. Hama–Magome; Ox 5.
    PC.

S80.14

14. Ōboshi Chikara Yoshikane, aged fifteen, seated on a stool, with a spear. Cens. Hama–Magome; Ox 5.
    PC.

15. Fuwa Katsuyemon Masatane, aged thirty-three, standing, three-quarter back view. Cens. Mera–Watanabe; eng. Mefuji; Ox 3.
    PC.

16. Yoshida Chūzayemon Kanesuke, aged sixty-two, seated, with an earnest expression. Cens. Hama–Magome; Ox 5.
    PC.

17. Isogaya Jurozayemon Masahisa, aged twenty-four, seated, back view, face in profile. Cens. Hama–Magome; Ox 5.
    PC.

18. Orinabe Yasubei Taketsune, aged thirty-

three, standing with drawn sword, shading his eyes. Cens. Mera–Watanabe; Ox 3.
    PC.

19. Ōishi Seizayemon Nobukiyo, aged thirty-four, standing with a spear and a hand on his sword-hilt. Cens. Mera–Watanabe; eng. Take; Ox 3.
    B; PC. *Bidwell 1968*, Pl.136.

20. Okuta Sadayemon Yukitaka, aged twenty-four, standing, back view, face in profile. Cens. Mera–Watanabe; eng. Take; Ox 7.
    PC.

21. Chiba Saburohei Mitsutada, aged fifty, seated holding his bow. Cens. Mera–Watanabe; eng. Mefuji; Ox 3.
    PC.

S81

Yeiyū rokkasen ('Six select heroes'). *Ōban*.

Title on oblong red cartouche with hero's name adjoining on narrow yellow panel. Full-length single figures on fully coloured background. Pub. Hayashi-ya Shōgorō; cens. Fuku–Muramatsu; date-seal Ox 10, November 1853.

S81.1

1. Baba Mino no Kami Nobufusa, in full armour, kneeling to tie up his sandal by a river-bank.
    VAM; MFA; PC.

2. Kusunoki Masatsura making his last stand at Shijō-nawate; river behind.
    VAM; MFA.

3. Nitta Sachūjō Yoshisada, fully armed, seated on a camp-stool; dark mountain behind.
    VAM; MFA; PC.

4. Onchi Sakon Mitsukazu, in jet-black

armour (with blind printing), making a sword-stroke; waterfall behind.

VAM; RSM; MFA.

5. Onikojima Yatarō Kazutada, back view in armour, holding his spear and a severed head; river and mountain behind.

VAM; MFA; PC.

6. Yamamoto Kansuke Nyūdō Dōkisai, wounded to death, grasping his spear and a severed head by a bundle of bamboo poles; mountain and warriors behind.

VAM; RSM; MFA; PC.

S82

Kōyō nijūshi shō no hitori ('Twenty-four generals of eastern Kai province, one by one', sc. Takeda followers at Kawanakajima). *Ōban.*

Title on oblong cartouche with narrow panel adjoining, giving name of character. Single figures in armour against a background of white tent-curtain bearing the Takeda *mon* in black. Pub. Yamaguchi-ya Tōbei; cens. Fuku–Muramatsu; eng. Take; date-seal Ox 10, November 1853.

1. Takeda Daizendayū Harunobu Nyūdō Shingen, seated, wearing his usual helmet with white mane and demon's horns, and voluminous robes.

PC.

2. Takeda Sama-no-suke Nobushige, in court cap, adjusting his armour.

VAM.

3. Yamamoto Kansuke Haruyuki on one knee, face in profile; this is quite unlike Kuniyoshi's many other representations of this redoubtable character.

PC.

4. Yamagata Saburohei Masakage adjusting

S82.4

his gauntlet, his spear resting in a hook at his girdle.

PC.

5. Naitō Shuri Masatoyo adjusting his armour.

VAM.

S83

Echigo jūhasshō ('Eighteen generals of Echigo province', sc. Uyesugi followers at Kawanakajima). *Ōban.*

Title on red oblong cartouche incorporating the character's name; a companion set to the preceding, the Uyesugi *mon* replacing that of the Takeda on the tent-curtain background. Pub. Mikawa-ya Kihei; cens. *aratame*; date-seal Ox 12, January 1854.

S83.1

1. Arakawa Idzu no Kami Tamemitsu adjusting his armour-sleeve, an armour-box behind him.

PC.

2. Naoye Yamashiro no Kami Kanetsugu.

PC.

S84

Yeiyū Yamato jūni-shi ('Japanese heroes for the Twelve Signs'). *Ōban.*

Title on shaded oblong cartouche incorporating the name of the hero, and surmounted by the character for the Sign, accompanied by a punning subtitle, on a red disc. Pub. Mikawa-ya Kihei; cens. *aratame*; date-seal Tiger 7 intercalary, September 1854.

1. Rat (not seen).

2. Ox. (Pl.28) Yamamoto Kansuke Nyūdō Dōki, wounded to death at Kawanakajima, leaning on his spear and resting on a dead

horse; river and silhouetted warriors behind.

PC. *Kennedy*, 1979.39.

3. Tiger. Watōnai (Katō Kiyomasa) confronting a tiger in the snow in Korea.

MFA.

S84.4

4. Hare. Shinodzuka Iga no Kami standing on the shore, in black armour (blind printing) and a white-maned helmet with forecrest of hare's ears, grasping his spear and shouting.

PC.

5. Dragon. Musashi-bō Benkei hurling the great bell of Miidera into the ravine.

PC.

6. Snake. Yegara Heita, dirk in hand, crouching on an overhanging rock, and watching a huge serpent that has caught a pheasant.

MFA; PC.

7. Horse. Shirafuji Hikoshichirō carrying his horse.

PC.

8. Goat (not seen).

9. Monkey. Onzōshi Ushiwaka Maru playing with monkeys by a cascade in a pine-wood by moonlight.

PC.

10. Cock. Sasaki Saburō Moritsuna looking over the Inland Sea; a cock in a basket hangs behind him.

PC.

11. Dog. Hata Rokurozayemon, spear in hand, on a rock by a large pine-tree, looks down on his faithful dog, and two warriors, Tayū-bō Kakushun and Akuhachi, getting over a wall.

PC.

12. Boar (not seen).

S85

Yakushi jū-shi den ('Stories of ten distressed children'). *Ōban.*

Title on short oblong red cartouche, with shaded panel adjoining, containing brief descriptive text. Pub. Sano-ya Tomigorō; cens. *aratame*; date-seal Tiger 9, November 1854.

S85.1

1. Ōtani Furuinosuke, as a boy, overcoming a large boar with his bare fists in a wooded ravine by a stream. It was from this incident that he derived his name (*furu-i*, 'old boar'; *ō-tani*, 'big ravine').
PC.

(No further prints noted from this series.)

S86

Kanadehon Chūshingura (title of the theatrical drama of the Forty-Seven *Rōnin*: literally, 'Forty-seven syllable pattern of the treasury of loyal hearts'). *Ōban yokoye* with 'dog-tooth' frame.

Title and subtitle on rectangular coloured, shaded, or patterned cartouche. A scene from each of the twelve acts of the drama. Pub. Tsujioka-ya Kamekichi; cens. *aratame*; date-seal Tiger 11, December 1854–January 1855.

1. Act I (*daijō*). The lady Kaoyo ascending steps towards Moronao and the Imperial envoy; Yenya and Wakasa on either side.
PC.

2. Act II. Wakasa seated overlooking his garden, while Honzō prepares to cut a branch from a pine-tree.
PC.

3. Act III. Yenya's attack on Moronao; he is being restrained, while the latter falls.
PC.

S86.9

4. Act IV. Yuranosuke outside the castle by night, holding the dirk with which his lord had performed *seppuku*.
PC.

5. Act V. Meeting between Kampei and Senzaki Yagorō at Yamazaki.
PC.

6. Act VI. O-Karu being hustled into a *kago* by Ichimonjiya, to go to her brothel.
PC.

7. Act VII. The spy Kudayū dragged from under the flooring; Yuranosuke and O-Karu above.
PC.

8. Act VIII. The bridal journey (*michiyuki*) of Konami and her mother Tonase; they rest under a tree, with Fuji in the background.
PC.

9. Act IX. Rikiya attacking Honzō with a spear; Yuranosuke in the doorway.
PC. *Stewart*, Pl.49.3.

10. Act X. Gihei in his shop, and his wife Sono knocking on the door outside.
PC.

11. Act XI. The *Rōnin* in the snow surrounding Moronao, who has been dragged from the charcoal-shed.
PC.

12. Act XII. Yuranosuke and the *Rōnin* laying the head of Moronao on their lord's tomb.
PC.

S87

Honchō musha kagami ('Mirror of warriors of our country'). *Ōban.*

Title on oblong red cartouche; name of character in small red label near the figure. Pub. Tsujioka-ya Bunsuke; cens. *aratame*; date-seal Hare 4–5, May–June 1855.

1. Iga Jutarō and Takiyasha-hime, he reading a scroll, and she holding a sword; a large toad in the background.
MFA.

2. Jiraiya loading his gun among rocks by a waterfall; a huge snake looms above him, and a blotched yellow toad crawls among the rocks.
MFA; PC.

3. Kamigashi-hime, in armour of Chinese style, attacking an earth-spider in its lair.
VAM; MFA.

4. (Pl.31) Kiyo-hime turning into a dragon as she entwines the bell of Dōjōji, with the wretched monk Anchin inside.
MFA.

5. Yogo Shōgun Taira no Koreshige, amid falling maple-leaves, draws his sword on a demon-woman behind him.
VAM.

6. Kwaidō Maru seizing Raijin the Thunder-God, as a thunderbolt falls to earth.
MFA.

7. Shiranui-hime, in the dress of incantation (candles on the head, mirror on the breast, carrying hammer, nails, and a straw doll), struggling with two roughs by whom she has been attacked in the forest by night. Eng. Mino.
VAM.

8. Tachibana-hime on a rock below a bridge fighting a dragon which emerges from the waves.
PC. *Speiser*, p.123.

S87.8

S88

Wakan nazoraye Genji ('Japanese and Chinese comparisons for the Chapters of Genji'). *Ōban*.

Title and subtitles in large square shaded *Genji-mon*. Pub. Ise-Yoshi; cens. *aratame*; eng. Shōji; date-seal Hare 7–11, August 1855–January 1856.

1. *Kiritsubo*. Chichibu Shōji Shigetada carrying his blindfolded horse down the precipice of Hiyodori-goye.
   VAM; PC.

2–5. (not seen)

6. *Suyetsumuhana*. Mukwan-no-tayū Atsumori riding out into the sea at Ichi-no-tani, while Kumagaye Naozane hails him from the shore.
   VAM.

7. (not seen)

8. *Hana no yen*. Shanaō (Yoshitsune) leaping among the pine-trees of Kuramayama to the astonishment of his *tengu* fencing-partners and their king, who sits in the background.
   VAM; PC.

9–11. (not seen)

12. *Suma*. Kwaidō Maru up a tree with the monkeys, watched by his mother Yama-uba below.
   VAM.

13. *Akashi*. Baba Mino no Kami cutting down a foeman while charging up a hill.
   BM; VAM.

14. (not seen)

15. *Yomogiū*. Momotarō ('little peachling') and his companions, the monkey, the badger, and the pheasant, with a captive demon; on a

stand behind are the Precious Things.
   VAM; PC. *FH*, 11; *Speiser*, p.125.

16. *Sekiya*. The Chinese hero Kwanu destroying the Five Barriers; mounted on a prancing horse and wielding his famous glaive, he lops off heads right and left. An opposing officer of European appearance in the background.
   VAM; MFA; PC.

17. *Ye-awase*. Iga Jutarō, on foot, seizes a mounted foeman by the girdle; trees of European type behind.
   VAM; PC.

18. (not seen)

19. *Usugumo*. The sick Raikō drawing his sword as the Earth-Spider envelops him in its web.
   VAM; MFA; PC. *Robinson 1963*, Pl.31.

20. (not seen)

21. *Otome*. The Indian prince Hansoku, and the Nine-tailed Fox resuming her shape as she flies away (cf. S66.4).
   VAM; B; PC. *Düsseldorf 1961*, 51; *Riccar 1978*, 71; *Bidwell 1980*, 196.

22. *Tamakadzura*. Takeshiuchi-no-sukune looking over the side of his ship, and being offered two magic jewels, *senju* and *manju*, by the Dragon King.
   VAM; PC.

23. *Hatsune*. Keyamura Rokusuke wrestling before an audience of nobles.
   VAM; PC.

24. (not seen)

25. *Hotaru*. Shinodzuka Iga no Kami on board ship hoisting the sail single-handed, to the astonishment of members of the crew.
   VAM; PC.

26. (not seen)

27. *Kagaribi*. Yamatotakeru-no-mikoto using the 'grass-mowing sword' (*Kusanagi-no-tsurugi*) to foil the barbarians' attempt to trap him in burning grass (cf. S4b.5).
   VAM; PC.

28. *Nowake*. Kidō Maru, seated on a buffalo, draws his sword as Raikō and his followers approach over the Ichihara moor.
   VAM.

29. *Miyuki*. Hyōshitō Rinchū, one of the *Suikoden* heroes, emerging from a temple, spear in hand, and watching three straw-cloaked men in discussion.
   VAM; PC.

30. *Fujibakama*. Watōnai (Katō Kiyomasa) on the Korean shore with two retainers.
   VAM.

31. *Makibashira*. Sagi-no-ike Heikurō wrestling with a giant python in the mountains.
   VAM; PC.

32. (not seen)

33. *Fuji no uraba*. Takeda Shingen of Kai seated, armed, at the foot of Mount Asama.
   VAM.

S88.34

34. *Wakana*. The rebel Abe no Sadatō on horseback trying to make his escape; Hachiman-tarō Yoshi-iye in the background, aiming an arrow.
   VAM; PC.

35 and 36. (not seen)

37. *Yokobuye*. Ushiwaka Maru playing his flute on Gojō bridge; Benkei lurking in the background.
   VAM; PC.

38. *Suzumushi*. Kyumonryō Shishin, the great wrestler in the *Suikoden*, seated on a bamboo bench beneath which are two piglets; a woman and child behind.
   VAM.

39. (not seen)

40. *Minori*. Suzuki Sayemon Shigeyuki aiming his pistol from ambush at Nobunaga (cf. S62.41 and S76.2).
   VAM.

41. (not seen)

42. *Niou-miya*. Mega Magosaburō at the battle of Miidera, defending the gateway amid a hail of arrows.
   VAM; PC.

43–47. (not seen)

48. *Sawarabi*. The *Suikoden* hero Gyōja Bushō overcoming a tiger with his bare hands.
   VAM; MFA; PC.

49 and 50. (not seen)

51. *Ukifune*. Nogi Nyūdō Raigen paddling a wooden shield (*tate*) with his *naginata* under a bridge, amid flying arrows.
   VAM.

52. *Kagerō*. Akushichibyōye Kagekiyo, resist-

ing arrest, struggles with several men in front of a broken wooden grating.

VAM; PC.

53 and 54. (not seen)

S89

Meitō yeiyū soroi ('Set of famous leading heroes'). *Ōban.*

Title on red cartouche surmounted by a demon's head and patterned with Kuniyoshi's *kiri* (paulownia) device; subtitle on scroll ad-joining, which occupies the upper part of the print. Historical scenes. Various pub.; cens. *aratame*; date-seal Dragon 9–11, October–December 1856.

1. Asahina Saburō Yoshihide breaking down the gate. Pub. Jōshū-ya Kinzō.
VAM.

2. Gen Sammi Yorimasa, attended by Ii no Hayata, taking aim at the *Nuye* above the Imperial palace. Pub. Mikawa-ya Tetsugorō.
VAM.

S89.5

3. Hōzō-in Kakuzen seated on a river-bank by moonlight, holding a spear; an owl in a pine-tree beside him. Pub. Mikawa-ya Tetsugorō.
VAM.

4. The robber chief Kumasaka Chōhan receiv-ing a cup of *sake* from one of his men, whilst another keeps a look-out in a tree. Pub. Tsujioka-ya Bunsuke.
VAM.

5. Miyamoto Musashi defeating his enemy Sasaki Ganryū on the sea-shore, using only two sticks against Ganryū's sword. Pub. Fujioka-ya Keijirō.
VAM; PC.

6. Nitta Shirō Tadatsune killing the mon-strous wild boar during Yoritomo's hunting-party on the moor below Mount Fuji. Pub. Mikawa-ya Tetsugorō.
VAM.

7. Sasaki Saburō Moritsuna, in armour with court cap, on a rock above the Inland Sea, while the fisherman Tōdayū points out the shallows where troops can cross. Pub. Mikawa-ya Tetsugorō.
VAM; PC.

8. Satō Tadanobu, wearing Yoshitsune's armour, leaping down on Yokogawa Kakuhan from the snow-covered roof of the Yoshino temple. Pub. Mikawa-ya Tetsugorō.
VAM.

9. Ushiwaka Maru and Benkei on Gojō bridge by moonlight. Pub. Fujioka-ya Keijirō.
VAM.

S90

Seichū gishin meimei kagami ('Mirror of the true loyalty of the faithful retainers, individ-ually', sc. the Forty-Seven *Rōnin*). *Ōban.*

Each print represents one of the *Rōnin* in action, and the upper part is occupied by the title, on a black *tsuba*-shaped cartouche, ad-joined by an allusive design by one of Kuni-yoshi's daughters, and a poem. The set is 'numbered' by the *iroha* syllables (see *Koop*, p.21), each in a small lozenge-shaped label, but sometimes they are omitted. Pub. Ise-ya Isaburō; cens. *aratame*; date-seal Snake 3–8, April–October 1857.

NOTE. As the *iroha* 'numbering' is not com-plete, and in some cases doubtful, the order of prints in this series has been aligned with that of S54.

1. Ōboshi Yuranosuke Yoshio beating a drum by the waterside in snow. Snake 4.
VAM.

2. Ōboshi Rikiya Yoshikane with a mallet, attacking an opponent hiding under a *koto*. Snake 6.
MFA; PC.

3. Yatō Yomoshichi Norikane. Snake 6.
MFA.

4. Fuwa Katsuyemon Masatane, in ordinary

clothes, chastising two *kago*-bearers. Snake 3.
MFA; PC. *Düsseldorf 1961*, 53.

5. Shikamatsu Hanroku Yukishige. Snake 4.
MFA.

6. Yoshida Kawayemon Kanesada in a furred helmet, spear in hand, running along the water's edge. Snake 3.
RSM; MFA.

7. Sakagaki Genzō Masakata. Snake 4.
MFA.

8. Yodogawa Kampei Munenori running past a stone lantern in pursuit of a fleeing adversary. Snake 6.
RSM; MFA.

9. Onodera Jūnai Hidekazu in the snow tying his girdle, his armour and swords on the ground behind him. Snake 6.
RSM; MFA.

10. Isoai Juroyemon Masahisa and a foeman chasing each other round a large standing screen. Snake 3.
RSM; MFA.

11. Okano Kinyemon Kanehide, his sword held in his mouth, wringing out his skirts in the snow. Snake 6.
RSM; MFA.

S90.12

12. Senzaki Yagorō Noriyasu, a wounded foeman behind him, cuts at a flying faggot. Snake 3.
RSM; MFA.

13. Yazama Jūjirō Moto-oki (not seen).

14. Ōtaka Dengo Tadao striking the gate of Moronao's mansion with a huge mallet. Snake 6.
VAM; MFA.

15. Kataoka Dengoyemon Takafusa (not seen).

16. Nakamura Kansuke Masatoki cutting the strings of several bows with his sword. Snake 6.
MFA.

17. Toshima Yasōyemon Tsuneki, having tied two roughs to a tree, pinions a third on the ground. Snake 3.
RSM; MFA; PC. *Düsseldorf 1961*, 52.

18. Teraoka Heiyemon Nobuyuki carrying two buckets of water through the snow. Snake 3.
RSM; MFA.

19. Uramatsu Handayū Takanao trying an unmounted sword on a doorpost, watched by the amazed owner, whilst a cat runs off. Snake 3.
RSM; MFA.

20. Tokuda Tadayemon Yukitaka pulling back a sliding door to disclose two terrified retainers of Moronao. Snake 3.
RSM; MFA.

21. Horibe Yahei Kanamaru beheading an opponent, the severed head flying into the air. Snake 6.
VAM; RSM; MFA.

22. Kimura Okuyemon Sadayuki parrying a spear-thrust amidst a shower of domestic utensils. Snake 4.
RSM; MFA.

23. Kazuta Shinyemon Taketaka pouring water from a bucket with a dipper on to a bed of hot ashes. Snake 6.
RSM; MFA.

24. Takebayashi Sadashichi Takashige making a stroke that has disarmed his opponent, whose right leg appears above. Snake 3.
RSM; MFA.

25. Karahashi Zensuke Takeyuki drinking *sake* from a tub, watched apprehensively by the cellar-man. Snake 3.
RSM; MFA.

26. Aibara Yesuke Munefusa chastising two porters by a river. Snake 3.
RSM; MFA.

27. Tomimori Sukeyemon Masakata receiving a jar of ashes hurled at him by a young retainer of Moronao. Snake 3.
RSM; MFA.

28. Ashioda Matanojō Mitsutoki, spear in hand, hauling a lurking foeman from his hiding-place. Snake 3.
RSM; MFA.

29. Hayami Sōzayemon Mitsutaka attacked while falling backwards into icy water. Snake 6.
RSM; MFA.

30. Onodera Kōyemon Hidetomi chasing a stumbling foeman on a veranda. Snake 4.
VAM; MFA.

31. Chiba Saburohei Mitsutada cutting open the head of an opponent. Snake 6.
MFA; PC.

32. Ōboshi Seizayemon Nobukiyo (not seen).

33. Sugatani Inojō Masatoshi standing by a moat, his foot on a stone and a spear in his hand. Snake 8.
RSM; MFA.

34. Horibe Yasubei Taketsune destroying decorative woodwork with a large mallet. Snake 6.
RSM; MFA; PC. *Kruml*, 13.14.

35. Hayano Wasuke Tsunenari, sword in hand, threatening a squirming adversary. Snake 3.
RSM; MFA.

36. Yata Gorozayemon Suketake escalading the wall and shaking his sword at three barking dogs. Snake 4.
RSM; MFA.

37. Okada Magodayū Toyonari killing a bear, from whose body arises the ghost of a villainous monk. Snake 3.
RSM; MFA.

38. Kō no Moronao (not seen).

39. Yenya Hangwan Takasada making his attack on Moronao in the palace. Snake 8.
RSM; MFA.

40. Yazama Shunroku Mitsukaze. Snake 4.
MFA.

41. Mase Magokurō Masatoki swimming under water among the fish. Snake 3.
RSM; MFA; PC. *Kruml*, 13.15.

42. Uramatsu Kihei Hidenao in a covered boat on the river. Snake 6.
RSM; MFA.

43. Yazama Kihei Mitsunobu, bareheaded in the snow, holding his spear and helmet. Snake 4.
RSM; MFA.

44. Mase Chūdayū Masa-aki, with lantern and open umbrella, watching frogs at night. Snake 6.
RSM; MFA.

45. Kadono Jūheiji Tsugifusa. Snake 6.
MFA.

46. Hara Gōyemon Mototoki thrusting his spear at an opponent falling into the water. Snake 8.
RSM; MFA.

47. Hayano Kampei Tsuneyo, seated before a torn lamp, contemplates his sword before performing *seppuku*.
RSM; MFA.

48. Kaiga Yazayemon Tomonobu. Snake 6.
MFA.

49. Nimura Jirozayemon Kanetsune warming himself at a blazing log fire. Snake 6.
RSM; MFA.

50. Yoshida Chūzayemon Kanesuke (not seen).

S91

Yeiyū goshiki awase ('Heroes matched to the Five Colours'). *Ōban.*

Title on shaded oblong cartouche with narrow yellow border; names of characters adjoining in narrow rectangular panels. Famous historical single combats. Pub. Sanoya Kihei; cens. *aratame*; eng. Fukagawa Hori-Chō; date-seal Snake 5, June 1857.

1. Satsuma no Kami Tadanori holding down Okabe Rokuyata Tadazumi under a large pine-tree, behind which Tadazumi's retainer approaches.
   MFA.
NOTE. This is the only print of this series so far noted, but two finished drawings for it are in private possession; unfortunately the names of the characters are not written in (*Geneva 1978*, 104; *Schack* (see S31.3), Pl.71).

S92

Honchō yeiyū kagami ('Mirror of our country's heroes'). *Ōban.*

Title on rectangular cartouche with pierced corners; name of character on smaller panel adjoining. Heroes in action. Pub. Kaga-ya Kichiyemon; date-seal Horse 6–8, July–September 1858.

1. Kudō Shōhei Mototsugu with a battleaxe in front of a waterfall.
   MFA.

2. Sasaki Shirobei Takatsuna crossing the Uji river under the ancient pine-tree of Karasaki.
   MFA.

3. Satō Shirobei Tadanobu laying about him with the *go*-board.
   MFA.

4. Yamaki Hangwan Kanetaka at bay in his mansion; one of Yoritomo's men pushes a decoy helmet from behind the *shōji* on the point of his *naginata*.
   MFA.

S92.5

5. Yamamoto Kansuke Haruyuki, wounded to death at Kawanakajima, is given a drink of water by an exhausted follower.
   MFA; PC.

S93

Rokuyōsei Kuniyoshi jiman ('Six conditions of nature, Kuniyoshi's pride'). *Ōban.*

Title in bold script on oblong red cartouche, incorporating two-character subtitle (astrological names for various days, auspicious and otherwise); name of character on smaller panel adjoining. Pub. Uo-Yei; date-seal Monkey 10 with *aratame*, November–December 1860 (from designs of *c.*1835).

1. *Butsumetsu*, a most unlucky day. Hori Ran Maru spearing Yasuda Sakubei in the defence of the Honnōji temple against Akechi Mitsuhide (*Hawley*, 349).
   PC.

2. *Senshō*, a day for official business. Inagawa

S91.1

Yoshimoto in his last fight at Okehazama, 1560 (*Hawley*, 71).

PC.

3. *Tai-an*, a good day for travelling. (Fig.15) Kwaidō Maru by a waterfall wielding a huge axe, his foot on the head of a prostrate bear-cub; a monkey behind him.

PC.

4. *Sembū*, not a very lucky day. (Pl.29) Mongaku Shōnin doing penance under the waterfall; Fudō's two acolytes, Kongara and Seitaka, appear above him.

PC.

S93.5

5. *Shakku*, not a good day. Ōmori Hikoshichi about to draw his sword by a stream, in which appears the demon reflection of the beautiful woman standing behind him.

PC.

6. *Tomobiki*, a bad day for funerals. Sasaki Takatsuna (*sic*, in error for Moritsuna) being shown the crossing-place of the Inland Sea by the fisherman Tōdayū.

PC.

S94

Meishō shi-ten kagami ('Mirror of the quartets of retainers of famous generals'; for *shitennō*, see *Koop*, p.101–2). *Ōban*.

Title on rectangular cartouche, the upper outline convex and the lower concave, incorporating the name of the general concerned. Groups, on plain coloured or shaded background. Pub. Jōshū-ya Kinzō; date-seal Boar 9 with *aratame*, October–November 1863 (from designs of *c*.1848). Published posthumously.

1. Minamoto no Yorimitsu (Raikō) Ason; his four retainers are all seated in court robes and caps. Clockwise from the top: Usui Sadamitsu,

S94.1

Urabe Suyetake, Watanabe no Tsuna, and Sakata no Kintoki.

PC.

2. Minamoto no Yoshinaka Ason; both he and his retainers wear armour. Clockwise from the top: Imai Shirō Kanehira, Tate Rokurō Chikatada, Higuchi Jirō Kanemitsu (with a large axe), and Nenoi Daiyata Yukichika.

PC.

3. Nitta Yoshisada Ason; both he and his retainers wear armour. Clockwise from the top: Kuriu Sayemon Norihisa, Watari Shinza-

yemon Yasumasa, Shinodzuka Iga no Kami Sadatsuna, and Hata Rokurozayemon Toki-yoshi.

MFA; PC.

S95

This is the inevitable final catch-all or miscellany comprising untitled and unclassified warrior-prints which do not fit in with either the regular series or the triptychs. So far as possible they have been arranged in convenient groups.

S95a

Ōban yokoye showing strong western influence; *c*.1830–5.

1. *Chūshingura jūichi damme yo-uchi no dzu* ('The *Chūshingura*, Act XI, the night-attack'). Moonlit street-scene with western effects of clouds and shadows; the *Rōnin* scaling the wall of Moronao's mansion.

BM; B; City Art Gallery, Bristol. *Inouye*, Pl.20; *Bidwell 1968*, Pl.25; *Riccar 1978*, 86; *Bidwell 1980*, 28.

2. *Ōmi no kuni no yūfu O-Kane* ('O-Kane, the brave woman of Ōmi province'). In an unearthly landscape with sensational cloud effects, O-Kane steps on the leading-rein of a splendid brown horse, which kicks up its heels towards her. Pub. Yamaguchi-ya Tōbei (Kin-kōdō); cens. *kiwame*.

PC. *Inouye*, Pl.21 (col. Pl.2).

3. *Shinzan no tsuribito* ('Anglers in the depths of the mountains'). Heavily wooded landscape (western style) with river and pool; two fishers on a ledge, and a huge snake appearing under the water and partly among the trees.

MFA (key-block pull only).

S95a.1

S95b.1

S95c.1

S95b

Other *ōban yokoye* prints; *c.*1835.

1. Sanada Yoichi Yoshisada and Matano Gorō Kagehisa struggling on the sea-shore at Ishibashiyama. Pub. Takenouchi Magohachi (Hōyeidō); cens. *kiwame* (combined with pub.).

    PC.

2. Katō Kiyomasa fighting the Korean tiger; plain background flecked with orange. Pub. Takenouchi Magohachi; cens. *kiwame*.

    PC.

3. Yorimasa and his retainer Ii no Hayata dispatching the monster *Nuye*. *Unsigned.* Pub. Takenouchi Magohachi; cens. *kiwame*.

    VAM.

S95c

Vertical diptychs (*kakemono-ye*); *c.*1840–5.

1. Tokiwa-gozen and her children in the snow; a village in the background. Pub. Idzumi-ya Ichibei.

    PC.

2. Shizuka-gozen in her *shirabyōshi* costume beneath a rolled bamboo blind. Pub. Idzumi-ya Ichibei.

    B. *Bidwell 1968*, Pl.78; *Riccar 1978*, 166.

3. Kaga no Chiyo with her bucket by the well, looking down at morning glory flowers. Pub. Idzumi-ya Ichibei.

    MFA.

4. Takeda Daizendayū Harunobu Nyūdō Shingen, in his traditional helmet, holding his war-fan charged with astrological symbols, and with fangs visible at the corners of his mouth. No pub. visible (only the upper sheet seen); cens. Muramatsu; eng. Okamoto Jirobei.

    MFA.

5. Uyesugi Danjō Daihitsu Terutora Nyūdō Kenshin, with a monk's hood over his helmet, the forecrest of paulownia between horns. Pair to the preceding; same pub., cens., and eng. (only the upper sheet seen).

    MFA.

S95d

Chūban in pairs, either undivided, or forming diptychs; *c.*1840–3.

1. Two mounted warriors confronting one another: on the right, Akiyama Shin-kurando armed with a huge axe; on the left, Abo (his *nanori* cut off in the only available copy), bareheaded with a sword. Pub. Arita-ya Seiyemon; cens. *kiwame*.

    PC.

2. Musashi-bō Benkei reading his subscription scroll to Togashi Sayemon at the Ataka Barrier. Pub. Arita-ya Seiyemon; cens. *kiwame* (Tanaka on later printings).

    PC.

3. Gen Sammi Yorimasa holding a torch over the fallen *Nuye*, which is about to be dispatched by his squire I no Hayata. Pub. Arita-ya Seiyemon; cens. Tanaka.

    PC.

4. The severed head of the Shuten-dōji, belching flames, in the air above Watanabe no Tsuna, while Raikō poises his sword in readiness. Pub. Arita-ya Seiyemon; cens. Tanaka.

    PC.

5. The fight between Ushiwaka Maru and Kumasaka Chōhan at the inn; bales and a torch on the ground, and Kisanda in the distance. Pub. Arita-ya Seiyemon; cens. Tanaka.

    PC.

S95e

Fan-prints (*uchiwa-ye*); *c.*1835–40.

1. *Ukishima no hara* ('The moor of Uki-shima'). Yoritomo's troops passing before him in review. No pub. or other mark.

    VAM. *Crighton*, V12.

2. *Funa Benkei* ('Benkei in the boat'). Yoshi-tsune and his men in a storm at sea; Benkei in the bows exorcizing the Taira ghosts. No pub. or other mark.

    VAM. *Crighton*, V13.

3. Title on a book surrounded with cherry-blossom: *Kōjō chaban Ishiyama aki no tsuki* ('Verbal farce: autumn moon on Ishiyama'). The lady Murasaki with a maid on a veranda under the moon. No pub. or other mark.

    B. *Riccar 1978*, 175; *Bidwell 1980*, 20.

4. The poet Abe no Nakamaro in China, seated at a table, and watched intently by a Chinese dignitary. No pub. or other mark.

    VAM.

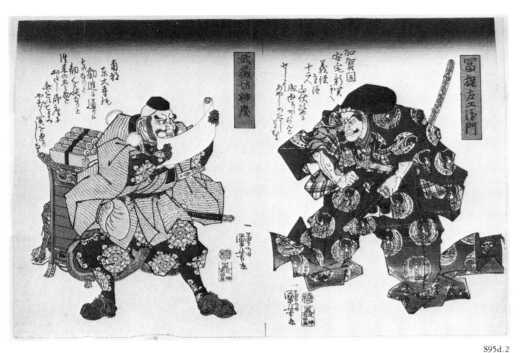

S95d.2

S95e.2

upper right; central panel of Kohōgi Sōkō enthroned, presiding over a meeting of six principal heroes round a table, and surrounded by all the others, each in a named and numbered compartment. Pub. Tsuru-ya Ki-yemon, Sano-ya Kihei, Kaga-ya Kichiyemon, Nishimura-ya Yohachi; *c.*1830.

PC. *Riccar 1979*, 46.

3. *Harimaze* print, the l.h. portion consisting of a *chū-tanzaku* representation of Inudzuka Shino on the roof-crest of Hōryūkaku, looking down on Inukai Kempachi, with geese flying below a full moon. The other two designs of the *harimaze* are by Hiroshige and Kunisada (Hanabusa Ittai). No pub.; Horse 9, October 1858.

B; PC. *Inouye*, Pl. 110; *Suzuki–Oka*, 55; *UT*, 35; *Riccar 1978*, 72.

4. *Yoshitsune yeiyū roku* ('Engraving of Yoshitsune's heroes'). *Ōban.* A group of twenty-three figures in all, on plain blue ground, with Yoshitsune himself at the top and Benkei at the bottom, all in armour except Shidzuka-gozen, who holds a *naginata.* Pub. Echizen-ya Heisaburō; *c.*1840.

PC.

5. Set of three *ōban* prints, which may have been intended to form a triptych, each representing a champion on the Takeda side in the Kawanakajima campaign, seated and armoured, with biographical text above by Shōtei Kinsui, the top of each print shaded off with Takeda *mon* reserved. They are: Kosaka Danjō-no-jō Masanobu, an armillary sphere behind him; Takeda Hosshō-in Harunobu Nyūdō Shingen with a fan and horned helmet; and Yamagata Saburohei Masakage with a huge iron club. Pub. Tsu-Sawa; cens. Hama; *c.*1845.

MFA; PC.

S95f.1

5. Series, **Reppuden** ('Stories of chaste women'). Shūshiki the poetess holding a roll of paper, having just hung a poem on a blossoming cherry-tree. Pub. Iba-ya Sensaburō.

VAM.

S95f
Miscellaneous oddments.

1. *Chūban* tetraptych. **Kawanakajima ō-kassen** ('The great battle of Kawanakajima'). Double portrait of (r.) Takeda Daizen-no-daibu Harunobu Nyūdō Shingen with rosary and war-fan, and (l.) Uyesugi Danjō-no-taihitsu Terutora Nyūdō Kenshin with large bamboo staff, both seated, armoured, under their respective banners. Above is a long account of the campaign. Pub. Mura-Tetsu; cens. Fu; *c.*1845.

PC.

2. **Suikoden gōketsu sugoroku** ('*Sugoroku* of the *Suikoden* heroes'). A large sheet (49.5×89 cm.) of the heroes of the *Suikoden,* adapted to the game of *sugoroku,* in which dice were thrown to determine rate of progress from one section to another. Title in large script,

Note on Catalogue Entries in Part II

Like the series in Part I, the triptychs are listed, so far as possible, in chronological order of publication. The first few words of the titles are transcribed to assist in identification. References placed directly following the titles indicate the triptychs which are reproduced in this book, either as Plates or as illustrations in the Introduction (Figs.). For an explanation of the abbreviations used, please consult the Note to Part I (p.98).

Part II: Triptychs and Diptychs

T1

(No title) The ghosts of Tomomori and the other Taira warriors slain at Dan-no-ura attacking Yoshitsune and Benkei in their ship. This is recorded (Iijima Kyoshin, rev. Tamabayashi Seirō, *Ukiyoye-shi: Utagawa retsuden*, Tokyo, 1941, p.259) as the first of Kuniyoshi's historical triptychs. Pub. Adzuma-ya Daisuke; cens. *kiwame*; 1818.

MFA; B; PC. *Robinson 1961*, Pl.2; *Or.Art*, Spring 1961, p.24; *Riccar 1978*, 87; *Bidwell 1980*, 1.

T2

(No title) Tadanobu in Yoshitsune's armour, with his men, fighting Yokogawa Kakuhan and his monks amid a hail of arrows in the snows of Mount Yoshino. Pub. Tsuru-ya Kihei; cens. *kiwame*; *c*.1820.

MFA.

T3

(No title) Raikō's retainers advancing on Kidō Maru, who raises his buffalo-hide disguise. Pub. Ise-ya Rihei; *c*.1820.

PC. *Takagi*, 1.

T4

(No title) (Pl.34) The Earth-Spider and his demons attacking the sick Raikō and his retainers. Pub. Yamamoto-ya Heikichi; cens. *kiwame*; *c*.1820.

BM; PC. *Apollo*, May 1949, p.125; *Düsseldorf 1961*, 1; *Düsseldorf 1962*, 13.

T5

(No title) Ushiwaka Maru fighting Kumasaka Chōhan and his gang at the post-station. Pub. Yamamoto-ya Heikichi; cens. *kiwame*; *c*.1820.
PC.

T6

(No title) Kuriu Sayemon, Hata Rokurozayemon, Shinodzuka Iga no Kami, and Watari Shinzayemon, retainers of Nitta Yoshisada, breaking up a haunted temple. Pub. Yamamoto-ya Heikichi; cens. *kiwame*; *c*.1820-5.
PC.

T7

(No title) (Pl.35) The *Nuye*, shot down in a swirling black cloud by Gen Sammi Yorimasa, about to be dispatched by Ii no Hayata. Pub. Yamamoto-ya Heikichi; cens. *kiwame*; *c*.1820-5.

RSM; PC. *Takagi*, 3; *Robinson 1961*, Pl.4.

T8

Hakone reigen izari no ada-uchi. The revenge of Iinuma Katsugorō, with the apparition of his wife Hatsu-hana in the waterfall. Pub. Nishimura-ya Yohachi; cens. *kiwame*; *c*.1825.
PC.

T9

Yehon Gappō tsuji. Takahashi Kambō defending himself on a huge image against a swarm of attackers. Pub. Tsuru-ya Kihei; cens. *kiwame*; *c*.1825.

VAM; RSM; PC.

T10

Kiyomori Nyūdō Nunobiki no taki yūran Akugenda Yoshihira no rei Namba Jirō wo utsu. (Pl.38) The ghost of Akugenda Yoshihira striking down his killer, Namba Jirō, at the Nunobiki waterfall before Kiyomori and his suite. Pub. Ise-ya Sanjirō; cens. *kiwame*; *c*.1825.

VAM; MFA; B; PC. *Robinson 1961*, Pl.5; *Düsseldorf 1961*, 2; *Riccar 1978*, 88; *Bidwell 1980*, 4.

T11

Chūshingura: gishi Takanawa hikitori no dzu. The Forty-Seven *Rōnin*, their task accomplished, retire to Takanawa; their leader Yuranosuke interviewing a priest of the temple. The date Bunsei 10 (1827) appears on one of the buildings. Pub. Kaga-ya Kichiyemon; cens. *kiwame*; 1827.

MFA; B; PC. *Riccar 1978*, 126.

T12

Chūshingura: yo-uchi no dzu. The night-attack in the *Chūshingura*; fight in the garden between the Forty-Seven *Rōnin* and the retainers of Moronao, some of whom (l.) are defending their master's hiding-place. Pub. Kaga-ya Kichiyemon; cens. *kiwame*; *c*.1827-30.

B; PC. *Riccar 1978*, 125; *Bidwell 1980*, 3.

T13

Chūshingura: yo-uchi no dzu. The night-attack in the *Chūshingura*; the Forty-Seven *Rōnin* beginning to go over Moronao's wall by rope-ladders on either side of the main gate. Pub. Kaga-ya Kichiyemon; *c*.1827-30.

B; PC.

T14

Chūshingura jūichi damme: Ryōgoku-bashi sei-soroi dzu. Eleventh act of the *Chūshingura*: the Forty-Seven *Rōnin* assembled at sunrise in the snow at Ryōgoku bridge; a flight of wild geese. Pub. Kaga-ya Kichiyemon; *c*.1827-30.

MFA; B. *Bidwell 1968*, Pl.3; *Riccar 1978*, 124.

T15

Chūshingura: gishi Ryōgoku-bashi hikitori no dzu. The Forty-Seven *Rōnin*, having crossed Ryōgoku bridge on their triumphant return, are interviewed by a mounted official. Pub. Kaga-ya Kichibei; cens. *kiwame*; *c*.1827-30.

PC.

T16

(No title) Preparations for the defence of the Horikawa palace: Shidzuka-gozen is handed a *naginata* by one of her maids, while Tadanobu gets out his armour (l.); Yoshitsune, armed with a *naginata*, hurries along the veranda (c.); and Benkei, grasping an iron club, gives directions (r.). Pub. Nishimura-ya Yohachi; cens. *kiwame*; *c*.1830.

MFA.

T17

Yashima ō-kassen. Yoshitsune executing his 'eight boat leap' (*hassō-tobi*), cutting through a rudder and a wooden shield that have been thrown at him. Black sky in some printings. Pub. Ise-ya Rihei; cens. *kiwame*; *c*.1830.

VAM; PC.

T18

Ujigawa kassen no dzu. The fording of the Uji river: Takatsuna leading, followed by Kagesuye and Shigetada. Pub. Yezaki-ya Tatsuzō; cens. *kiwame*; *c*.1831 (also a reissue, *c*.1845, cens. Hama).

VAM; PC.

T19
Yamashiro no kuni Kasagi ishi-iye kassen no dzu. Defence of Kasagi castle by the loyalists against the Rokuhara forces (1331) with tree-trunks and rocks being hurled down on the attackers (*Taiheiki*, pp.70ff.). Pub. Tsuru-ya Kiyemon; cens. *kiwame*; *c*.1832.
VAM; RSM; MFA.

T20
Kuramayama no dzu. Ushiwaka Maru practising fencing with the *tengu* under the direction of Sōjō-bō; Kisanda in attendance. Pub. Yezaki-ya Tatsuzō; cens. *kiwame*; *c*.1832.
PC.

T21
Ōyeyama Shuten-dōji shūzui no dzu. The drinking-bout of Raikō and his retainers with the Shuten-dōji in the latter's palace on Mount Ōyeyama. Pub. Daikoku-ya Heikichi; cens. *kiwame*; *c*.1832.
VAM; RSM; MFA; PC.

T22
Nitta Ashikaga ō-watashi ō-kassen. Nitta Yoshisada and his troops swimming across a river by a broken bridge to attack a fortified position on the opposite bank (perhaps the Iruma river; *Taiheiki*, p.279). Pub. Sōshū-ya Yohei; cens. *kiwame*; *c*.1832.
PC.

T23
Gyakushin Masakado wa Rokurō Kintsura ga isame no etc. (Pl.39) Musashi Gorō Sadayo striking Rokurō Kintsura with his fan before the latter's brother Masakado. Pub. Akamatsu-ya Shōtarō; cens. *kiwame*; *c*.1833–4.
RSM; MFA; PC.

T24
Shimotsuke no kuni Nasu no hara kimmō hakumen kyūbi no akko taiji no dzu. The Nine-tailed Fox slain on Nasu moor by Miurano-suke Tsunetane and Kadzusa no Suke Hirotsune. Pub. Yamaguchi-ya Tōbei; cens. *kiwame*; *c*.1834.
RSM; MFA; PC.

T25
Yoshinaka hata-age kassen no dzu. The first battle at the setting-up of Yoshinaka's standard in Shinano (1180): Jō Shirō Nagamochi on horseback cutting at Tayū-bō Kakumei, and Tomoye-gozen killing Kurotsuka Hachirō. Pub. Takenouchi Magohachi; cens. *kiwame*; *c*.1834.
MFA; PC.

T26
Yengen gwan-nen go-gwatsu nijūgo-nichi Minatogawa ō-kassen. The battle of the Minatogawa on 4 July 1336: fighting on a hill, and the Ashikaga fleet seen approaching in the distance. Pub. Tsuru-ya Kiyemon; cens. *kiwame*; *c*.1834.
VAM; MFA; PC.

T27
Kanshin mata-kuguri no dzu. The humility of Kanshin, crawling between the legs of a fisherman, to the amusement of the latter's companions. Pub. Sano-ya Kihei; cens. *kiwame*; *c*.1835 (later printing, *c*.1843, cens. Tanaka).
BM; VAM; RSM; B; PC. *Riccar 1978*, 208; *Bidwell 1980*, 91; *Kruml*, 18.26.

T28
Sanada no Yoichi Yoshihisa: Matano no Gorō Kagehisa: Sanada no Yoichi wa kokon ni hiideshi wakamusha etc. (Pl.33) Struggle between Yoshihisa and Kagehisa at the battle of Ishibashiyama (1180); very large figures. Yoshihisa in error for Yoshitada. Pub. Yama-guchi-ya Tōbei; cens. *kiwame*; *c*.1835.
PC. *Riccar 1978*, 89.

T29
Igagoye kataki-uchi no dzu. The Igagoye revenge: Karaki Masayemon (c.) fighting against odds; Busuke and Magohachi defending a bridge (r.); spectators in the background. Pub. Sōshū-ya Yohei; cens. *kiwame*; *c*.1835.
PC.

T30
Higo no kuni Midzumata no kaijō nite Tametomo nampū chii etc. (Pl.36) Tametomo's ship wrecked in a storm by a dragon in the clouds and a great fish; *tengu* fly in to the rescue. Pub. Fujioka-ya Keijirō; cens. *kiwame*; *c*.1836.
RSM; MFA; PC. *Takagi*, 4.

T31
(No title) Asahina Saburō on the sea-shore with a group of freakish inhabitants of foreign lands. Pub. Maru-ya Seijirō; cens. *kiwame*; *c*.1836.
MFA; B; PC. *Takagi*, 2.

T32
Yoshitsune no jūku-shin. Yoshitsune and his nineteen chief retainers in a ship (cf. T319). Pub. Idzumi-ya Ichibei; cens. *kiwame*; *c*.1836.
VAM; PC.

T33
Miyamoto Musashi Shirakura ka dokushu no etc. Miyamoto Musashi bursting out of the bath-house, to the consternation of Shirakura Gengoyemon, his wife, and followers, who had intended to boil him alive there. Pub. Yamamoto-ya Heikichi; cens. *kiwame*; *c*.1836.
VAM; PC.

T34
Kusunoki Masashige no shin Tsujikaze Itamochi no ryō-yūshi Fujiidera no kassen ni Kazu-uji wo ikedokoro dzu. (Pl.42) The battle of Fujiidera in driving rain: Kazu-uji and Moronao, the Ashikaga generals, seized by the Kusunoki (1348). Pub. Sōshū-ya Yohei; cens. *kiwame*; *c*.1836.
MFA; PC.

T35
Kenkyū yo-nen go-gwatsu nijūhachi-nichi Fuji no Susono Soga kyōdai yo-uchi hommō no dzu. The Soga brothers laying about them in the camp-enclosure after killing Suketsune (28 June 1193). Pub. Yamamoto-ya Heikichi; *c*.1836.
MFA; PC.

T36
Inuzaka Keno Tanetomo Ōmori to Suzu-no-mori no etc. The three *Hakkenden* heroes Inuzaka Keno Tanetomo, Inuda Kobungo, and Inukawa Shōsuke Yoshitomo engaged in a running fight with numerous opponents; Mount Fuji behind. Pub. Idzumi-ya Ichibei; cens. *kiwame*; *c*.1836.
VAM; RSM; B; PC.

T37
Nitta Yoshisada Ashikaga Taka-uji ō-kassen. The great battle (probably of Hyōgo, 1335) between Nitta Yoshisada and Ashikaga Taka-uji: a general mêlée, with Shinodzuka Iga no Kami grappled with Satō Tōtōmi no Kami (l.). Pub. Tsuru-ya Kiyemon; cens. *kiwame*; *c*.1836.
RSM; MFA; PC.

T38
Gempei kassen: Settsu Banshū no Naniwa-gata Heike no etc. Battle on the shore outside the Taira fortified camp at Ichi-no-tani (1184): Hirayama Suyeshige (r.), Kumagaye Naozane (c.), Kumagaye Sada-iye and Etchū Moritsugu (l.). Pub. Maru-ya Seijirō; cens. *kiwame*; *c*.1836.
PC.

T39
Dzushū Ishibashiyama Tobi-no-gake ni Minamoto no Yoritomo seijū shichi-ki gaboku ni naka ni kakure dzu. The battle of Ishibashiyama (1180) in the rain, showing Yoritomo and his seven companions hiding in the hollow tree, and the combat of Kagehisa and Yoshisada. Pub. Yebi-ya Rinnosuke; cens. *kiwame*; *c*.1836.
MFA; PC.

T40
Akasaka no shuku nite Ushiwaka Maru gōtō wo kiru. Ushiwaka fighting Chōhan and his gang at the post-station. Pub. Yamamoto-ya Heikichi; cens. *kiwame*; *c*.1836.
RSM; MFA; B; PC.

T41
Hakkenden no uchi: Hōryūkaku. (Pl.43) Inudzuka Shino at bay on the Hōryūkaku roof

against Inukai Kempachi and his men, a favourite episode from the *Hakkenden*. Pub. Idzumi-ya Ichibei; cens. *kiwame*; *c*.1836–7.

BM; VAM; MFA; B; PC. *Bidwell 1968*, Pl.123; *Riccar 1978*, 90; *Bidwell 1980*, 87.

T42

Inuyama Dōsetsu Tadatomo shujin Orima-uji no kataki isoko no etc. Battle with a burning castle in the distance; Inukai Kempachi and Inumura Daikaku in white coats; Inuyama Dōsetsu and Inudzuka Shino in armour (from the *Hakkenden*). Pub. Idzumi-ya Ichibei; cens. *kiwame*; *c*.1836–7.

MFA; PC.

T43

. . . Etchū . . . Kurikaradani . . . kassen etc. (Title partly cut off the only available copy.) The battle of Kurikaradani (1183) by moonlight: Tomoye-gozen heaving a rock upon foemen clinging to a steep bank (l.), Kiso Yoshinaka grappled with Mikawa no Kami Tomonori (c.), and warriors fighting on a road (r.). Pub. not visible; *c*.1837–8.

MFA.

T44

Minamoto no Raikō jōraku Sagami no kuni Ashigarayama ni etc. Genji Tsuna watches Kwaidō Maru knocking a bear-cub over a precipice; the latter's mother Yama-uba (l.) is also present. Pub. Fujioka-ya Hikotarō; cens. *kiwame*; *c*.1837–8.

VAM; B; PC.

T45

Udaishō Yoritomo-kō Heike tsuitō to shite etc. Reception of Yoshitsune and Noriyori by Yoritomo and his assembled nobles after their victory over the Taira. Pub. Idzumi-ya Ichibei; cens. *kiwame*; *c*.1837–8.

PC.

T46

Minamoto no Yorimitsu no Shitennō tsuchi-gumo taiji no dzu. (Pl.37) Raikō's retainers about to kill the Earth-Spider in the midst of its web. Pub. Maru-ya Seijirō; cens. *kiwame*; *c*.1838.

MFA; PC. An original drawing for the r.h. sheet is in the Kunsthalle, Bremen, No.13/622.

T47

Yoshitsune ichidaiki: Gojō-bashi no dzu. (Pl.40) The moonlight fight between Yoshi-tsune and Benkei on Gojō bridge, Kyoto; Kisanda behind. Pub. Fujioka-ya Hikotarō; cens. *kiwame*; *c*.1839.

BM; VAM; B; Baur; PC. *Apollo*, May 1949, p.126; *Robinson 1961*, Pl.45; *Robinson 1963*, Pl.4; *Bidwell 1968*, Pl.52; *Riccar 1978*, 91; *Bidwell 1980*, 93.

T48

Mitate musha rokkasen. Group of six choice warrior-poets: Gen Sammi Yorimasa, Satsuma no Kami Tadanori, Kenrei-monin, Udaijin Sanetomo, Udaishō Yoritomo, and Kumagaye Renshō-bō (Naozane). Pub. Yamato-ya; *c*.1839–41.

VAM; PC.

T49

Osanashi-dachi buyū soroi. Set of heroic children: a group of the boys of Japanese history with their 'Maru' names and those they bore in later life, thirty-six in all. Pub. Idzumi-ya Ichibei; *c*.1839–41.

MFA; PC.

T50

Morokoshi Shin no Shikōtei chōsei furo no etc. The great ships full of boys and girls sent in search of Hōraizan by the Chinese Emperor Shih Huang Ti (Shikōtei), *c*.219 BC. Pub. Hoso-Sen; *c*.1839–41 (later printing, *c*.1843, cens. Kinugasa).

BM; MFA; PC.

T51

Jingō Kōgō Sankan seibatsu no dzu. The punitive expedition of the Empress Jingō to Korea (traditional date, 200): Takeshiuchi-no-sukune, backed by the Empress and her troops, attacking the Koreans on the sea-shore. Pub. Nuno-Kichi; *c*.1839–41.

PC.

T52

Hachiman-tarō Yoshi-iye: Kōhei nenkan Yoritoki Sadatō no chōteki etc. The captive rebel Abe no Munetō brought before Fujiwara no Mitsuyori by Yoshi-iye (1064). (A later printing has altered banners and other details.) Pub. Takahashi-ya; *c*.1839–41.

VAM; RSM (both versions); PC.

T53

Jōan yo-nen etc. Ushiwaka Maru fighting Chōhan and his gang at the inn; one shining a lantern (1174). Pub. Iba-ya Sensaburō; *c*.1839–41.

RSM; MFA; PC.

T54

(Diptych; no title) Ushiwaka Maru fighting Benkei on Gojō bridge. Pub. Nuno-Kichi; *c*.1839–41.

B; PC. *Riccar 1978*, 94; *Bidwell 1980*, 94.

T55

(Title unknown, if any; only available copy incomplete) Sayemon-no-suke Taira no Shigemori and his troops in a battle in the snow (probably during the troubles of Hōgen, 1156, or Heiji, 1159). Pub. Jōshū-ya Kinzō; *c*.1839–41.

VAM.

T56

Jishō yo-nen Minamoto no Yoritomo-kō gihei wo age Sunshū etc. The interview between the brothers Yoritomo and Yoshitsune at the base of Mount Fuji (1180). Pub. Iba-ya Sensaburō; *c*.1839–41.

VAM; PC.

T57

Sumidagawa batto no dzu. Yoritomo and his troops crossing the Sumida river on rafts (August 1180). Pub. Idzumi-ya Ichibei; *c*.1839–41.

B; PC.

T58

Gempei seisuiki: Suruga no kuni Fujikawa kassen. At the battle of Fujikawa, a flight of wild geese warns the Minamoto of a Taira ambush (10 November 1180). Pub. Jōshū-ya Kinzō; *c*.1839–41.

VAM; RSM; B; PC.

T59

Gempei seisuiki: Awa no kuni Katsu-ura kassen. The battle of Katsu-ura in the province of Awa: Yoshitsune and his troops marching along the shore to attack the castle of Yoshitō (20 March 1185). Pub. Jōshū-ya Kinzō; cens. *kiwame*; *c*.1839–41.

VAM; B; PC.

T60

Gempei seisuiki: Kaga no kuni Ataka kassen. The battle of Ataka in the province of Kaga, with Tomoye-gozen and Yamabuki, the warrior-mistress and wife respectively of Yoshinaka, attacking the Taira under Kagekiyo (1183). Pub. Jōshū-ya Kinzō; cens. *kiwame*; *c*.1839–41.

VAM; RSM; PC.

T61

Gempei Hokuyetsu ō-kassen. The great battle between Yoshinaka and the Taira in northern Echizen province. Jō Shirō Nagamochi, the amazon Hangaku, and Jō Kurō Sukemori are among those engaged. Pub. Tsuru-ya Ki-yemon; cens. *kiwame*; *c*.1839–41.

PC.

T62

Ujigawa ō-kassen. The battle of the Uji river (5 March 1184): Takatsuna about to land, followed by Kagesuye and the main body still in mid-stream; broken bridge in the background. Pub. Yezaki-ya Tatsuzō; cens. *kiwame*; *c*.1839–41.

VAM; PC.

T63

Awadzu-ga-hara ō-kassen: Yoshinaka Shitennō Imai Shirō Kanehira etc. Prowess

of Imai Kanehira at the battle of Awadzu (March 1184); he is shown fighting under the pine-tree of Karasaki on the shore of Lake Biwa; Yoshitsune (l.). Pub. Sōshū-ya Yohei; *c.*1839–41.
PC.

T64
Washi-no-o no Saburō Ichi-no-tani Hiyodori-goye no annaisha to naru dzu. Washio Saburō struggling with a black bear, watched by Yoshitsune and his retainers (21 March 1184). Pub. Maru-ya Seijirō; cens. *kiwame*; *c.*1839–41.
VAM; B; PC. *Riccar 1978,* 92.

T65
Yoshitsune no gumpei Ichi-no-tani saka-otoshi no dzu. Yoshitsune leading his men in the descent of the Hiyodori-goye defile at the battle of Ichi-no-tani (21 March 1184). Pub. Kawaguchi-ya Uhei; cens. *kiwame*; *c.*1839–41.
MFA; PC.

T66
Banshū Suma-ga-mori no sakura ni Yoshi-tsune kōsatsu wo tatsuru dzu. Yoshitsune and his suite under the cherry-trees of Suma receiving Naozane with the head of Atsumori in a box (21 March 1184) after the battle of Ichi-no-tani. Pub. Kaga-ya Kichibei; cens. *kiwame*; *c.*1839–41.
RSM; PC.

T67
Minamoto no Yoshitsune Kajiwara sakaro sōron no dzu. The quarrel between Yoshitsune and Kajiwara Kagetoki about 'reversed oars' (*sakaro*) before the battle of Yashima (23 March 1184). Pub. Arita-ya Seiyemon; cens. *kiwame*; *c.*1839–41. (See *Heike,* p.647.)
VAM; RSM; PC.

T68
Gempei Yashima ō-kassen. The great battle of Yashima (23 March 1184): Yoshitsune's 'eight boat leap' (c.), Noritsune (l.), Benkei on a large boat, and Munemori clinging to a piece of floating wood (r.). Pub. Kawaguchi-ya Uhei; cens. *kiwame*; *c.*1839–41.
MFA; PC.

T69
Nagato no kuni Akama-ga-ura Gempei ō-kassen. The great battle of Akama-ga-ura (usually known as Dan-no-ura): Yoshitsune performing his 'eight boat leap' pursued by Noritsune (there seems to have been some uncertainty whether this occurred at Yashima or Dan-no-ura), and Moritsugu laying about him. Pub. Kawaguchi-ya Chōzō; *c.*1839–41.
RSM; PC.

T70
Sesshū Daimotsu-no-ura ni Heike no onryō

arawaruru no dzu. The ghosts of the Taira attacking Yoshitsune's ship in Daimotsu bay in the province of Settsu (28 November 1185). Pub. Nuno-Kichi; *c.*1839–41.
BM; VAM; PC. *Takagi,* 6; *Kruml,* 22.41; *Kennedy,* 1980.86.

T71
Udaishō Yoritomo-kō Susono maki-gari seisen dzu. Yoritomo's hunting-party assembling on Suso moor under Mount Fuji (1193). Pub. Arita-ya Seijirō; cens. *kiwame*; *c.*1839–41.
PC.

T72
Kenkyū yo-nen Minamoto no Yoritomo Fuji maki-gari no dzu. (Pl.46) *Chōban* format. Tadatsune about to receive the charge of the monstrous boar, watched by Yoritomo and his suite (1193). Pub. Mori-ya Jihei; *c.*1839–41.
PC.

T73
Yoritomo-kō Fuji no mi-kari no dzu. Yoritomo and his suite watching Tadatsune killing the monstrous wild boar. Pub. Sano-ya Kihei; *c.*1839–41.
VAM; PC.

T74
Udaishō Yoritomo-kō sumō go-ran no dzu. The great wrestling-match before Yoritomo and his son Sanetomo: Chōkyō wrestling with Chikatsune, umpired by Ogata Saburō Masa-yoshi. Pub. Fujioka-ya Hikotarō; *c.*1839–41.
MFA; PC.

T75
(No title) Yegara Heita Tanenaga, having been swallowed by a giant python, cuts his way out, while Idzumi Kojirō Chikahira and Wada Kojirō Yoshishige control the monster. Pub. Jōshū-ya Kinzō; *c.*1839–41.
VAM.

T76
Taiheiki Tenryūgawa no ukihashi no dzu. Nitta Yoshisada and Funada Nyūdō together leaping the gap in the broken bridge across the Tenryūgawa (1335). The text is by Kuniyoshi himself. See *Bertin,* p.259. Pub. Yezaki-ya Tatsuzō; cens. *kiwame*; *c.*1839–41.
RSM; PC.

T77
Miidera kassen: Nitta no Shitennō etc. A charge led by Wakiya Uyemon-no-suke Yoshisuke at the battle of Miidera; he was the younger brother of Nitta Yoshisada. Pub. Sōshū-ya Yohei; cens. *kiwame*; *c.*1839–41.
VAM; PC.

T78
Nitta Sachūjō Yoshisada jūroku-gi no yeiyū to tomo ni etc. (Pl.44) Nitta Yoshisada and his

little band of heroes on the shore awaiting the host of Ashikaga Taka-uji, whose ships are seen approaching in the mist; this was just before the battle of the Minatogawa (1336). Pub. Jōshū-ya Kinzō; cens. *kiwame*; *c.*1839–41.
VAM; RSM; PC.

T79
Kusunoki Masatsura kyōgun mi hatsukō wo mite etc. Kusunoki Masatsura, on a hillock surrounded by his staff, watches the massing of the Ashikaga troops under the opposing cliff. Pub. Sano-ya Kihei; cens. *kiwame*; *c.*1839–41.
BM; RSM; MFA; PC.

T80
Ryakuō nen-chū Yenya Hangwan keshi shi-jūshichi ki etc. Night-attack of the Forty-Seven *Rōnin*: the fight in Moronao's garden, crossed by a long wooden gallery. Pub. Sano-ya Kihei; *c.*1839–41.
B; PC.

T81
Chūshingura shijūshichi-nin: gishi shōkō no dzu. The Forty-Seven *Rōnin,* having accomplished their revenge, burning incense before the tomb of their master Yenya Hangwan. Pub. Maru-ya Jimpachi; cens. *kiwame*; *c.*1839–41.
B; PC.

T82
Kwanzeon no reigen: hitotsuya no furu-koto rōba no sekiaku etc. The Hag of Adachi-ga-hara in the Lonely House (*hitotsuya*) with her girl-victim, and the apparition of Kwannon. Pub. Minato-ya Kohei; *c.*1839–41.
VAM; RSM; MFA; B; PC; Museum voor Volkenkunde, Leyden.

T83
Heishōgoku Nyūdō wa Go-Shirakawa-tei no otoshigo nite etc. (Pl.41) Kiyomori at Miyaji-ma arresting the sunset by incantations, so that work could proceed on his new buildings. Pub. Tsuji-ya Yasubei; cens. Taka; *c.*1842–3.
VAM; RSM; MFA; PC.

T84
Minamoto no Yoshitsune Ichi-no-tani chōjō jin soroi dzu. Yoshitsune and his men looking down on the Taira position at Ichi-no-tani from the precipice of Hiyodori-goye. Pub. Idzumi-ya Ichibei; cens. Fukatsu (large oblong seal); *c.*1842–3.
PC.

T85
Ushiwaka Maru Ōshū gekō no toki etc. Ushiwaka outside the house of Jōruri-hime serenading her on his flute, which she accompanies within on her *koto.* Pub. Jōshū-ya Kinzō; cens. Fu; *c.*1842–3.
VAM; RSM; PC.

T86

Yoritomo-kō Tsuru-ga-oka no shinzen ni oite Shidzuka-gozen no mai wo miru no dzu. Shidzuka-gozen dancing as a *shirabyōshi* before Yoritomo and his assembled nobles at Tsuru-ga-oka. Pub. Kawaguchi-ya Chōzō; cens. Fu; c. 1842–3.
RSM; PC.

T87

Kamakura sei Ōshū shimpatsu no dzu. Yoritomo and his men marching north to Mutsu in 1189. Pub. Jōshū-ya Kinzō; cens. Fu; c. 1842–3.
PC.

T88

Yoritomo hata-age kassen Yamaki Hangwan ga tachi ni yo-uchi no dzu. The battle of the setting-up of Yoritomo's standard: his night-attack on the palace of Yamaki Hangwan Kanetaka (9 September 1180). Pub. Kawaguchi-ya Uhei; cens. Tanaka; c. 1842–3.
PC.

T89

Shōgun Tarō Yoshikado mikata wo atsumen ga tame etc. The magic toads watched by Yoshikado (c.), his sister Takiyasha (l.), Iga Jutarō (r.) and their followers. Pub. Tsuru-ya Kiyemon; cens. Mura; c. 1842–3.
VAM; RSM; MFA; PC.

T90

Kwaidō Maru yeboshi gi no dzu. Kwaidō Maru being prepared by ladies to assume the formal dress of manhood. Pub. Takahashi-ya; cens. Mura; c. 1842–3.
VAM; MFA.

T91

Higo no kuni mononofu Aso no Saburō Taira no Tadakuni ga musume Shiranui etc. Girls throwing branches of cherry-blossom at Tametomo at the time of his betrothal to Shiranui, daughter of Aso Tadakuni of Higo. Pub. Iba-ya Sensaburō; cens. Mura; c. 1842–3.
VAM; RSM; PC.

T92

Chinzei Hachirō Tametomo Oniyasha wo annai to shite etc. Tametomo and his followers in their ship, with Oniyasha at the prow. Pub. Nuno-Kichi; cens. Mura; c. 1842–3.
RSM; PC.

T93

Minamoto no Yoshitsune Ōshū gekō Hiraidzumi tachi ni Hidehira no oyako ni taimen no dzu. Formal reception of Yoshitsune and his men by Hidehira at his castle of Hiraidzumi in the province of Mutsu. Pub. Nuno-Kichi; cens. Mura; c. 1842–3.
VAM; RSM; B; PC.

T94

Jishō yo-nen hachi-gwatsu nijūni-nichi yo Gempei Ishibashiyama etc. The battle of Ishibashiyama (14 September 1180), with the single combat of Sanada Yoshisada and Matano Kagehisa on a rock (r.), Takatsuna fighting against odds (c.), and Yoritomo shooting (l.). Pub. Iba-ya Sensaburō; cens. Mura; c. 1842–3.
PC.

T95

Kiso Yoshinaka no omoimono Tomoye-gozen to iu shita etc. Tomoye-gozen pulling the ear of Nagase Hangwan in the presence of Tedzuka Tarō Mitsumori, Yoshinaka, and Yamabuki-gozen. Pub. Yebi-Ne; cens. Mura; c. 1842–3.
MFA; PC.

T96

Bunji gen-nen san-gwatsu Antoku-tei Heike no hito mi ni etc. Mitsutoki reporting to Tomomori at the battle of Dan-no-ura (25 April 1185) in the presence of Dainagon Tenji, Nii no Ama, Kenrei-monin, Go-Tenji, and the boy-Emperor Antoku. Pub. Yamaguchi-ya Tōbei; cens. Mura; c. 1842–3.
VAM; PC.

T97

Go-Shirakawa no Hō-ō no Horikawa no gosho wo ba etc. Benkei (blowing a conch), Shidzuka-gozen, and Yoshitsune preparing to meet Tosa-bō Shōshun's attack on the Horikawa palace. Pub. Taka-Ji; cens. Mura; c. 1842–3.
RSM; PC. *Takagi,* 8.

T98

Minamoto no Yoritomo Daibutsu kuyō no dzu. The attempted arrest of Kagekiyo in the precincts of the Tōdaiji temple (April 1195). Landscape background and background figures by Hiroshige. Pub. Yoshimi-ya Sonokichi; cens. Mura; eng. Renkichi; c. 1842–3.
VAM; B; PC.

T99

Yoritomo-kō mikari no dzu. Tadatsune killing the monstrous wild boar, watched by Yoritomo and his suite. Pub. unidentified; cens. Mura; eng. Renkichi; c. 1842–3.
PC.

T100

Soga no Hako-ō Maru wa haha etc. Hako-ō Maru (Soga Gorō) before Kudō Suketsune, with noblemen in attendance. Pub. Koga-ya Katsugorō; cens. Mura; c. 1842–3.
VAM; PC.

T101

Wada Yoshimori ichimon kujūsan-gi Ōiso ni oite etc. Soga Gorō outside the *shōji*, while the great feast given by Wada Yoshimori at Ōiso proceeds within. Pub. Takahashi-ya; cens. Mura; c. 1842–3.
VAM; RSM; PC.

T102

Soga monogatari: sono toki Tokimune ōi-ni ikari kobushi wo etc. Asahina Saburō (c.) knocks down Yawata Shichirō (l.), watched by the Soga brothers (r.). Figures on plain background. Pub. Yebi-ya Rinnosuke; cens. Mura; c. 1842–3.
RSM; PC.

T103/T104

(Double triptych) R.h. half: *Soga Tokimune hon-i wo* etc. Soga Gorō fighting his way towards Yoritomo, who sits surrounded by his suite. L.h. half: *Soga yo-uchi no dzu.* Soga Jurō engaged by Nitta Shirō Tadatsune. The whole scene in pouring rain. Pub. Sakurai; cens. (r.h.) Watari, (l.h.) Mura; c. 1842–3.
RSM (l.h. only); B; PC.

T105

Kusunoki Masatsura Nagaragawa no funabashi wo kitte Ashikaga etc. (Pl.48) The battle of the Nagaragawa (1347), with Masatsura's troops crossing a bridge of boats. Pub. Iba-ya Sensaburō; cens. Mura; c. 1842–3.
VAM; RSM; MFA; B; PC.

T106

Iga Kōdzuke ada-uchi. The Igagoye revenge (*Mitford,* 'Kazuma's Revenge'): Shidzuma engaging Matagorō (r. and c.), while Masayemon fights against odds (l.). Pub. Yezaki-ya Tatsuzō; cens. Mura; c. 1842–3.
B; PC.

T107

Nijō-in no toki etc. Gen Sammi Yorimasa standing with his bow (r.), his wife Ayame-no-maye seated (c.), and his squire Ii no Hayata Tadazumi (l.) also seated. Figures on plain background. Pub. Iba-ya Sensaburō; cens. Watari; eng. Matsushima Fusajirō; c. 1842–3.
RSM; Berlin, Museum für Ostasiatische Kunst.

T108

Minamoto no Ushiwaka Maru Yahagi no chōja ga moto tachiyori tamau dzu. (Pl.45) Ushiwaka and Kisanda being summoned by one of Jōruri-hime's maids (large half-length figures); Jōruri herself plays the *koto* in the house behind. Pub. Iba-ya Kyūbei; cens. Watari; eng. Renkichi; c. 1842–3.
PC.

T109

Gempei seisuiki: Sanshū Yashima kassen. The battle of Yashima in the province of Sanuki (23 March 1184): Kagekiyo chasing Kunitoshi along the shore, while Tsuginobu, shielding Yoshitsune, is shot by Noritsune from his boat. Pub. Jōshū-ya Jūzō; cens. Watari; c. 1842–3.
VAM; PC.

T110

Saimyōji Tokiyori Nyūdō shokoku shugyō no etc. Tokiyori, the Hōjō regent, in monk's habit, at the house of Tsuneyo in the snow; the latter's daughter Shirataye cuts the dwarf trees (*bonsai*) to make a fire. Pub. Sakurai; cens. Watari; c.1842–3.

B; PC.

T111

Taira no Masakado isshi Shōgun Tarō Yoshikado etc. Iga Jutarō (l.), Yoshikado (c.), and his sister Takiyasha (r.) with their gang in the old temple where they lived. Pub. Minato-ya Kohei; cens. Hama; c.1842–3.

RSM; PC.

T111a

Yoshi-iye Mikawa Zenji ga musume ni etc. Hachiman-tarō Yoshi-iye cuts off the corner of a *go*-board with his sword, while Nareginu, daughter of Mikawa Zenji, holds up a lantern, and Abe no Munetō stands glowering outside. Pub. Fujioka-ya Hikotarō; cens. Hama; c.1842–3.

PC.

T112

Konoye-no-in no gyo-u Nimpyō san-nen etc. Yorimasa shooting down the *Nuye* from above the palace of the Emperor Konoye (1153). Pub. Sōshū-ya Yohei; cens. Hama; c.1842–3.

B; PC. *UT*, 174/176; *Riccar 1978*, 97; *Bidwell 1980*, 109.

T113

Chinzei Hachirō Tametomo Idzu no Ōshima nite etc. Tametomo (l.) sinking the foremost ship of Mochimitsu's fleet with a single arrow; his mistress Sasaraye and his henchman Oniyasha, armed with a *naginata* and an iron club respectively, and the rough islanders look on in admiration. Pub. Tsujioka-ya Yasubei; cens. Hama; c.1842–3. (See also T140.)

RSM; PC.

T114

Minamoto no Yoritomo-kō shoshō wo atsume etc. Yoritomo presiding at a war-council of all his chief followers. Pub. Kadzusa-ya Iwazō; cens. Hama; c.1842–3.

RSM; PC.

T115

Minamoto no Yoritomo Sumidagawa hata-age chakutō seizoroye no dzu. Presentation of a *naginata* to Hatakeyama Shigetada by Hōjō Tokimasa before Yoritomo on the banks of the Sumida river (1180); many warriors in attendance. Pub. Tsuta-ya Kichizō; cens. Hama; c.1842–3.

RSM; PC.

T116

Kiso Kwanja Yoshinaka Heike wo horobasan to ichizoku etc. Yoshinaka's farewell parade on going to war with the Taira (1180); Tomoye-gozen rides off (l.). Pub. Kagi-ya Hanjirō; cens. Hama; c.1842–3. (Cf. T244.)

B; PC.

T117

Minamoto no Yoshitsune Heike wo horoboshite nochi etc. The composition of Yoshitsune's plea to his brother Yoritomo (the text of which occupies the upper part of the print) after his victory over the Taira (3 July 1185). Pub. To-Sawa; cens. Hama; c.1842–3.

VAM; B; PC.

T118

Udaishō Yoritomo-kō Tsuru-ga-oka Hachi-man-gū ye hōraku no tame etc. Yoritomo releasing 1,000 cranes (a pious Buddhist practice) on the shore at Tsuru-ga-oka. Pub. Sano-Ichi; cens. Hama; c.1842–3.

MFA; PC; Berlin, Museum für Ostasiatische Kunst.

T119

Minamoto no Yori-iye-kō Kamakura Kotsubo no umi-yūran Asahina etc. Asahina Yoshihide's fight with two crocodiles in the sea off Kamakura, watched by the Shōgun Yori-iye and his nobles in boats. Pub. Sōshū-ya Yohei; cens. Hama; c.1842–3.

RSM; PC.

T120

Dainagon Suketomo-kō no soku Chūnagon Suketoshi-kō etc. Kumawaka Maru, son of Dainagon Suketomo, and the wife of Shino-dzuka Iga no Kami outside a house in the snow. Pub. Fujioka-ya Keijirō; cens. Hama; c.1842–3.

RSM; B; PC.

T121

Hyōgo no omote ō-kassen no dzu. Encounter of the troops of Kusunoki Masashige and the Ashikaga in mid-stream (1336). Pub. Jōshū-ya Jūzō; cens. Hama; c.1842–3.

VAM; PC.

T122

Genke shotō sofu koden. An illustrated family tree of the main line of the Minamoto clan from Sadazumi Shinnō (874–916), son of the Emperor Seiwa, to Yoshitsune. Pub. Idzumi-ya Ichibei; cens. Muramatsu; c.1842–3.

PC.

T123

Gempei seisuiki: Idzu no kuni Yamaki kassen. Yoritomo's attack on the Yamaki palace at night takes Kanetaka and his retainers by surprise (1180). Pub. Jōshū-ya Kinzō; cens. Muramatsu; c.1842–3. (See Catalogue illustration to S18.)

PC. Preliminary sketches for this triptych are reproduced in F. E. Loewenstein, *Die Handzeichnungen der japanischen Holzschnittmeister*, Plauen im Vogtland, 1922.

T124

Ōshū Takadachi kassen Yoshitsune etc. Yoshitsune leading a sortie from the castle of Takadachi over the moat bridge; Benkei laying about him (c.) (1189). Pub. Ki-ya Sōjirō; cens. Muramatsu; c.1842–3.

MFA; PC.

T125

(No title) (Fig.24) The Soga brothers with Tegoshi no Shōshō in the rain outside the tent of Kudō Suketsune. Large figures. Pub. Jō-Yasu; cens. Muramatsu; c.1842–3.

PC.

T126

Kaga no kuni Ataka no shin-seki nite Yoshitsune shūjū etc. Benkei reading his scroll (*kwanjinchō*) to Togashi Sayemon at the Ataka Barrier, he and his party dressed as monks. Pub. Yeshima; cens. Yoshimura; c.1842–3.

B; PC.

T127

Yoshinoyama nite Yoshitsune shūjū etc. The parting of Shidzuka-gozen from Yoshitsune and his followers among the snows of Mount Yoshino. Pub. Kadzusa-ya Iwazō; cens. Mera; c.1842–3.

B.

T128

Minamoto no Yorimitsu-kō no tachi ni tsuchi-gumo yōkwai nasu no dzu. The Earth-Spider and his troop of demons tormenting the sick Raikō (Yorimitsu), while the latter's retainers play at *go*. This is the print that got Kuniyoshi into trouble with the authorities (see *Robinson 1961*, p.14). Pub. Iba-ya Sensaburō; no cens.; 1843.

VAM; RSM; B; PC. (B also has an original coloured drawing of it; *Bidwell 1968*, Pl.138.) *Takagi*, 5; *Robinson 1961*, Pl.42; *Speiser*, p.79; *UT*, 76; *Riccar 1978*, 278; *Bidwell 1980*, 137.

T129

Koromo no Toji ga musume nite Wataru ga tsuma etc. Yendō Musha Moritō approaching Kesa-gozen over the roof with a drawn sword; in the background (l.) a servant about to adjust the sandal of Watanabe Wataru, her husband. Pub. Murata-ya Ichibei; cens. Tanaka; c.1844.

PC.

T130

Gompachi wa Inshū no kin nari etc. Shirai Gompachi fighting off a gang of roughs on the shore, one of whom he has thrown into a fire, watched by Banzui Chōbei. This seems to be an illustration of a stage production, with Ichimura Uzayemon XII as Gompachi, and Ichikawa Danjurō VIII as Chōbei, but it has not been possible to trace it. Pub. Ise-ya Kisuke; cens. Fu; c.1844.

VAM; PC.

T131

Hikosan ada-uchi no dzu. Kyōgoku Takumi engaged by O-Sono and O-Sada, daughter and widow respectively of Yoshioka Ichimisai, watched by Keyamura Rokusuke and a nobleman with his retainers. Large figures, plain ground. Pub. Yamaguchi-ya Tōbei; cens. Fu; *c.*1844.

PC.

T132

(No title) The Soga brothers standing over the sleeping Kudō Suketsune; Tegoshi no Shōshō on the right (1193). Pub. Chita-ya; cens. Fu; *c.*1844.

RSM; PC.

T133

Yoshitsune ichidaiki no uchi: Minamoto no Yoshitsune-kō Yoshino-yama no naka ni etc. (Pl.50) Yoshitsune, his wife Kita-no-kata (Kyō-no-kimi), and Benkei in the snows of Mount Yoshino (1186). Large half-length figures. Pub. Sen; cens. Mura; *c.*1844.

PC.

T134

Heike no ichimon horobite hōken wa saikai ni etc. Yoshitsune, Benkei, and Yoshimori listening to the report of two *ama*, mother and daughter, named Oimatsu and Wakamatsu, who had tried to recover the sacred Sword of the regalia from the sea-bottom after the battle of Dan-no-ura (1185). Pub. Tsujioka-ya Bunsuke; cens. Mura; *c.*1844.

VAM.

T135

Horikawa yo-uchi: Tosa-bō Shōshun toyose no dzu. Benkei, Shidzuka-gozen, and Yoshitsune preparing to meet the attack of Tosa-bō Shōshun on the Horikawa palace (10 November 1185). Large half-length figures. Pub. Iba-ya Kyūbei; cens. Mura; eng. Renkichi; *c.*1844.

VAM; RSM; PC. *Düsseldorf 1961*, 20; *Kruml*, 12.49; 21.60.

T136

Takeda Shingen Uyesugi Kenshin to gogwatsu jūgo-nichi ryōshō etc. Kenshin and Shingen face each other across the river to discuss peace terms during the Kawanakajima campaign (1553–63). Pub. Sano-ya Kihei; cens. Mura; *c.*1844.

RSM; MFA; PC.

T137

Rokusuke wa Buzen no kuni Hikosan no fumoto Keyamura no domin etc. O-Sono fighting her father's murderer, Kyōgoku Takumi, by a river; Keyamura Rokusuke coming to her assistance. Pub. Fujioka-ya Keijirō; cens. Watari; *c.*1844.

VAM.

T138

Sōma no furu-dairi ni Masakado no himegimi Takiyasha etc. (Pl.52) The witch Takiyasha, daughter of Taira no Masakado, calling up a monstrous skeleton-spectre to frighten Mitsukuni. Pub. Hachi; cens. Watari; *c.*1844.

BM; VAM; RSM; MFA; Baur; PC. *Takagi*, 14; *Robinson 1961*, Pl.43; *Crighton*, V65; *UT*, 36/38; *Riccar 1978*, 100; *Geneva 1978*, 60; *Illing 1978*, 2, 3; *Kruml*, 9.46.

T139

Taira no Kiyomori-kō wa sono sembushin yori idete etc. The dying Kiyomori in his last feverish sickness surrounded by Taira nobles and ladies (20 March 1181). Pub. Sugi-ya Seibei; cens. Hama; *c.*1844.

VAM; PC.

T140

Tametomo wa Seiwa-tei hasse no son etc. (Pl.47) Reprint of T113 with altered title. Pub. Ōmi-ya Suke . . .; cens. Hama; *c.*1844.

B; PC. *Geneva 1978*, 65.

T141

Somoku honchō sumai no okori-hara wa etc. Kawadzu Saburō Sukeyasu and Matano Gorō Kagehisa wrestling before Yoritomo, umpired by Sanada Yoichi Yoshitada (*c.*1170). Pub. To-Sawa; cens. Hama; *c.*1844.

MFA; B; PC.

T142

Nitta Sachūjō Yoshisada Kamakura etc. Nitta Yoshisada throwing his sword into the sea as an offering to the sea-gods to enable him to attack the Hōjō in Kamakura (1333). Pub. Yezaki-ya Tatsuzō; cens. Yoshimura; *c.*1844.

VAM; RSM; B; PC. *Bidwell 1968*, Pl.113.

T143

Kennin san-nen Minamoto no Yori-iye-kyō Fuji-no mi-kari no etc. (Pl.53) Nitta Tadatsune encounters the goddess of Mount Fuji and her dragon in a cave in the mountain, in which are stalactites and a waterfall (1203). Pub. Tsuji-ya Yasubei; cens. Yoshimura; *c.*1844.

B; PC. *Riccar 1978*, 102; *Bidwell 1980*, 132.

T144

Dan-no-ura tatakai no dzu. (Pl.49) The end of the battle of Dan-no-ura (25 April 1185): Tomomori, the great anchor tied about him, about to cast himself into the sea, flanked by his retainer Sagami Gorō and his mistress Tenji-no-tsubone. Pub. Koga-ya Katsugorō; cens. Yoshimura; *c.*1844.

BM; VAM; RSM; MFA; B; PC. *Takagi*, 10; *Or.Art*, Spring 1961, p.27; *Bidwell 1968*, Pl.134; *Geneva 1978*, 73.

T145

Nin-ō jūgo-dai Jingō Kōgō Sankan seibatsu

Takenouchi etc. (Pl.55) Under the direction of Takeshiuchi-no-sukune Japanese troops lever an enormous rock over a precipice above a Korean city. Pub. Yamashiro-ya Heisuke(?); cens. Fu; eng. Kōkō Iwa; *c.*1845.

RSM; PC. *Kruml*, 22.52.

T146

Kiso Yoshinaka Hokkoku ni hei wo agete Miyako ye etc. The battle of Kurikaradani (2 June 1183): Kagekiyo, Tomoye-gozen, and Yoshinaka struggling with Tomonori; behind, the Taira troops falling over the cliff. Pub. Kagi-ya Hanjirō; cens. Fu; *c.*1845.

VAM; B; PC.

T147

Daimotsu-no-ura Yoshitsune shūjū etc. (Fig.12) The Taira ghosts rising from the sea to attack Yoshitsune's ship. Pub. Kiyomidzu-ya; cens. Fu; *c.*1845.

PC. *Robinson 1963*, Pl.16.

T148

Chū-kō-gi-yū: oji no ada-uchi. Yasubei's revenge on Murakami Shōyemon and his men for the death of his uncle, watched by his mother and sister. Pub. Ise-ya Ichibei; cens. Fu; *c.*1845.

VAM; RSM; PC.

T149

Ushiwaka Maru Ōshū no kin-akibito to tomo ni gekō no etc. Ushiwaka Maru, travelling to Mutsu with Kichiji the gold-merchant, has his sandals removed at the inn where he was later attacked by Chōhan and his gang. Pub. Sumiyoshi-ya Masagorō; cens. Mura; 1842–3.

VAM; PC.

T150

Benkei ga yūriki tawamure ni Miidera no tsurigane wo etc. Benkei dragging off the great bell of Miidera, watched by Yoshitsune in the background. Pub. Iba-ya Sensaburō; cens. Mura; *c.*1845.

BM; VAM; B; PC. *Takagi*, 13; *Riccar 1978*, 101; *Bidwell 1980*, 145; *Kruml*, 18.24.

T151

Yoshitsune no jūku-shin. Group of Yoshitsune and his nineteen chief retainers, their names written large above. Pub. Nuno-Kichi; cens. Mura; *c.*1845.

VAM; RSM; PC.

T152

Heike no ichimon ikusa kado-ide no shuyen Tomomori etc. The great feast of the Taira before going to war, with Tomomori dancing. Pub. Yezaki-ya Tatsuzō; cens. Mura; *c.*1845.

RSM; PC.

T153

Ikuta-no-mori oite Gempei ō-kassen etc. (Fig.19) Kajiwara Kagesuye in the forest of

Ikuta, having lost his helmet, defends himself against several Taira warriors under an old plum-tree; in the background his father Kagetoki rides to his assistance (*Heike*, p.549). Pub. Yamaguchi-ya Tōbei; cens. Mura; *c*.1845.
    PC.

T154

Kawanakajima ō-kassen: Kenshin no kuruma-gakari wo mite etc. Kansuke reporting Kenshin's movements to Shingen, surrounded by his staff on the river-bank. Pub. Sano-ya Kihei; cens. Mura; *c*.1845.
    RSM; PC.

T155

Taira no Kiyomori Yoshitomo wo horobosu sono shō Tokiwa wakagimi wo etc. Tokiwa-gozen and her children brought before Kiyomori (who may be intended for Nakamura Utayemon IV in *Gempei Soga*, produced at the Nakamura theatre at the beginning of 1845). Pub. Yebi-Ne; cens. Watari; *c*.1845.
    VAM; PC.

T156

Sesshū Ichi-no-tani Gempei kassen no dzu. The fight on the sea-shore at Ichi-no-tani, with the Taira fleet out in the bay (21 March 1184). Pub. Hachi; cens. Watari; *c*.1845.
    RSM; PC.

T157

Kenkyū gwan-nen Udaishō Yoritomo shōraku no go Nanto Tōdaiji etc. The attempted arrest of Kagekiyo in the courtyard of the Tōdaiji temple at Nara. Pub. Hayashi-ya Shōgorō; cens. Watari; *c*.1845 (also a reprint with date-seal Horse 7, 1858).
    VAM; RSM; PC.

T158

Kenkyū yo-nen go-gwatsu Minamoto no Yoritomo-kō Fuji no Susono nite etc. Soga Jurō dancing before Kudō Suketsune (1193). Pub. Yebi-ya Rinnosuke; cens. Watari; *c*.1845.
    PC.

T159

Fuji Susono Soga kyōdai hommō wo togeru dzu. The Soga brothers' last fight (1193): Gorō fighting against odds (c.), Jurō about to be killed by Tadatsune (r.), and Gorō Maru emerging from the tent-enclosure (l.); pouring rain. Pub. Yamaguchi-ya Tōbei; cens. Watari; *c*.1845.
    BM; RSM; B; PC. *Robinson 1961*, Pl.44.

T160

Takeda Uyesugi Kawanakajima ō-kassen no dzu. An adaptation of T25, Nagamochi and Tayū-bō becoming Uyesugi Kenshin and Takeda Shingen respectively; the r.h. sheet blocks recut to eliminate Tomoye-gozen, and the signature also recut. Pub. Yamamoto-ya

Heikichi; cens. Watari; *c*.1845.
    MFA; Museum voor Volkenkunde, Leyden.

T161/T162

(Double triptych) R.h. half: *Yamamoto Kansuke Haruyuki Nyūdō Dōkisai uchijini no dzu.* Yamamoto Kansuke riding to his death through the Uyesugi troops at Kawanakajima. L.h. half: *Kawanakajima Shingen Kenshin hatamoto ō-kassen no dzu.* The irruption of Kenshin into Shingen's camp-enclosure. Pub. Kawaguchi-ya Uhei; cens. (r.h.) Muramatsu, (l.h.) Watari; *c*.1845.
    VAM; B; PC.

T163

Nagato no kuni Akama-no-ura ni oite Gempei ō-kassen etc. The battle of Dan-no-ura (25 April 1185): Yoshitsune's leap (l.) (often associated with the battle of Yashima), the Imperial barge (c.), and other boats engaged (r.). Pub. Yenshū-ya Matabei; cens. Muramatsu; *c*.1845.
    VAM; PC.

T164

Minamoto no Yoshitsune rotō wo insotsu shite etc. Benkei beating Yoshitsune before Togashi at the Ataka Barrier; Kyō-no-kimi protesting. Pub. Man-Kyū; cens. Muramatsu; *c*.1845.
    PC.

T165

Shinshū Kawanakajima ō-kassen no dzu. Encounter of Shingen and Kenshin on the river-bank at Kawanakajima: Kenshin on a rearing horse raises his sword; Shingen prepares to receive the blow on his war-fan. Pub. Idzumi-ya Ichibei; cens. Muramatsu; *c*.1845.
    VAM; RSM; MFA; PC. (A preliminary sketch is in the Leyden Museum voor Volkenkunde; see *Lieftinck*, No.27.) *Düsseldorf 1961*, 23.

T166

Sōma ni Tarō Yoshikado wa chichi no metsubō no toki tōsai etc. (Pl.51) The Toad Spirit (here called Gama Sennin) instructing Yoshikado and his sister Takiyasha in magic by causing a woman to materialize on his breath. Pub. Yezaki-ya Tatsuzō; cens. Hama; *c*.1845.
    B; PC. *Riccar 1978*, 99; *Bidwell 1980*, 121.

T167

Yoshitsune Ōshū-ye gekō shite Koromogawa no tachi etc. Fujinoye, seated reading, approached by Yoshitsune; her husband Tadahira behind. Pub. Jōshū-ya Kinzō; cens. Hama; *c*.1845.
    VAM.

T168

Satō Shirō Tadanobu Horikawa no tachi wo ochiru etc. Satō Tadanobu standing at bay before his attackers, the *go*-board overturned.

Pub. Yezaki-ya Tatsuzō; cens. Hama; *c*.1845.
    VAM; PC.

T169

Minamoto no Yorimitsu Ason Tamba no kuni Ichihara-no etc. The ambush of Kidō Maru discovered by the retainers of Raikō (Yorimitsu) on Ichihara moor in the province of Tamba. Pub. Han; cens. Yoshimura; *c*.1845.
    PC.

T170

Yoshioka Ichimisai no musume chichi no ada etc. The daughters of Yoshioka Ichimisai, backed by Keyamura Rokusuke, fighting Kyōgoku Takumi, their father's murderer. Pub. Sawa-ya Kōkichi; cens. Kinugasa; *c*.1845.
    VAM; RSM.

T171

(No title) (Pl.54) Oniwaka Maru about to leap into the river to attack the monstrous carp that had swallowed his mother. Pub. Mino-ya Chūsuke; cens. Mera; *c*.1845.
    VAM; RSM; B; PC. *Takagi*, 9; *Apollo*, January 1949, p.4; *Riccar 1978*, 98; *Bidwell 1980*, 122; *Ronin*, 73.

T172

Gi-yū-kō-shin-yei-yū soroi. O-Seki watching a trial of strength between the two wrestlers Nuregami Chōgorō and Hanaregoma Chōkichi. Pub. Wakasa-ya Yoichi; cens. Mera; *c*.1845.
    VAM; RSM; PC.

T173

Yuki kure te	When the day is done
konoshita kage wo	I take a tree for my lodge.
yado to seba	On my weary way,
hana ya ko yoi no	Lying under its broad boughs,
aruji nara mashi.	A flower is my sole host.
	(tr. *Heike*, p.558)

Satsuma no Kami Tadanori writing his last poem (which forms the title of the triptych) under the cherry-trees on the evening before his death at Ichi-no-tani (21 March 1184). Pub. Yamaguchi-ya Tōbei; cens. Murata; *c*.1846.
    VAM.

T174

Fukushū kagami ni maze no ki. Composite picture of various dramatic stories of revenge. Pub. Jingi Kikubei; cens. Hama; *c*.1846.
    PC.

T175

Kawanakajima ō-kassen: Kenshin Shingen tachi-uchi no dzu. Personal encounter of Shingen and Kenshin in the river at the battle of Kawanakajima (*c*.1560). Pub. Yamashiro-ya Jimbei; cens. Mura; *c*.1846.
    VAM; RSM.

T176

Mitate hakkei: seiran. Miyamoto Musashi

laying about him with a broken beam by a mill-stream, when attacked by Shirakura Dengoyemon and his men. Pub. Iba-ya Kyūbei; cens. Hama; c.1846.

VAM; B; PC.

T177

Mitate hakkei: takadono no rakugan. Masakado drinking *sake* on a terrace with Kikyō-no-maye and other ladies watching a flight of wild geese (939). Pub. Yenshū-ya Matabei; cens. Mura; c.1846.

VAM.

T178

Mitate hakkei: Shōshazan no banshō. Oniwaka Maru laying about him on the temple steps of Yenkyōji in the province of Harima. Pub. Yenshū-ya Matabei; cens. Mura; c.1846. (See Catalogue illustration to S39.)

VAM; PC.

T179

Mitate hakkei: Yashima no sekishō. Benkei looking through a telescope at the lady Tamamushi-no-maye and the fan on the pole at the battle of Yashima. Pub. Iba-ya Sensaburō; cens. Mura; c.1846.

BM; VAM.

T180

Mitate hakkei: kihan. Koman, swimming in Lake Biwa with the Minamoto banner, is attacked from the Taira barge by Sanemori. Pub. Ise-ya Ichibei; cens. Murata; c.1846.

VAM; RSM.

T181

Mitate hakkei: Kanzaki no shūgwatsu. The boatman Matsuyemon (formerly Higuchi Jirō Kanemitsu) hurling a huge anchor. Pub. Koshima; cens. Murata; c.1846.

VAM; PC.

T182

Mitate hakkei: ya-u. Tadamori and the oil-thief. *By Hiroshige.* c.1846.

VAM; Baur.

T183

Watōnai tora-gari no dzu. (Pl.58) Katō Kiyomasa (Watōnai) attacking a huge tiger in the snow in Korea which has carried off one of his men; other soldiers in the background force a tiger over a cliff. Pub. Yamashiro-ya Jimbei; cens. Murata; c.1846.

BM; RSM; B; PC. *Apollo,* May 1949, p.126; *Geneva 1978,* 87; *Riccar 1978,* 118.

T184

Chūsei gishinden, the title repeated on each sheet, and the whole matching the series *Seichū gishi den* (S54). Moronao's retainer Furubayashi Heihachirō Kaneyoshi defending himself against the two *Rōnin* Oribe Yasubei Taketsune (r.) and Takebayashi Sadashichi

Takashige in the snow. Pub. Kawaguchi-ya Uhei; cens. Hama–Kinugasa; 1847–8.

PC.

T185

Yoritomo-kō no mei wo ukete Tosa-bō Shōshun etc. Kisanda, Genzō, and Yoshitsune among palm-trees, observing the approach of Tosa-bō Shōshun and his party to attack the Horikawa palace. Pub. Sugi-ya Seibei; cens. Hama–Kinugasa; 1847–8.

VAM; PC.

T186

Ōboshi Yoshikane wo hajime shijūsho-nin no gishi hon-i wo etc. After carrying out their revenge, the Forty-Seven *Rōnin* burn incense in the temple, whilst attendants prepare food for them and keep back admiring crowds. Pub. Sano-ya Kihei; cens. Hama–Kinugasa; 1847–8.

B; PC; Dept. of Fine Arts, University of Colorado.

T187/T188

(Double triptych) *Akao no gishin yo-uchi karamete no kata (ōte-gata) yūshi chakutō no dzu.* The Forty-Seven *Rōnin* divided into the two groups that attacked Moronao's mansion from the back and front respectively, the titles of the two halves differing accordingly, as above. Pub. Minato-ya Kohei; cens. Hama–Kinugasa; 1847–8.

PC.

T189

Shidzu no ama otome Daishokkwan etc. The *ama* who has stolen the sacred jewel from the Dragon King's palace at the behest of Fujiwara no Kamatari (Daishokkwan) pursued through the waves by various fishy retainers. Pub. Kiyomidzu-ya Naojirō; cens. Muramatsu–Yoshimura; 1847–8.

VAM; RSM; B; PC. *Robinson 1961,* Pl.71.

T190

Yeiroku yo-nen ku-gwatsu yo-nichi Kawanakajima kassen ni etc. Yamamoto Kansuke and the remnant of his troops on a hillock mown down by the Uyesugi musketeers at Kawanakajima (12 October 1561). Pub. Minato-ya Kohei; cens. Muramatsu–Yoshimura; 1847–8.

VAM; RSM; MFA; B; PC. *Or.Art,* Spring 1961, p.28; *Bidwell 1968,* Pl.132.

T191

(No title) The fording of the Uji river (1184): Takatsuna riding up the bank, met by Noritaka; Shigetada and Kagesuye in the river behind. Pub. Yamaguchi-ya Tōbei; cens. Muramatsu–Yoshimura; 1847–8.

VAM; B; PC.

T192

Kiso Yoshinaka wa tatewaki senshō Yoshi-

kata no ko ni shite etc. Pursuit of Yoshinaka by a bamboo-grove at the battle of Awadzu (1184). The two outer sheets are signed by Ichijusai Yoshikazu. Pub. Jōshū-ya Jūzō; cens. Muramatsu–Yoshimura; 1847–8.

PC.

NOTE. This is not the usual version of Yoshinaka's fall (cf. T265, T315). It may perhaps be a disguised representation of Suye Harukata (see S74.37).

T193

(No title, but three long panels of text) Kajiwara Genda Kagesuye with his horse (l.), Shōshō (c.), and the enraged Soga Gorō Tokimune (r.) by a fenced enclosure. Design of c.1840. Pub. Naka-ya Tokubei; cens. Muramatsu–Yoshimura; 1847–8.

MFA.

T194

Heike no kyōshaku akugyaku wo sō mi Kurama etc. Discomfiture of Benkei on Gojō bridge by Yoshitsune, assisted by the *tengu.* Pub. Yenshū-ya Hikobei; cens. Murata–Mera; 1847–50.

VAM; RSM; MFA; B; PC. *Düsseldorf 1961,* 28; *Düsseldorf 1962,* 15; *Kruml,* 13.1; *Lewis,* 1975.13.

T195

Heike no meishō Taira no Shigemori hachi-jin wo hiite teki wo etc. Arrest of Akugenda Yoshihira in the snow by Taira no Shigemori and his men (1160). Pub. Tsujioka-ya Bunsuke; cens. Murata–Mera; 1847–50.

PC.

T196

(Title?—only one sheet seen) Fujinoye, wife of Tadahira, by the sea-shore, holding a poem-card. Pub. Nōshū-ya Yasubei; cens. Mera–Murata; 1847–50.

VAM.

T197

Ishibashiyama ō-kassen no dzu. The battle of Ishibashiyama (1180), with Sanada Yoichi Yoshihisa (*sic*) struggling with Matano Gorō Kagehisa by a waterfall, and Sasaki Takatsuna fighting with two swords. Pub. Yamaguchi-ya Tōbei; cens. Mera–Murata; 1847–50.

PC.

T198

Kenkyū no hajime Kamakura no tachi ni shoshi taikei wo etc. Quarrel over a game of *go* in the palace of Kamakura, between Kudō Suketsune and Sasaki Nobutsuna; Mount Fuji behind. Pub. Ka-wa-chō; cens. Mera–Murata; 1847–50.

MFA; PC.

T199/T200

(Double triptych) (i) *Minamoto no Yoritomo-kyō Fuji maki-gari no dzu.* (ii) *Kenkyū yo-*

nen go-gwatsu no koro Udaishō Yoritomo-kō Fuji etc. Tadatsune receiving the charge of the giant wild boar, in a panorama of Yoritomo's hunting-party under Mount Fuji (June 1193). Pub. Jōshū-ya Kinzō; cens. Mera–Murata; 1847–50.
VAM, RSM, MFA (ii) only; PC.

T201

Shinshū Odai kassen no dzu. The last fight of Odai Matarokurō Yorisada, who has spitted three foemen on his spear, and his henchman Iwatsu Tetsuyemon Shigenobu outside their burning castle (mid sixteenth century). Pub. Kiyomidzu-ya Naojirō; cens. Mera–Murata; 1847–50.
VAM; RSM; PC. *Lieftinck* No.25 is a preliminary sketch for this triptych.

T202

Inaba sanchū ni oite etc. Dōji Yoshiharu (Horio Yoshiharu) overthrowing a giant boar, watched by warriors among the trees. Pub. Tajima-ya; cens. Mera–Murata; 1847–50.
B.

T203

Satō Masakiyo suikyō no rōnin ryō-ko no yū wo torihishigu dzu. Satō Masakiyo (Katō Kiyomasa) fighting two drunken *rōnin* by a river, watched by soldiers armed with staves. Pub. Tajima-ya Ya . . .; cens. Mera–Murata; *c.*1847–50.
MFA.

T204

Oda Harunaga-kō jo no hei hyakkannen kudzure etc. The rebuilding of Kiyosu castle in three days under the direction of Naka-ura Sarukichirō (Toyotomi Hideyoshi), who is shown reporting to Harunaga (Nobunaga) (see *Hawley*, 26, 27). Pub. Yamamoto-ya Heikichi; cens. Mera–Murata; *c.*1847–50.
VAM; RSM; MFA; PC.

T205

Shidzu-ga-mine kassen no dzu. The defeat of Shibata Katsuiye by Hideyoshi at Shidzu-ga-mine (1583): the attack of Katō Kiyomasa and his men carrying bamboos in place of banners, to which severed heads are attached (see *Hawley*, 501). Pub. Yamamoto-ya Heikichi; cens. Mera–Murata; *c.*1847–50.
VAM; PC.

T206

Sono seki kokon musō no yūshi Sama-no-suke Mitsuharu wa etc. Akechi Mitsuharu with his horse resting under the pine-tree of Karasaki on the shore of Lake Biwa after his defeat at the battle of Uchide-hama, 1582 (cf. *Hawley*, 413). Pub. Yamamoto-ya Heikichi; cens. Mera–Murata; *c.*1847–50.
VAM; RSM; MFA; B; PC.

T207

Yūshi kōmyō no dzu. Battle in hilly country by a lake. The title gives no clue, and none of the figures is named. Pub. Yamashiro-ya Jimbei; cens. Mera–Murata; *c.*1847–50.
RSM; PC.

T208

Miyamoto Musashi wa Higo no dan ni shite etc. Miyamoto Musashi plunging his sword into an enormous whale off the coast of Higo. Pub. Kawaguchi-ya Shōzō; cens. Mera–Murata; *c.*1847–50.
RSM; B; PC. *Suzuki–Oka*, 56/58; *UT*, 180/182; *Riccar 1978*, 108; *Bidwell 1980*, 183.

T209

Gishi shijūshichi-nin hommō wo toge etc. The Forty-Seven *Rōnin* crossing Ryōgoku bridge after carrying out their revenge; Yuranosuke bowing to a mounted official on the near side. Pub. Yamamoto-ya Heikichi; cens. Mera–Murata; *c.*1847–50.
MFA; B; Baur; PC. *Zürich 1936*, 3; *Düsseldorf 1962*, 47; *Kruml*, 9.60; *Lewis*, 1975.16.

T210

Gishi hommō wo tatsushite Sengokuji ye hikitori katame no dzu. The Forty-Seven *Rōnin* assembling outside the temple after carrying out their revenge. Pub. Yorodzu-ya Kichibei; cens. Mera–Murata; *c.*1847–50.
MFA; B; PC. *Lewis*, 1975.17.

T211

Gitora hommō wo toge bozen ye tamuke no dzu. The Forty-Seven *Rōnin* washing the head of Moronao in the well. Pub. Naka-Ni; cens. Mera–Murata; *c.*1847–50.
RSM; PC.

T212

(No title?—only one sheet seen) Yamanaka Dankurō shot through by a gun amid clouds of smoke; *hibachi* and sword-rack in the background. Pub. Tada-ya Takichi; cens. Mera–Murata; *c.*1847–50.
PC.

T213

Yasubei no kataki-uchi. (Fig.30) Yasubei engaging a number of opponents in a natural arena, watched by his mother and sister. Pub. unidentified; cens. Mera–Murata; *c.*1847–50.
VAM; MFA; PC.

T214

Tametomo wa rōdō amata meshitsure etc. Tametomo watches his henchman Oniyasha shouldering a stranded boat off a rock. Pub. Yamaguchi-ya Tōbei; cens. Kinugasa–Yoshimura; early 1849.
VAM; PC.

T215

Yoshitsune kōshin: shitennō shusse kagami no uchi: Kamei Rokurō. (Pl.57) Kamei Rokurō Shigekiyo making his debut as one of Yoshitsune's retainers by fighting a black bear in the snow, watched by Yoshitsune and other retainers. Pub. Nishimura-ya Yohachi; cens. Kinugasa–Yoshimura; early 1849.
PC. *Robinson 1961*, Pl.67.

T216

Hyōye-no-suke Yoritomo-dono Jishō yo-nen no aki etc. (*Yokoye* diptych, or two-thirds of a triptych.) The gathering of Yoritomo's troops before the battle of Ishibashiyama (14 September 1180). Pub. Jōshū-ya Kinzō; cens. Kinugasa–Yoshimura; early 1849.
B.

T217

Ujigawa kassen no dzu. (Pl.60) The rival generals swimming the Uji river to attack Yoshinaka: Takatsuna (c.), Kagesuye (l.), and Shigetada further off (r.); sunset sky. Pub. Yenshū-ya Hikobei; cens. Kinugasa–Yoshimura; early 1849.
BM; MFA; PC.

T218

Kamakura Shōgun Yori-iye-kyō Kotsubo-no-hama ni ryōsen to etc. (Pl.56) Asahina Saburō Yoshihide struggling with two crocodiles on the sea-shore, watched by the Shōgun Yori-iye from a rock. Pub. Kiyomidzu-ya Tsunejirō; cens. Kinugasa–Yoshimura; early 1849.
VAM; PC.

T219

Shōgun Tarō Yoshikado mikata no sei wo atsumuru dzu. The gathering of Yoshikado, his sister Takiyasha, the old retainer Iga Jutarō, and their gang in the old temple. An earlier design (*c.*1835) for T111 above. Pub. Sawamura-ya Rihei; cens. Kinugasa–Watanabe; late 1849–50.
MFA.

T220

Banshū Sodegawa-jiri Fujito hama Sasaki Moritsuna etc. Sasaki Moritsuna and his troops fording the Inland Sea at sunrise to attack the Taira at Kojima castle, Bizen (1 November 1184) (*Heike*, p.635). Pub. Yamaguchi-ya Tōbei; cens. Kinugasa–Watanabe, black *aratame*; late 1849–50.
VAM; RSM; MFA; PC.

T221

Yoshitsune kyū-ryū no dzu. Yoshitsune recovering his bow from the sea at the battle of Yashima (may form a double triptych with T256 below). Pub. Hayashi-ya Shōgorō; cens. Kinugasa–Watanabe, black *aratame*; late 1849–50.
VAM; RSM; PC.

T222

Dan-no-ura ō-kassen no dzu. The battle of Dan-no-ura: Yoshitsune's leap, with Noritsune leaping after him. Pub. Tsuta-ya Umejirō; cens. Kinugasa–Watanabe, black *aratame*; late 1849–50.
VAM.

T223

Higo no kuni Aso no kōri Aso no Saburō Taira no Tadakuni etc. The betrothal of Tametomo (r.) and Shiranui-hime (l.) before her father Aso Tadakuni, in the time of cherry-blossom. Pub. Ise-ya Kanekichi; cens. Hama–Magome; 1849–52.
VAM; PC.

T224

Obaka shuku yo-uchi no dzu. (Fig. 17) Ushiwaka Maru engaging Kumasaka Chōhan and his gang at the inn; a flaming torch flies through the air. Pub. Amatsu; cens. Hama–Magome; 1849–52.
VAM; MFA; PC.

T225

(No title) The fording of the Uji river: Hatakeyama Shigetada, Sasaki Shirō Takatsuna, and Kajiwara Genda Kagesuye. Pub. Yebi-ya Rinnosuke; cens. Hama–Magome; 1849–52.
MFA; PC.

T226

Ichi-no-tani ō-kassen no dzu. Confusion in the Taira camp at Ichi-no-tani caused by Yoshitsune's descent of Hiyodori-goye: Naozane calling after Atsumori (l.). Pub. Yamamoto-ya Heikichi; cens. Hama–Magome, black *aratame*; 1849–52.
PC.

T227

(No title) In a mountainous landscape, Matano Gorō Kagehisa, half-naked on a rock, waving his fist at Sanada Yoichi Yoshitada, mounted and in hunting costume (l.); Yoshitsune and his suite seated (r.). Pub. Fujioka-ya Keijirō; cens. Hama–Magome; 1849–52. (This may perhaps be part of a double triptych; it appears incomplete at both ends.)
PC.

T228

(No title) The battle of Ichi-no-tani: Naozane (l.) calling after Atsumori (c.); on shore, Hirayama Suyeshige fighting (r.), and behind him Tadanori slain by Okabe Rokuyata Tadazumi; Taira fleet off shore. Pub. Tsujioka-ya Bunsuke; cens. Hama–Magome; 1849–52.
VAM; MFA.

T229

Yashima ō-kassen. The battle of Yashima; fight on the shore, with the Taira fleet in the offing. Naozane and Atsumori, locked in struggle, fall from their horses (actually they fought at Ichi-no-tani); Tajima no Kami Tsunemasa mounted; Norimori wrestling with Yoshiyasu. Pub. Yebi-ya Rinnosuke; cens. Hama–Magome; 1849–52.
MFA; PC. Preliminary sketch, PC.

T230

Yashima ō-kassen. The battle of Yashima: Yoshitsune's leap, with Noritsune shaking his fist (l.), and a general mêlée (r.) in which Benkei and Kikuō Maru are prominent. Pub. Ise-Gen; cens. Hama–Magome, black *aratame*; 1849–52.
VAM; RSM; MFA; PC.

T231

Kawanakajima kassen: Kenshin no shaki. Uyesugi Kenshin charging at the head of a wedge formation of his troops at the battle of Kawanakajima. Pub. Tsujioka-ya Bunsuke; cens. Hama–Magome; 1849–52.
PC.

T232

Miyamoto Musashi michi ni ijin ni yotte etc. Miyamoto Musashi being shown a magic glass by an eccentric stranger at a post-station on the road. Pub. Fujioka-ya Keijirō; cens. Hama–Magome; 1849–52.
RSM; B; Baur; PC.

T233

Hakkenden chūyū soroi. Group of Fuse-hime and the eight 'Dog Heroes' of Bakin's novel *Hakkenden*. Pub. Sa-Yo; cens. Hama–Magome, black *aratame*; 1849–52.
VAM.

T234

(No title) Takeshiuchi-no-sukune on his ship heading for Korea. Pub. Ise-ya Tsurujirō; cens. Fuku–Muramatsu; 1849–52.
B; PC.

T235

(No title) Tametomo receiving a deputation of toys (owl, dog, Daruma, etc.) on the sea-shore. Pub. Yorodzu-ya Kichibei; cens. Fuku–Muramatsu; 1849–52.
B.

T236

(No title) Tametomo, in full armour and carrying his bow, meets the Hosogami, or Gods of the Small-Pox, on the sea-shore. Pub. Ise-ya Chūsuke; cens. Fuku–Muramatsu; 1849–52.
VAM.

T237

(No title) Tametomo in his island kingdom, seated on a rock, watching native women picking fruit and diving for *awabi*. Pub. Chū; cens. Fuku–Muramatsu; 1849–52.
VAM.

T238

Kumasaka Chōhan mono-mi no matsu no dzu. Kumasaka Chōhan and his gang round a camp-fire under their 'look-out' pine-tree. Pub. Yamaguchi-ya Tōbei; cens. Fuku–Muramatsu; 1849–52.
VAM.

T239

Minamoto no Yoritomo Yamaki no tachi ye yo-uchi no dzu. Yamaki Kanetaka leading the defence of his palace against Yoritomo's night-attack (1180). Pub. Kawaguchi-ya Uhei; cens. Fuku–Muramatsu; 1849–52.
PC.

T240

Echigo (no) kuni no jū-nin Jō Shirō Nagamochi Heike no seisoku etc. (Fig. 18) Jō Shirō Nagamochi, about to go to war in the Taira cause, sees an apparition of the Thunder-God on the sea-shore. Pub. Yamaguchi-ya Tōbei; cens. Fuku–Muramatsu; 1849–52.
MFA; PC. *Kruml*, 18.16.

T241

Daimotsu-no-ura sakaro ron no dzu. The quarrel about 'reversed oars' between Yoshitsune and Kajiwara Kagetoki before the battle of Yashima. Pub. Tsujioka-ya Bunsuke; cens. Fuku–Muramatsu; 1849–52.
RSM; MFA; PC.

T242

Minamoto no Yoshitsune Miyako wo uchitachi Saikoku ye etc. The Taira ghosts, silhouetted against the sky, attacking Yoshitsune's ship amid mountainous waves. Pub. Yenshū-ya Hikobei; cens. Fuku–Muramatsu; 1849–52.
BM; VAM; MFA; B; PC. *Inouye*, Pl.94; *Takagi*, 12; *Bidwell 1968*, Pl.98; *Riccar 1978*, 104; *Bidwell 1980*, 185.

T243

Taiheiki Hyōgo kassen. Shirafuji Hiko-shichirō ransacking the sacred books before the horrified monks in a temple. Pub. Jōshū-ya Kinzō; cens. Fuku–Muramatsu; 1849–52.
VAM; MFA; PC.

T244

Nitta Chūjō Yoshisada Sesshū Minatogawa shutsujin no dzu nari. Departure parade of Yoshisada's troops before the battle of the Minatogawa. This is an adaptation of T116 above, with the head of Tomoye-gozen recut as Wakiya Yoshisuke, while Yoshinaka has become Yoshisada, and Yamabuki-gozen is Kōtō-no-naishi. Pub. Kagi-ya Hanjirō; cens. Fuku–Muramatsu; 1849–52.
VAM.

T245

Taiheiki kassen no dzu. A battle in the wars of the Taiheiki: a mounted warrior pitches another over an embankment, and a mounted archer shoots at a cavalier who catches the arrows on his spear. None of the figures is named. Pub. unidentified; cens. Fuku–Muramatsu; 1849–52.

VAM.

T246
Takeda Shingen Suwa Yorishige no jinchū wo uchi-kudzusu dzu. (Fig.27) Takeda Shingen directing the discharge of a large cannon across a river, blowing up part of the fortified ćamp of Suwa Yorishige (*c.*1540). Pub. Tsujioka-ya Bunsuke; cens. Fuku–Muramatsu; 1849–52.

RSM; PC.

NOTE. There is a chronological difficulty here. Gunpowder was introduced by the Portuguese into Japan in 1542 (*Papinot*, p.644, s.v. Tanegashima), which was the year of Yorishige's death, a year or two after his defeat by Shingen (ibid., p.611).

T247
Shinshū Kawanakajima kassen no dzu. Prowess of Yamamoto Kansuke at the battle of Kawanakajima. Pub. Yamaguchi-ya Tōbei; cens. Fuku–Muramatsu; 1849–52.

VAM.

T248
Kanadehon Chūshingura: daijō. (Fig.28) First act of the *Chūshingura*: departure of the Imperial envoy (l.), with Moronao, Yenya, the lady Kaoyo, and nobles on a terrace (r.). Pub. Yebi-ya Rinnosuke; cens. Fuku–Muramatsu; 1849–52.

VAM; PC. *Geneva 1978*, 35.

T249
Gishi yo-uchi midare-iri no dzu. Night-attack of the Forty-Seven *Rōnin*: the fight in the garden, and the defence of Moronao's hiding-place. Pub. Hayashi-ya Shōgorō; cens. Fuku–Muramatsu; 1849–52.

RSM; B; PC.

T250
Igagoye kataki-uchi no dzu. The Igagoye revenge: beginning of the engagement between Masayemon, Shidzuma, and their men on the one hand, and Sakurai Rinzayemon, Matagorō, and their party on the other. Pub. Hayashi-ya Shōgorō; cens. Fuku–Muramatsu; 1849–52.

VAM; RSM; MFA; PC.

T251
Meishō Kyūshū yori jōraku no toki Buzen no kuni etc. Story of the ship's captain Yojibei: a nobleman leaping from a ship to a rock in a storm. Pub. Mikawa-ya Tetsugorō; cens. Fuku–Muramatsu; 1849–52.

VAM; RSM; MFA; PC. *Riccar 1978*, 111.

T252
Masakado muhon no kuwadate ototo Rokurō Kintsura kore wo isamu. Rokurō Kintsura driven from the court of his brother Masakado after protesting at the latter's rebellious schemes. Pub. Idzumi-ya Ichibei; cens. Kinugasa–Murata; 1851–2.

VAM; RSM; PC.

T253
(No title) (Pl.64) Vertical triptych. The penance of Mongaku Shōnin under the waterfall of Nachi, encouraged by Fudō and his acolytes Kongara and Seitaka. Pub. Sumiyoshi-ya Masagorō; cens. Kinugasa–Murata; 1851–2.

B; Baur; PC; City Art Gallery, Bristol. *Robinson 1961*, Pl.60a; *UMS*, 17a; *Riccar 1978*, 122; *Bidwell 1980*, 166.

T254
Tametomo no yumi no ikioi no dzu. Tametomo, attended by his followers, sinking the leading ship of Mochimitsu's fleet with a single arrow; a small whirlpool (l.). Pub. Tsuta-ya Umejirō; cens. Kinugasa–Murata, black *aratame*; 1851–2.

VAM; B; PC.

T255
Mutsu no Kami Hidehira hyōjō no dzu. Fujiwara no Hidehira, Lord of Mutsu and protector of Yoshitsune, holding court. Pub. Fujioka-ya Keijirō; cens. Kinugasa–Murata; 1851–2.

MFA; PC.

T256
Yashima ō-kassen. The battle of Yashima: Noritsune (l.) shooting Satō Tsuginobu; behind, the Taira fleet, with Nasu no Yoichi shooting the fan off the pole (may form a double triptych with T221 above). Pub. Hayashi-ya Shōgorō; cens. Kinugasa–Murata; 1851–2.

VAM; RSM; PC.

T257
Yoshino-yama kassen. Vertical triptych. Satō Tadanobu on top of the Yoshino pagoda wearing the armour of Yoshitsune; the monk Yokogawa Kakuhan below. Pub. Sumiyoshi-ya Masagorō; cens. Kinugasa–Murata, black *aratame*; 1851–2.

B; PC. *Memphis 1961*, 106; *UMS*, 17b; *Riccar 1978*, 123; *Bidwell 1980*, 172.

T258
Kawanakajima kassen sonaye wo tatenaosu dzu. Takeda Shingen reviewing his troops, who carry large inscribed banners, in preparation for the battle of Kawanakajima. Pub. Tsujioka-ya Bunsuke; cens. Kinugasa–Murata; 1851–2.

PC.

T259
Kawanakajima ō-kassen no dzu. Prowess of Yamamoto Kansuke at the battle of Kawanakajima. Pub. Idzumi-ya Ichibei; cens. Kinugasa–Murata; 1851–2.

VAM; RSM; PC.

T260
Chūshingura yo-uchi no dzu. The seizing of Moronao by the Forty-Seven *Rōnin*, while the fight goes on in the garden and palace. Pub. Tsujioka-ya Bunsuke; cens. Kinugasa–Murata; 1851–2.

PC.

T261
(No title) Raikō and his retainers attacking the drunken monster Shuten-dōji. Pub. Amatsu; cens. Mera–Watanabe; 1851–2.

VAM; MFA; B; PC. *Riccar 1978*, 110; *Bidwell 1980*, 165.

T262
(No title) Kidō Maru, making a rush at Raikō, is seized by the latter's retainers. Pub. Yamaguchi-ya Tōbei; cens. Mera–Watanabe; 1851–2.

B; PC. *Riccar 1978*, 112.

T263
Sanuki no in kenzoku wo shite Tametomo wo sukuni dzu. (Fig.16) Tametomo, shipwrecked by a giant fish, is rescued by *tengu*. Pub. Sumiyoshi-ya Masagorō; cens. Mera–Watanabe; 1851–2.

BM; VAM; MFA; B; PC. *Takagi*, 15; *Robinson 1961*, Pl.58; *Illing 1976*, 74; *Riccar 1978*, 103; *Bidwell 1980*, 173; *Kruml*, 9.69.

T264
Minamoto (no) Ushiwaka Maru Sōjō-bō no shitagau bujutsu wo etc. Ushiwaka Maru, attended by Kisanda, practising fencing with the *tengu* in the forest at night under the direction of their king, Sōjō-bō. Pub. Yenshū-ya Hikobei; cens. Mera–Watanabe; 1851–2.

VAM; B; PC. *Düsseldorf 1961*, 29; *Düsseldorf 1962*, 77; *Bidwell 1968*, Pl.53; *Crighton*, V20; *Riccar 1978*, 105; *Bidwell 1980*, 174.

T265
Awadzu-ga-hara ō-kassen no dzu. The battle of Awadzu moor: Tomoye-gozen given a drink of water by Kaneyuki (c.), Yoshinaka urging his horse into the frozen bog (r.), and Kanehira fighting off the pursuit. Pub. Maru-ya Seijirō; cens. Mera–Watanabe; 1851–2.

MFA; PC.

T266
Daimotsu-no-ura kaitei no dzu. (Fig.22) The ghosts of Tomomori, with his huge anchor, and the other slain Taira warriors at the bottom of the sea; some, in the form of crabs, hurry off to attack Yoshitsune's ship. Pub. Fujioka-ya Keijirō; cens. Mera–Watanabe; 1851–2.

MFA; B; PC. *Takagi*, 11; *Riccar 1978*, 107; *Bidwell 1980*, 184; *Kruml*, 13.41.

T267
Horikawa yo-uchi no dzu. (Fig.21) Yoshitsune and his men (Benkei and Shidzuka in the lead) on a wooden platform fighting off the troops of Tosa-bō Shōshun attacking the Horikawa palace. Pub. Sano-ya Kihei; cens. Mera–Watanabe; 1851–2.
PC.

T268
Ōshū Takadachi kassen. Hatakeyama Shigetada, a large mounted figure, reconnoitring the castle of Takadachi across the moat (*Heike*, p.293). Pub. Fujioka-ya Keijirō; cens. Mera–Watanabe; 1851–2.
PC.

T269
Soga kyōdai chichi no ada-uchi no dzu. The Soga brothers' revenge: Gorō, after killing Suketsune, lays about him among Yoritomo's retainers, whirling one of them by the arm, while Jurō is engaged by Tadatsune. Pub. Sano-ya Kihei; cens. Mera–Watanabe; 1851–2.
BM; VAM; PC. *Kruml*, 9.79; 18.22.

T270
Rokuhara han Tōji kwaisen. The fight at the Eastern Temple, Rokuhara, Kyoto (1333) (*Taiheiki*, p.256), defended by the Hōjō against Mega Magosaburō Nagamune (l.) and the Imperial troops. Pub. Fujioka-ya Keijirō; cens. Mera–Watanabe; 1851–2.
BM; PC.

T271
Nanke yūshi Shijō-nawate nite uchijini. (Pl.59) The last stand of the Kusunoki at Shijō-nawate (1348): (l. to r.) Masatsura, Masatomo, and Genshū. Pub. Fujioka-ya Keijirō; cens. Mera–Watanabe; 1851–2.
BM; VAM; B; PC. *Binyon–Sexton*, Pl.XLV; *Robinson 1961*, Pl.59; *Memphis 1961*, 26; *Riccar 1978*, 106; *Geneva 1978*, 82; *Bidwell 1980*, 179.

T272
Gishi hommō wo togeru no dzu. Moronao and one of his retainers captured and surrounded by the Forty-Seven *Rōnin*; the captives addressed by Yuranosuke. Pub. Maru-ya Seijirō; cens. Mera–Watanabe; 1851–2.
MFA; PC.

T273
Gishi hyōjō no dzu. The Forty-Seven *Rōnin* in council in their lord's palace. Pub. Yenshū-ya Hikobei; cens. Mera–Watanabe; 1851–2.
RSM; PC.

T274
(Title?—only one sheet seen) A revenge fight at sunrise; the principal figure is Takiguchi-no-suke. Pub. Fujioka-ya Keijirō; cens. Mera–Watanabe; 1851–2.
MFA.

T275
Ashikaga Taka-uji hyōjō no dzu. Ashikaga Taka-uji presiding at the preparation of a feast. Pub. Yamamoto-ya Heikichi; cens. Mera–Watanabe; Rat 3, April–May 1852.
VAM; RSM; PC.

T276
Seichū gishi no kikigaki no uchi: uchi-iri hommō no dzu. The Forty-Seven *Rōnin* scaling the wall of Moronao's palace with bamboo ladders by moonlight. Pub. Mita-ya Kihachi; cens. Mera–Watanabe; Rat 3, April–May 1852.
B; PC. *Riccar 1978*, 128.

T277
Sangokushi: Chōhan hashi no dzu. Chōhi defending Chōhan bridge, mounted on a black charger and armed with his formidable spear; Sōsō in flight. Pub. Tsuta-ya Kichizō; cens. Kinugasa–Murata; Rat 6, July–August 1852.
B; PC. *Düsseldorf 1962*, 12; *Bidwell 1968*, Pl.133; *Riccar 1978*, 114.

T278
Chūtatsu Kōmei kakomi no dzu. The castle of Kōmei beleaguered by the Shiba army. Pub. Tsuta-ya Kichizō; cens. Kinugasa–Murata; Rat 6, July–August 1852.
PC.

T279
Shōtoku Taishi Mononobe no Moriya chūbatsu no dzu. Prince Shōtoku, mounted and attended, quells Mononobe no Moriya with a death-ray glance (587). Pub. Tsuta-ya Kichizō; cens. Kinugasa–Murata; Rat 6, July–August 1852. (Cf. *Hawley*, 503.)
VAM; RSM; PC.

T280
Raikō Ōyeyama kijin no dzu. The triumphant return of Raikō and his men with the monstrous head of the Shuten-dōji. Pub. Yamaguchi-ya Tōbei; cens. Kinugasa–Murata; Rat 6, July–August 1852.
VAM.

T281
Wada kassen: Yoshihide sōmon wo oshi-yaburu. (Pl.62) Asahina Saburō Yoshihide breaking down the great gate during the revolt of the Wada against the Hōjō (1213). Pub. Yamaguchi-ya Tōbei; cens. Kinugasa–Murata; Rat 6, July–August 1852.
VAM; B; PC.

T282
Horikawa yo-uchi no dzu. Tosa-bō Shōshun brought captive by Benkei before Yoshitsune and Shidzuka-gozen. Pub. Tsuta-ya Kichizō; cens. Kinugasa–Murata; Rat 6, July–August 1852.
VAM; RSM; PC.

T283
Minamoto no Yoritomo-kō Fuji-mine maki-gari no dzu. Comical panoramic representation of Yoritomo's hunting-party under Mount Fuji. Pub. Tsuta-ya Kichizō; cens. Kinugasa–Murata; Rat 6, July–August 1852.
B; PC.

T284
Kōyetsu Kawanakajima ō-kassen. (Fig.25) Cavalry engagement amid rolling clouds of battle-smoke at the battle of Kawanakajima. Strong western influence. Pub. Yamaguchi-ya Tōbei; cens. Kinugasa–Murata; Rat 6, July–August 1852.
RSM; PC. *Inouye*, Pl.95; *Riccar 1978*, 115.

T285
Chūshingura yo-uchi no dzu. Night-attack of the Forty-Seven *Rōnin*: the fighting in the garden spreads to Moronao's palace, where he is being hidden by his retainers behind a picture. Pub. Hayashi-ya Shōgorō; cens. Kinugasa–Murata; Rat 6, July–August 1852.
RSM; B; PC.

T286
Gempei bajutsu mari-ashi-sobi no dzu. A game of *dakyū*, the Japanese polo. Pub. Sawaya Kōkichi; cens. Fuku–Muramatsu; Rat 6, July–August 1852.
VAM.

T287
Honchō sanyūshi. Fuwa Banzayemon trying to frighten Nagoya Sanzaburō and Umanosuke with an inflated ghost-figure in a ruined temple (*Mitford*, 'Kazuma's Revenge' and 'Funakoshi Jiuyemon'). Pub. Kaga-ya Yasubei; cens. Fuku–Muramatsu; Rat 6, July–August 1852.
VAM; B; PC. *Kruml*, 22.40.

T288
(Title?—only available copy incomplete) Comical representation of men scrambling for coins watched with amusement by seated nobles. Pub. Yamaguchi-ya Tōbei; cens. Hama–Magome; Rat 9, October–November 1852.
PC.

T289
Kawanakajima kassen: Shingen-kō hatamoto no yūshi etc. Takeda Shingen reviewing his troops before the battle of Kawanakajima. Pub. Hayashi-Ji; cens. Hama–Magome; Ox 1, February 1853.
PC.

T290
Igagoye kataki-uchi. The Igagoye revenge: Karaki Masayemon (r.) fighting against odds, and Sawai Matagorō engaged by Wada Shidzuma (l.). Pub. Mori-ya Jihei; cens. Hama–Magome; Ox 1, February 1853.
RSM; PC.

T291

Sangokushi no uchi: tōyen ni gi wo musubu dzu. Gentoku, Kwanu, and Chōhi taking their oath of loyalty in the peach-orchard, waited on by girls. Pub. Tsuta-ya Kichizō; cens. Mera–Watanabe; Ox 3, April 1853.
VAM; RSM; MFA; PC.

T292

Kawanakajima kassen: Kenshin-kō Shingen-kō no hatamoto etc. Uyesugi Kenshin engaged by Wakatsuki Heidayū (l.) and Nagasaka Gengorō (r.) at the battle of Kawanakajima. Pub. Mori-ya Jihei; cens. Mera–Watanabe; Ox 3, April 1853.
RSM; PC. *Riccar 1978*, 116.

T293

Tsūzoku Sangokushi no uchi: Kwanu ga gishin Sōsō wo yurusu dzu. Kwanu, mounted at the head of his troops, interviewing Sōsō. Pub. Tsuta-ya Kichizō; cens. Kinugasa–Murata; Ox 4, May 1853.
B; PC.

T294

Tsūzoku Sangokushi no uchi: Gentoku mitabi setchū ni etc. Gentoku, Kwanu, and Chōhi visiting the house of Kōmei in the snow. Pub. Tsuta-ya Kichizō; cens. Kinugasa–Murata; Ox 4, May 1853.
VAM; B; PC. *Riccar 1978*, 117; *Kruml*, 22.42.

T295

Tsūzoku Sangokushi no uchi: kwa-i hone wo kezurite Kwanu etc. Kwanu playing at *go* whilst his wounded arm is dressed. Pub. Tsuta-ya Kichizō; cens. Kinugasa–Murata; Ox 4, May 1853.
B; PC.

T296

Tsūzoku Sangokushi no uchi: Gentoku uma wo odorasu Tan-kei etc. (Pl.61) Gentoku leaping his horse into the gorge of Tan; the ox-boy (*ushidōji*) on the opposite bank. Pub. Tsuta-ya Kichizō; cens. Hama–Magome; Ox 5, June 1853.
MFA; B; PC.

T297

Tsūzoku Sangokushi: Kwanu go-kwan wo yaburu no dzu. Kwanu, mounted, receives the submission of Sōsō and his followers on a bridge. Pub. Tsuta-ya Kichizō; cens. Hama–Magome; eng. Shōji; Ox 5, June 1853.
PC.

T298

Raikō Ōyeyama iri no dzu. Raikō severing the head of the Shuten-dōji, which springs in the air; his followers destroy the other demons. Pub. Yamamoto-ya Heikichi; cens. Hama–Magome; Ox 5, June 1853.
VAM; PC.

T299

Ryūgū Tamatori-hime no dzu (on some copies, *Asakusa Okuyama iki ningyō*). Tamatori-hime, the *ama* who stole the sacred jewel, pursued through the waves by a great dragon and various fishes. Pub. Yamaguchi-ya Tōbei; cens. Fuku–Muramatsu; eng. Sashichi; Ox 6, July 1853.
MFA; B; Baur.

T300

Kurikaradani kassen: Kiso Yoshinaka Heishō Tomonori wo uchitori etc. The battle of Kurikaradani (1183): Yoshinaka kills the Taira commander Tomonori, while Kagekiyo fells three of the oxen with burning brushwood attached to their horns by which the Taira were thrown into a panic. Pub. Yamaguchi-ya Tōbei; cens. Fuku–Muramatsu; Ox 6, July 1853.
RSM; PC.

T301

Tsūzoku Sangokushi no uchi: Hakumonro ni Sōsō Ryofu wo kiru no dzu. The captives Ryofu, Kōjun, and Chinkyū brought before Gentoku and Sōsō. Pub. Tsuta-ya Kichizō; cens. Kinugasa–Murata; Ox 8, September 1853.
PC.

T302

(*Tsūzoku Sangokushi* series) *Ryofu wo ou to shite Tōtaku* etc. Ryofu flees (l.) as the gross Tōtaku falls backwards and Riju hastens to his aid; the Lady Chōsen observes from a balcony (r.). Pub. Tsuta-ya Kichizō; cens. Kinugasa–Murata; eng. Shōji; Ox 8, September 1853.
MFA; B.

T303

Hokkoku ō-kassen. The battle of Kurikaradani (1183): Yoshinaka struggling with Tomonori, whilst Unno Kotarō has just knocked a man and his horse over a cliff. Pub. Idzumi-ya Ichibei; cens. Kinugasa–Murata; Ox 8, September 1853.
PC.

T304

Kenkyū yo-nen go-gwatsu nijūhachi-nichi Soga kyōdai ada-uchi no dzu. The Soga brothers about to strike down Kudō Suketsune in his tent, by a smoking brazier (28 June 1193). Pub. Maru-ya Jimpachi; cens. Hama–Magome; Ox 9, October 1853.
B; PC.

T305

Ōyeyama fukuju shusei. Raikō and his men entertaining the Shuten-dōji and his demons with *sake* and dancing. Pub. Ki-ya Sōjirō; Ox 10, November 1853.
VAM; MFA; PC.

T306

Tsūzoku Sangokushi no uchi: Bachō ōi ni sui-kyō ni tatakau etc. Battle between Bachō and Sōsō. Pub. Tsuta-ya Kichizō; cens. *aratame*; Ox 11, December 1853. (See Catalogue illustration to S75.)
B; PC.

T307

Tsūzoku Sangokushi no uchi: Ryū Gentoku Hokkai ye kakomi otoku. Kwanu, Gentoku, and Chōhi in an engagement outside a castle. Pub. Tsuta-ya Kichizō; cens. *aratame*; Ox 11, December 1853.
PC.

T308

(Title?—only one sheet seen) Tokiwa-gozen and her children in the snow. Design of *c.*1845. Pub. Idzutsu-ya Shōkichi; cens. *aratame*; Ox 12, January 1854.
PC.

T309

Tsūzoku Sangokushi no uchi: Kōchū Gi-yen wo chōsha ni tatematsuru. The old warrior Kōchū overthrown by Kwanu. Pub. Tsuta-ya Kichizō; cens. *aratame*; Tiger 8, October 1854.
PC.

T310

Tsūzoku Sangokushi no uchi: Kōmei mutabi Mōkwaku wo toriko ni su. Shukuyū Fujin, wife of Mōkwaku, overthrowing Chōki and Machū. Pub. Tsuta-ya Kichizō; cens. *aratame*; Tiger 8, October 1854.
VAM.

T311

Tsūzoku Sangokushi no uchi: Kwanu Gi no shichi-gun wo hitasu. Kwanu destroying the Seven Armies of Gi (Wei) in a great river-battle. Pub. Tsuta-ya Kichizō; cens. *aratame*; Tiger 8, October 1854.
VAM; PC.

T312

Yoritomo hata-age: Yamaki no yakata yo-uchi no dzu. Yoritomo's night-attack on the palace of Yamaki: Kanetaka at bay (l.), attacked by Yendō Hyōtarō and Katōji Kagekado (1180). Pub. Yamamoto-ya Heikichi; cens. *aratame*; Tiger 8, October 1854.
VAM; PC.

T313

Yeiroku yo-nen ku-gwatsu Kawanakajima ō-kassen: Yamamoto Kansuke etc. (Pl.63) Yamamoto Kansuke rallying his exhausted troops on a hill for their last stand at the battle of Kawanakajima (October 1561). Pub. Yamamoto-ya Heikichi; cens. *aratame*; Tiger 8, October 1854.
RSM; PC.

T314

Kawanakajima ō-kassen: Kenshin Saijōzan ni oite sarugaku etc. Uyesugi Kenshin originating the Monkey Dance at Saijōzan during the Kawanakajima campaign. Pub. Kiya Sōjirō; cens. *aratame*; eng. Kane; Tiger 11, January 1855.
VAM; PC.

T315

Awadzu kassen. The battle of Awadzu (1184): Tomoye-gozen wielding a tree-trunk, while Yoshinaka is shot riding through the bog; Wada Yoshimori (r.). Pub. Tsujioka-ya Bunsuke; cens. *aratame*; Tiger 12, January–February 1855.
PC.

T316

Kawanakajima ō-kassen. Prowess of Onikojima Yatarō at the battle of Kawanakajima; he is shown overthrowing Nakanishi Dairokurō. Pub. Yamaguchi-ya Tōbei; cens. *aratame*; Hare 1, February–March 1855.
PC.

T317

Watōnai gunko tōshu no dzu. Katō Kiyomasa (Watōnai) and his men chasing tigers which are carrying off some Japanese soldiers across a river. Pub. Yamaguchi-ya Tōbei; cens. *aratame*; Hare 1, February–March 1855.
VAM; RSM; B; PC. *Riccar 1978*, 118.

T318

Asaji- (i.e. *Adachi-*) *ga-hara hitotsuya no dzu*. The Lonely House story: the Hag (c.) with a suppliant girl-victim, and the appearance of Kwannon (r.) behind a screen. Pub. Yamaguchi-ya Tōbei; cens. *aratame*; Hare 2, March–April 1855.
MFA; PC.

T319

Yoshitsune (no) jūku-shin. Yoshitsune and his nineteen retainers in a ship with Benkei at the prow. Pub. Idzumi-ya Ichibei; cens. *aratame*; Hare 6, July–August 1855.
RSM; MFA; PC.

T320

Minamoto no Yoritomo Ishibashiyama hata-age kassen. Aftermath of the battle of Ishibashiyama (1180): Yoritomo and his men hiding in the hollow tree, and Kagetoki diverting their pursuers. Pub. Daikoku-ya Kinjirō; cens. *aratame*; Hare 8, September–October 1855.
VAM; PC.

T321

Satō Tadanobu yūsen Yoshitoki ga sei wo utsuru dzu. (Fig.23) Tadanobu furiously resisting arrest, wielding the *go*-board with one hand and grasping the hair of his treacherous mistress with the other, the *go*-pieces flying in all directions. Design of *c*.1835. Pub. Yamaguchi-ya Tōbei; cens. *aratame*; Hare 9, October–November 1855.
RSM; MFA (crêpe); PC.

T322

Sagi-no-ike Heikurō Taka-uji no taigun etc. Sagi-no-ike Heikurō creating havoc among the Ashikaga troops. Pub. Mori-ya Jihei; cens. *aratame*; Hare 9, October–November 1855.
PC.

T323

Kusunoki Ashikaga ō-kassen. Ashikaga Taka-uji struck by a severed head flung by Sagi-no-ike Heikurō. Pub. Tsujioka-ya Bunsuke; cens. *aratame*; Hare 9, October–November 1855.
VAM; PC.

T324

Shinshū Kawanakajima Takeda no shōhei Saijōzan wo hikigayeshi etc. Amakasu Ōmi no Kami Kagetoki directing the attack of the Uyesugi troops at the battle of Kawanakajima. Pub. Hayashi-ya Shōgorō; cens. *aratame*; Hare 9, October–November 1855.
BM; VAM; RSM; PC. *Düsseldorf 1961*, 49.

T325

Kawanakajima kassen. (Fig.26) Close-up view of the face-to-face encounter of Takeda Shingen and Uyesugi Kenshin at Kawanakajima; Hachikawano Zensuke (r.) thrusting a spear at the latter. Pub. Jōshū-ya Kinzō; cens. *aratame*; eng. Sashichi; Hare 9, October–November 1855.
VAM; RSM; PC.

T326

Yoritomo Tō-Oku seibatsu: Saijō Totarō Kunihira taishō wo etc. During his punitive expedition to eastern Mutsu (1189), Yoritomo is attacked by Saijō Kunihira. Pub. Mori-ya Jihei; cens. *aratame*; Hare 12, January 1856.
VAM.

T327

Kaga no kuni Ataka no seki ni Benkei shūjū no kinan wo suku dzu. During their flight disguised as *yamabushi*, Benkei beats Yoshitsune to avert suspicion at the Ataka Barrier in the province of Kaga. Pub. Tsujioka-ya Bunsuke; cens. *aratame*; Dragon 2, March 1856.
VAM; MFA; PC.

T328

Chō chidori satsuki no irodori. The Soga brothers with Tora of Ōiso between them. Pub. Yebi-ya Rinnosuke; cens. *aratame*; Dragon 2, March 1856.
VAM; PC.

T329

Midzukame wo kudaite meiyo wo arawasu no dzu. Chibata Tatsuiye (Shibata Katsuiye) leading his successful sortie from the castle after breaking the water-jars. Pub. Tsuta-ya Kichizō; cens. *aratame*; Dragon 2, March 1856.
VAM; MFA; PC.

T330

(Diptych) *Adachi-ga-hara hitotsuya no dzu*. The Hag of the Lonely House with a girl-victim trussed up on the floor; apparition of Kwannon behind. Pub. Ōmi-ya Kyū . . .; cens. *aratame*; Dragon 3, April 1856.
PC. *Inouye*, Pl.76; *Robinson 1963*, Pl.33.

T331

Kōyetsu Kawanakajima ō-kassen. Encounter between Usami Suruga no Kami and Yamagata Saburohei on horseback at the battle of Kawanakajima; battle-smoke and infantry behind. Pub. Ōmi-ya Kyū . . .; cens. *aratame*; Dragon 4, May 1856.
MFA.

T332

Kawanakajima ryōshō jikisen no dzu. Kenshin charging into Shingen's camp-enclosure through rolling clouds of battle-smoke at the battle of Kawanakajima. Pub. Hayashi-ya Shōgorō; cens. *aratame*; Dragon 5, June 1856.
RSM; MFA; PC.

T333

Kusunoki no shin Tsujikaze Itamochi Hosokawa Sada-uji ikedori no dzu. The battle of Fujiidera (1348) in the rain: Hosokawa Sada-uji seized by the Kusunoki retainers Tsujikaze and Itamochi. Pub. Tsujioka-ya Bunsuke; cens. *aratame*; Dragon 7, August 1856.
PC.

T334

Ujigawa ō-kassen. The fording of the Uji river in Yoshitsune's campaign against Yoshinaka (1184): Kagesuye, Takatsuna, and their men, with Chichibu Shigetada emerging on the further bank. Pub. Sō-To; cens. *aratame*; Dragon 9, October 1856.
MFA; PC.

T335

Ganryūjima kataki-uchi no dzu. Miyamoto Musashi, fencing with two sticks, makes a leap as he fights the villain Sasaki Ganryū on the shore, watched by an appreciative crowd. Pub. Daikoku-ya Kinnosuke; cens. *aratame*; Dragon 9, October 1856.
RSM; MFA; PC.

T336

Kurikaradani yūsen no dzu. Combat of Wakagawa Kiyohide and Takuma Gemba at the battle of Kurikaradani (1183); so the print is inscribed, but it actually represents Nakagawa Kiyohide and Sakuma Gemba Morimasa at the battle of Shidzu-ga-mine (1583) (cf. *Hawley*, 502ff.). Pub. Tsuta-ya Kichizō; cens.

aratame; Dragon 10, November 1856.
VAM; MFA; B; PC.

T337

Daimotsu-no-ura ō-kassen. The battle of Dan-no-ura: Yoshitsune, sword in one hand and *naginata* in the other, makes his leap, pursued by Noritsune; the Imperial barge in the background. Pub. Mori-ya Jihei; cens. *aratame*; Dragon 10, November 1856.
RSM.

T338

Ōshū Takadachi-jō ō-kassen no dzu. The battle of Takadachi in the province of Mutsu: Benkei laying about him in the mêlée under the castle walls (1189). Pub. Tsuta-ya Kichizō; cens. *aratame*; Dragon 10, November 1856.
PC.

T339

Gempei ō-kassen. (Fig.20) Yoshitsune recovering his bow from the sea at the battle of Yashima (*Heike*, p.663). Pub. Fujioka-ya Keijirō; cens. *aratame*; Dragon 12, January 1857.
MFA; PC.

T340

Akazawa-yama yūshi sumō no dzu. Kawadzu Saburō Sukeyasu throwing Matano Gorō Kagehisa in their wrestling-match before Yoritomo, Ōba Kagechika, and others. Pub. Sen-Kiyo of Shiba; cens. *aratame*; Snake 2, March 1857.
PC.

T341

Kusunoki Masashige wara no ningyō no tsukuri etc. Kusunoki Masashige and his men making straw dummies to trick the enemy into exhausting their arrows. Pub. Mikawa-ya Tetsugorō; cens. *aratame*; Snake 3, April 1857.
PC.

T342

Wada kassen: Asahina Saburō Yoshihide mōyō kwairyoku no dzu. Asahina Saburō Yoshihide breaking down the great gate during the Wada rebellion against the Hōjō (1213). Pub. Jōshū-ya Jūzō; cens. *aratame*; Snake 4, May 1857.
VAM; MFA; PC.

T343

Nitta Ashikaga kyō-gassen: shōri no shogun wo atsumeru dzu. The troops of Nitta Yoshisada rallying on a hill after their victory over the Ashikaga. Pub. Jōshū-ya Jūzō; cens. *aratame*; Snake 4, May 1857.
PC.

T344

Kusunoki Masashige Minatogawa ō-kassen ni shōsei wo motte etc. Kusunoki Masashige rallying his men with the sounds of drum, conch, and bell at the battle of the Minato-gawa (1336). Pub. Jōshū-ya Jūzō; cens. *aratame*; Snake 4, May 1857.
PC.

T345

Takeda Uyesugi Kawanakajima ō-kassen no dzu. Encounter of Takeda Shingen and Uyesugi Kenshin in mid-stream at the battle of Kawanakajima. Pub. Daikoku-ya Heikichi; cens. *aratame*; Snake 4, May 1857.
VAM; RSM; MFA. *Hawley*, frontispiece.

T346/T347

(Double triptych) *Shijō-nawate nite Nanke no yeiyū taiteki wo* etc. The last stand of the Kusunoki at Shijō-nawate under a hail of arrows (1348): (r. to l.) Genshū, Masatsura, Masatomo, Masayuki, Koshirō Hyōgo, and Noda Shirō. Pub. Sō-To; cens. *aratame*; Snake 4 (r.h. half), Snake 8 (l.h. half), May and September 1857.
MFA (r.h. half only); PC. *Or.Art*, Spring 1961, pp.28–9; *Riccar 1978*, 119; *Lewis*, 1975.24 (l.h. half); *Kruml*, 18.21 (l.h. half).

T348

Sangokushi: Bachō Chōhi kahō seki tatakai. Mounted combat between Bachō and Chōhi, lit by fires and torches, and watched by two sovereigns in their carriages. Pub. Yenshū-ya Hikobei; cens. *aratame*; Snake 7, September 1857.
MFA.

T349

Soga jū-ban-giri no dzu. The Soga brothers' last fight: Gorō (c.), Jurō (top l.), and a tent-enclosure (r.). Pub. Yamaguchi-ya Tōbei; Horse 2, March–April 1858.
PC.

T350

Kusunoki Ashikaga ō-kassen no dzu. Battle on the shore between the Kusunoki and the Ashikaga (probably the Minatogawa, 1336): Masashige and his men charging, led by Onchi Sakon-tarō, Sagi-no-ike Heikurō, Wada Idzumi no Kami, and Hayase Sayemon. Design probably c.1850. Pub. Yamaguchi-ya Tōbei; Horse 2, March–April 1858.
PC.

T351

Ushiwaka Kurama shugyō dzu. Ushiwaka Maru practising fencing among the pine-trees of Kuramayama with the *tengu* under the supervision of their king, Sōjō-bō. The *tengu* here are completely birdlike. Pub. Maru-ya Kyūshirō; Horse 4, May–June 1858 (a later edition of September 1861—Cock 8—has the pub. Kagi-Shō).
RSM; PC. *Crighton*, V21.

T352

Kusunoki no jinchū ni Sugimoto Akiyuki wo tsumorite etc. In a seated assembly Sugimoto Akiyuki receives a famous sword from Kusunoki Masashige; all present weep. Pub. Yamamoto-ya Heikichi; Horse 4, May–June 1858.
VAM; MFA.

T353

Akazawa-yama ō-sumō. Matano Gorō Kagehisa thrown by Kawadzu Saburō Sukechika in their wrestling-match before Yoritomo, umpired by Yebina Gempachi. Large figures. Pub. Maru-ya Kyūshirō; eng. Kane; Horse 4, May–June 1858.
VAM. *Crighton*, V9.

T354

Ryūgūjō: Tawara Tōda Hidesato ni sanshu no tosan wo okuru. Tawara Tōda Hidesato escorted through the waves by the Dragon King's fishy retainers, having received the Three Gifts. Pub. Maru-ya Kyūshirō; Horse 4, May–June 1858 (a later edition of September 1861—Cock 8—has pub. Kagi-Shō; cf. T351 above).
VAM; RSM; MFA; PC.

T355

Akamatsu no shiro midzuzeme no dzu. The beleaguering of the castle of Akamatsu by water, with floating batteries, and a large lookout tower (l.). This is really Takamatsu castle besieged by Hideyoshi in 1582 (see *Papinot*, p.630; *Hawley*, 335). Pub. Idzumi-ya Ichibei; cens. *aratame*; Monkey 8, September–October 1860.
PC.

T356

Kataki-uchi kidan Jiraiya monogatari: Sōshū Shichiri-ga-hama etc. Jiraiya and his followers, seated on the shore, watch Amame Isobei catching two miscreants, whilst Onikubi Kōyemon engages the youth Masajirō and the maiden Midori in combat. Design of c.1836. Pub. Yamaguchi-ya Tōbei; cens. *aratame*; Cock 1, February 1861.
MFA.

T357

(No title) Raikō's retainers playing at *go*, with attempted interruptions by the Earth-Spider's demons. Large figures. Pub. Yamaguchi-ya Tōbei; cens. *aratame*; Cock 1, February 1861.
B; PC. *Takagi*, 18; *Düsseldorf 1961*, 54; *Speiser*, p.129; *Riccar 1978*, 121; *Bidwell 1980*, 200.

T358

Miyamoto Musashi Sōshū Hakone no sanchū ni etc. Miyamoto Musashi fighting off a pack of wolves in the Hakone mountains, watched by Sekiguchi Yatarō, seated smoking by a fire. Pub. Ki-ya Sōjirō; cens. *aratame*; Cock 6, July 1861.
MFA; PC.

SIGNATURES

The system of dating Kuniyoshi's prints by a combination of censorship seals and the artist's changes of handwriting, as shown in his signature, is explained in *Robinson 1961* (pp.25–33), and has been followed in this book. But it has been possible in the interval to expand the range of datable signatures there given, and the following examples, from almost every year of Kuniyoshi's life down to 1855, will, it is hoped, prove useful. The date-seals, introduced in 1852, give the year and month of publication for all subsequent prints, but there are several clear instances (e.g. S93, T321, T356) of the use of designs of up to twenty-five years earlier.

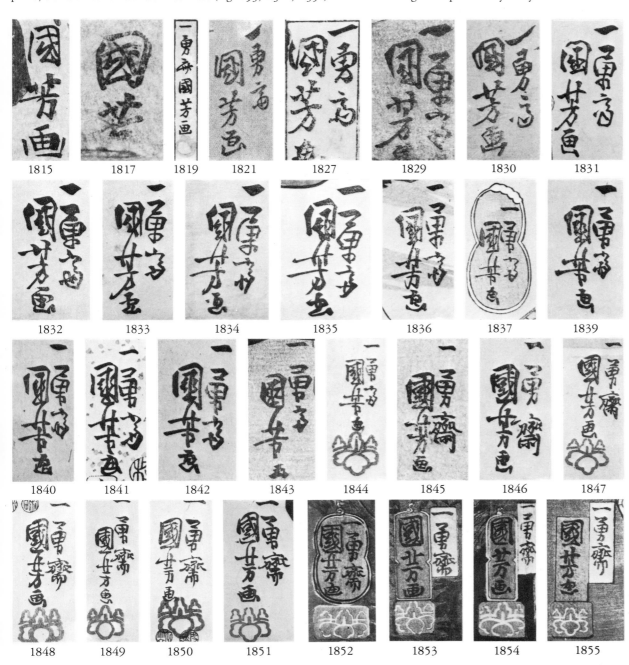

| 1815 | 1817 | 1819 | 1821 | 1827 | 1829 | 1830 | 1831 |

| 1832 | 1833 | 1834 | 1835 | 1836 | 1837 | 1839 |

| 1840 | 1841 | 1842 | 1843 | 1844 | 1845 | 1846 | 1847 |

| 1848 | 1849 | 1850 | 1851 | 1852 | 1853 | 1854 | 1855 |

GLOSSARY

ama: a fisher-woman who specialized in diving for *awabi*, q.v.

aratame: 'examined'; in seal form used as a censorship mark on prints, 1849–51, 1854–7, and 1859 onwards (combined with date).

ashigaru: the lowest rank of feudal retainer.

awabi: haliotis, or sea-ear; a rather coarse edible bivalve.

biwa: a four-stringed instrument shaped like a flat-backed lute.

bonji: debased and formalized Sanskrit characters signifying Buddhist divinities.

bonsai: artificially dwarfed trees in pots, sometimes of great age and value.

bugaku: ancient court dances performed in masks.

chidori: 'wave-birds'; sanderlings or plovers.

chōban: a print size about 50 × 20 cm.

chūban: a print size about 25 × 18 cm.

chū-tanzaku: a print size about 38 × 13 cm.

daimyō: a great lord, head of a feudal clan.

geisha: a girl trained to entertain with music, dancing, and conversation.

Genji-mon: a set of 54 rectilinear devices, each representing one of the chapters of the Romance of Prince Genji (*Koop*, pp. 119, 120).

go: a complicated form of chequers (B. H. Chamberlain, *Things Japanese*, s.v. *go*, gives a full account of the game).

gō: an additional art-name (see note following S1a.2).

gohei: a wand with strips of cut paper attached, a Shintō divine symbol.

hakama: long and very wide trousers worn on ceremonial occasions.

haori: a coat, esp. a military surcoat worn over armour.

harimaze: a print bearing several separate designs by different artists.

hibachi: a domestic brazier.

hinin: a criminal, beggar, or social outcast.

hoko: an early form of spearhead with a laterally projecting point.

iroha: the Japanese syllabary embodied in a poem of 47 syllables (*Koop*, p. 21).

jūmonji: the character for 'ten' (which is a cross); cross-shaped.

jūnishi: the Twelve Signs of the Zodiac (*Koop*, p. 63).

kago: a palanquin or sedan-chair.

kakemono: a hanging scroll-picture, so *kakemono-ye*, a vertical diptych or triptych designed to be mounted and hung as a *kakemono*.

kakihan: a 'hand seal' or personal device; *paraphe* in French.

kana: the Japanese characters representing the syllables of the *iroha* (q.v.), often written alongside the *kanji* characters to indicate correct pronunciation.

kappa: a river-sprite (see *Edmunds*, p. 428).

kesa: a Buddhist priest's robe worn slung across the shoulder.

kimono: general word for a garment, or clothing.

kiwame: 'approved'; in seal form used as a censorship mark on prints before 1842.

koban: a print size about 18 × 13 cm.

kogatana: a small knife carried in a slot in the sword-scabbard.

komusō: a *samurai* in temporary disgrace, usually represented with a *shakuhachi* (q.v.) and a deep straw hat concealing his face.

koto: a musical instrument consisting of a long sounding-box over which strings are stretched, each with its separate bridge, and plucked with plectra attached to the player's fingers.

kusudama: a hanging scented ball of artificial flowers, with streamers.

mempō: an armour mask, or visor.

mokugyo: a hollow wooden fish-shaped gong, struck by Buddhist priests.

mon: a heraldic device or badge ('crest' is *not* the correct equivalent).

naginata: a pole-arm with a long curved blade; a glaive.

nanori: the official name of a Japanese, such as 'Yoshitsune'.

Nō: Japanese classical dance-drama.

nodachi: a very long sword carried across the back.

ōban: the standard print size, about 38 × 25 cm.

obi: lady's silk brocade sash.

ō-tanzaku: a print size about 38 × 17 cm.

otokodate: chivalrous townsmen who championed the oppressed (see *Mitford*, introduction to 'A Story of the Otokodate of Yedo').

raijū: a fabulous beast of vaguely canine appearance, said to come to earth with thunderbolts.

Rakan: (Arhat) a disciple of Buddha (*Koop*, p. 112).

rimbō: the Buddhist 'Wheel of the Law', originally a Hindu weapon.

rōnin: 'wave man'; a *samurai* without a feudal lord.

saihai: a general's baton, with large tassel of cut paper attached, used in directing troops.

sake: Japanese rice wine, heated before drinking.

samisen: a three-stringed banjo-like instrument, played with a large plectrum.

sashimono: a flag attached to the back of the armour to facilitate recognition in battle.

Sennin: an 'Immortal', or saintly recluse.

seppuku: the formal method of suicide by cutting open the abdomen; *hara-kiri* is a vulgar synonym. See *Mitford*, Appendix A.

shakuhachi: a bamboo flute or pipe, blown at the end, and slightly curved.

shimenawa: a rope with tufts of cut paper at intervals, hung round Shintō shrines and other places to confer sanctity.

shirabyōshi: court dancing-girls in medieval times, distinguished by a white robe, court cap, sword, and *gohei*.

shirazaya: sheath and hilt of plain white wood in which sword-blades were kept when not in use.

shōji: window or sliding door covered with paper.

sode: an armour shoulder-piece.

surimono: a print, usually about 20.5×17.5 cm., on superior paper and exhibiting much technical refinement, used in the same circumstances as our greetings card.

tachi: a long sword mounted to be slung from the belt.

taibi: 'big tail'; the last of a series.

tate: a rectangular wooden shield, often set up for protection by troops in defensive positions.

tengu: a birdlike wood-sprite (see *Edmunds*, p.623).

torii: 'bird rest'; a wooden archway found outside Shintō shrines, and originally a perch for birds dedicated to the gods.

tsuba: a sword-guard, usually of circular or oval form.

tsudzumi: a hand-drum, the body of baluster or hour-glass form.

uchiwa: a non-folding fan with bamboo framework.

wakana: young greens.

wani: a crocodile or sea-monster.

yamabuki: the yellow rose, *Kerria japonica.*

yamabushi: a warrior-monk (lit. 'sleeping in the mountains').

yokoye: a horizontal, as opposed to vertical, composition.

BIBLIOGRAPHICAL REFERENCES

(in alphabetical order of the abbreviations employed)

PUBLICATIONS CONTAINING REPRODUCTIONS OF KUNIYOSHI'S PRINTS

Apollo	*Apollo*, a Magazine of the Arts, London, 1925–.
Bidwell 1968	(Merlin C. Dailey) *The Raymond A. Bidwell Collection of Prints by Utagawa Kuniyoshi*, Museum of Fine Arts, Springfield, Massachusetts, 1968.
Bidwell 1980	(Merlin C. Dailey) *Utagawa Kuniyoshi: an Exhibition . . . based on the Raymond A. Bidwell collection of Japanese Prints at the Springfield Museum of Fine Arts*, Springfield, Massachusetts, 1980.
Binyon–Sexton	Laurence Binyon and J. J. O'Brien Sexton, *Japanese Colour Prints*, London, 1923.
Boller	Willy Boller, *Masterpieces of the Japanese Colour Woodcut*, London, 1957.
Cologne 1963	*Kuniyoshi* (Ausstellung in der Eigelsteintorburg), Museum für Ostasiatische Kunst, Cologne, 1963.
Crighton	R. A. Crighton, *The Floating World: Japanese popular Prints 1700–1900*, Victoria and Albert Museum, London, 1973.
Düsseldorf 1961	*Kuniyoshi 1798–1861*, Kunstmuseum, Düsseldorf, 1961.
Düsseldorf 1962	*Kuniyoshi 1798–1861: Kunisada (Toyokuni III) 1786–1865*, Kunstmuseum, Düsseldorf, 1962.
Falteri	Falteri, Grafica antica e moderna, Cat. No.6: *Stampe Giapponesi da Koryusai a Shinsui*, Florence, 1981.
FH	(Walter Exner) *Frauen und Helden: Farbholzschnitte von Kuniyoshi*, Frankenau, 1962.
Geneva 1965	*Estampes japonaises*, Cabinet des Estampes (Musée d'Art et d'Histoire), Geneva, 1965.
Geneva 1978	*Kuniyoshi 1798–1861: une Collection particulière*, Cabinet des Estampes (Musée d'Art et d'Histoire), Geneva, 1978.
Graf	Oscar and Cäcilie Graf, *Japanisches Gespensterbuch*, Stuttgart, 1925.
Hawley	W. M. Hawley, *Pictorial Biography of Toyotomi Hideyoshi*, privately printed, Hollywood, 1975. (This publication consists of a set of reproductions of Kuniyoshi's illustrations to *Toyotomi kunkōki*, with brief captions.)
Hillier	J. Hillier, *Japanese Colour Prints*, London, 1966.
Illing 1976	Richard Illing, *Japanese Prints from 1700–1900*, Oxford, 1976.
Illing 1978	Richard Illing, *Later Japanese Prints*, Oxford, 1978.
Illing 1980	Richard Illing, *The Art of Japanese Prints*, London, 1980.
Inouye	Inouye Kazuo, *Kuniyoshi hangwa kessaku shū*, Kyoto, 1930.
Iserlohn 1963	*Kuniyoshi Farbholzschnitte*, Haus der Heimat, Iserlohn, 1963.
Johnes	Raymond Johnes, *Japanese Art*, London, 1961.
Kennedy	Robin Kennedy, periodical catalogues of Japanese prints, London, 1979–.
Kruml	Richard Kruml, periodical catalogues of Japanese prints, London, 1973–.
Lewis	R. E. Lewis, periodical catalogues of

Japanese prints, San Rafael, California, USA, 1970–.

Lieftinck B. W. Robinson, *Summary Catalogue of Drawings by Utagawa Kuniyoshi in the Collection of Ferd. Lieftinck*, privately printed, Groningen, 1953. (This collection is now in the Leyden Museum.)

Memphis 1961 (Merlin C. Dailey) *A Memorial Exhibition of the work of Utagawa Kuniyoshi on the 100th Anniversary of his Death*, Brooks Memorial Art Gallery, Memphis, Tennessee, 1961.

Or.Art *Oriental Art*, a Quarterly Publication devoted to all forms of Oriental Art, New Series, Oxford, 1955–.

Riccar 1978 *Exhibition of Ukiyo-e by Kuniyoshi*, Riccar Art Museum, Tokyo, 1978.

Riccar 1979 (Suzuki Jūzō) *Exhibition of Suikoden by Kuniyoshi*, Riccar Art Museum, Tokyo, 1979.

Robinson 1961 B. W. Robinson, *Kuniyoshi*, Victoria and Albert Museum, London, 1961.

Robinson 1963 B. W. Robinson and Werner Speiser, *Kuniyoshi: ein Meister des japanischen Farbholzschnitts*, Essen, 1963.

Ronin *Images of a Floating World*, Ronin Gallery, New York, n.d.

Speiser Werner Speiser, *Kuniyoshi*, Bad Wildungen, 1969.

Stewart Basil Stewart, *Subjects Portrayed in Japanese Colour Prints*, London, 1922.

Strange E. F. Strange, *Japanese Colour Prints*, Victoria and Albert Museum, London, 1904.

Suzuki–Oka Suzuki Jūzō and Oka Isaburō, *Masterworks of Ukiyo-e: the Decadents* (Kunisada, Kuniyoshi, and Yeisen), Tokyo, 1969.

Takagi Takagi Shigeru, *Mushaye fukkatsu*, Fukuoka, 1938.

UMS (Suzuki Jūzō) *Ukiyoye meisaku senshū*, Vol. 10: *Kuniyoshi*, Tokyo, 1968.

UT (Suzuki Jūzō, ed. Gotō Shigeki) *Ukiyoye Taikei*, Vol. 10: *Kunisada, Kuniyoshi, Yeisen*, Tokyo, 1974.

Zürich 1936 *Japanische Holzschnitt Triptychen*, Kunsthaus, Zürich, 1936.

WORKS OF REFERENCE

Edmunds W. H. Edmunds, *Pointers and Clues to the Subjects of Chinese and Japanese Art*, London, 1934 (reprint, Geneva, 1973). Edmunds catalogued Japanese prints for Sotheby's for many years, and his work, like *Koop*, grew out of his own needs and experience. It is full and most useful. A certain lack of cross-referencing in the original edition has been remedied by an excellent index in the reprint.

Joly H. L. Joly, *Legend in Japanese Art*, London, 1908 (reprint, 1972). Joly had a brilliant mind and a wide acquaintance with the Japanese sources, but he was a careless proof-reader.

Koop A. J. Koop and H. Inada, *Japanese Names and how to read them*, London, 1923 (reprint, 1972). Though primarily a character dictionary, indispensable to anybody aspiring to read titles and names on prints for themselves, this splendid book contains a mass of useful information in its introductory section, such as lists of the Hundred Poets, the Chapters of Genji, the Provinces, etc., and full chronological tables.

Papinot E. Papinot, *Historical and Geographical Dictionary of Japan*, Yokohama, 1909. The author was an eminent Jesuit scholar, and his book is concise and reliable; biographical entries are confined to strictly historical characters. There is a good set of maps, and appendices on the Provinces, chronology, etc. The work was originally published in French.

Weber V. F. Weber, *Kōji Hōten*, Paris, 1923 (reprint, New York and London, 1977). Two huge and lavishly illustrated volumes in French, covering a great deal of ground, and with useful appendices on heraldry, signatures on works of art, etc.

TRANSLATIONS OF JAPANESE TEXTS

Gikeiki Helen Craig McCullough, *Yoshitsune: a Fifteenth Century Japanese Chronicle*, Stanford (California), 1966. This translation of the *Gikeiki* reads very well, and has a most useful introduction. The whole of Yoshitsune's life is covered.

Heike Kitagawa Hiroshi and Bruce T. Tsuchida, *The Tale of the Heike (Heike Monogatari)*, Tokyo, 1975. A full and most valuable translation of the classic account of the wars of Gempei, with all the necessary background information in the Translator's Preface.

Kojiki B. H. Chamberlain, *Kojiki, or Record of Ancient Matters*, Yokohama, 1883. The most ancient Japanese chronicle (completed in 712) translated by the earliest and perhaps still the most brilliant British scholar in Japanese. From the Age of the Gods to the end of the seventh century.

Nihongi W. G. Aston, *Nihongi: Chronicles of Japan from the Earliest Times to A.D. 697*, London, 1896 (reprint, London, 1956). Invaluable for the earliest periods; the original is a more self-consciously scholarly (in the Chinese sense) work than the *Kojiki*, and covers much the same ground. We were indeed fortunate to have had both Chamberlain and Aston in the pioneering days of Japanese studies in this country.

Sadler A. L. Sadler, *The Ten-foot-square Hut and Tales of the Heike*, Sydney, 1928. A lucid,

Taiheiki
stylish, and highly readable translation of the *Heike monogatari*, though less full than *Heike*, together with the brief lament of the *Hōjōki*. Helen Craig McCullough, *The Taiheiki: a* *Chronicle of Mediaeval Japan*, New York, 1959. A splendid translation and introduction; the period covered is approximately 1318–33.

JAPANESE HISTORY AND LEGENDS RETOLD

Bertin
L. E. Bertin, *Les Grandes Guerres Civiles du Japon*, Paris, 1894. If one can acclimatize one's self to the author's highly idiosyncratic method of transcribing Japanese names, this is a valuable and comprehensive book, covering the period from the Age of the Gods to the end of the fourteenth century.

de Benneville
J. S. de Benneville, *Saitō Musashi-bō Benkei*, Yokohama, 1910. The author has an irritatingly facetious style, but the book contains virtually all the stories of Yoshitsune, Benkei, and their immediate forebears and successors.

Dening
Walter Dening, *The Life of Miyamoto Musashi* ('Japan in Days of Yore' IV), two vols., Tokyo, 1905.

Dickins
Frederick Victor Dickins, *Chiushingura, or The Loyal League*, London and Glasgow, 1930 (original edn., Yokohama, 1876). The two preceding works, by two eminent pioneers of Japanese studies in this country, provide excellent versions of these favourite episodes.

Hearn
Lafcadio Hearn, *Kwaidan* (Jonathan Cape, 'The Travellers' Library'), London, 1927. A delightful collection of Japanese ghost-stories, the first of which hinges on the battle of Dan-no-ura.

Mitford
A. B. Mitford, *Tales of Old Japan*, two vols., London, 1871 (and many later editions). This is a classic, and basic required reading in any branch of Japanese studies. Considering its early date, it is remarkable how faithfully the book captures the spirit of pre-Meiji Japan. The introductions and tailpieces to the stories (including a hair-raising eyewitness account of a formal *seppuku*) are a mine of valuable information.

Ozaki
Yei Theodora Ozaki, *Warriors of Old Japan and Other Stories*, London, 1909. Handy short versions of the lives of Tametomo, Yorimasa, Yoshitsune, and others.

The above list is not intended to be exhaustive, an extended bibliography being precluded by considerations of space. But it includes all the works which the writer has found most helpful in cataloguing Kuniyoshi's warrior-prints.

LIST OF ILLUSTRATIONS

BLACK-AND-WHITE ILLUSTRATIONS IN THE INTRODUCTION

1. The Chinese hero Konseimaō Hanzui attacked by demons. *c.*1827–30. S2.36.
2. Prince Hansoku of India subduing a lion. *c.*1849–50. S66.2.
3. Koshibe no Sugaru catching a thunder-beast. *c.*1834–5. S1c.2.
4. Minamoto no Yoshi-iye at the Nakoso Barrier. *c.*1843. S28.16.
5. Hatsu-hana under the waterfall. *c.*1841–2. S20.7.
6. The courtesan Jigoku. *c.*1845. S35.3.
7. Nagoya Sanzaburō wiping his sword. *c.*1845–8. S46.7.
8. The one-eyed general Yamamoto Kansuke. *c.*1845. S34.4.
9. Masayasu disintegrating before a volley of musketry. *c.*1848–9. S62.36.
10. Tametomo the great archer. *c.*1843–4. S31.19.
11. The *rōnin* and the ghost of his murdered wife. *c.*1845–6. S44.26.
12. *Triptych:* The Taira ghosts attacking Yoshitsune's ship. *c.*1845. T147.
13. Yamato-take-no-mikoto and his 'grass-mowing sword'. 1834–5. S4b.5.
14. The Empress Jingō and her fleet. *c.*1842–3. S21.5.
15. The strong boy Kwaidō Maru. 1860. S93.3.
16. *Triptych:* Tametomo shipwrecked by a great fish. 1851–2. T263.
17. *Triptych:* Ushiwaka fighting Chōhan at the inn. 1849–52. T224.
18. *Triptych:* Nagamochi and the apparition of the Thunder-God. 1849–52. T240.

19. *Triptych:* Kagesuye fighting at the forest of Ikuta. *c.*1845. T153.
20. *Triptych:* Yoshitsune recovering his bow at Yashima. 1857. T339.
21. *Triptych:* Yoshitsune defending the Horikawa palace. 1851–2. T267.
22. *Triptych:* The Taira ghosts preparing to attack Yoshitsune. 1851–2. T266.
23. *Triptych:* Tadanobu resisting arrest. 1855. T321.
24. *Triptych:* The Soga brothers and Tegoshi no Shōshō. *c.*1842–3. T125.

25. *Triptych:* The battle of Kawanakajima. 1852. T284.
26. *Triptych:* Kenshin attacking Shingen at Kawanakajima. 1855. T325.
27. *Triptych:* Shingen discharges his big gun. 1849–52. T246.
28. *Triptych:* First act of the *Chūshingura* drama. 1849–52. T248.
29. Inuyama Dōsetsu amid flames. 1852–3. S74.4.
30. *Triptych:* The revenge of Horiguchi Yasubei. *c.*1847–50. T213.

COLOUR AND BLACK-AND-WHITE PLATES

1. Inukai Kempachi, one of the eight heroes of the *Hakkenden*. *c.*1830. S4a.4.
2. Kane-jo stops the runaway temple-horse. *c.*1825–30. S1a.5.
3. The *Suikoden* hero Rōshi Yensei. *c.*1827–30. S2.50.
4. Abe no Yasuchika exorcizing the fox-woman Tamamo-no-maye. *c.*1834–5. S1c.1.
5. Fuse-hime saving the child Masashi from a thunderbolt. *c.*1836. S4c.3.
6. Inudzuka Shino fighting on the Hōryūkaku roof. *c.*1835. S5.1.
7. Kōmei conjuring the wind. *c.*1836. S10.1.
8. Struggle between Yoshinaka and Tomonori at Naminoyo. *c.*1836. S9.2.
9. Tokiwa-gozen with her three children in the snow. *c.*1841–2. S20.23.
10. Nichiren and the Seven-faced Divinity. *c.*1835–6. S6.6.
11. Appearance of a gourd-plant at the birth of Prince Shōtoku. *c.*1840. S14.1.
12. Kidō Maru learning magic from the *tengu*. *c.*1843. S1f.1.
13. Tomomori and the anchor with which he drowned himself. *c.*1845. S1f.7.
14. The Soga brothers at the tent of Kudō Suketsune. *c.*1836. S8.7.
15. Sasaki Takatsuna commandeering a farmer's horse. *c.*1840. S15.11.
16. Uneme exorcizing the monstrous serpent from the lake. *c.*1842–3. S23.23.
17. Yorimasa shooting at the monster *Nuye*. *c.*1845. S48.6.
18. Taira no Koremochi and the demon-woman. *c.*1843. S28.7.
19. Tametomo on the beach at Ōshima. *c.*1845. S49.3.
20. Masakiyo blown up by a land-mine at Kawanakajima. *c.*1848–9. S63.9.
21. Saitō Toshimoto and a Chinese general struggling under water. *c.*1848–9. S62.31.
22. Shidzuka-gozen in the dancing dress of a *shirabyōshi*. *c.*1843. S25.3.
23. The *Hakkenden* hero Inukai Kempachi. *c.*1845–6. S37.6.
24. Oniwaka Maru and the giant carp. *c.*1848. S1f.10.
25. Yeda Genzō at the defence of the Horikawa palace. 1852. S76.6.
26. Musashi Gorō Sadayo at the battle of Shimahiro-yama. 1847–8. S52.6.
27. Death of Shundō Jiroyemon in the moment of revenge. 1847–8. S51.9.
28. Yamamoto Kansuke wounded to death at Kawanakajima. 1854. S84.2.
29. Mongaku Shōnin under the waterfall. 1860. S93.4.
30. Amakasu Ōmi no Kami, a general of the Uyesugi at Kawanakajima. *c.*1845. S34.9.

31. Kiyo-hime and the bell of Dōjōji. 1855. S87.4.
32. Sōshin returning to help his injured mother. *c.*1840. S13.4.
33. *Triptych:* Sanada Yoichi fighting Matano Gorō at Ishibashiyama. *c.*1835. T28.
34. *Triptych:* The Earth-Spider tormenting the sick Raikō. *c.*1820. T4.
35. *Triptych:* Yorimasa shooting down the monster *Nuye*. *c.*1820–5. T7.
36. *Triptych:* Tametomo's shipwreck. *c.*1836. T30.
37. *Triptych:* The Earth-Spider slain by Raikō's retainers. *c.*1838. T46.
38. *Triptych:* The ghost of Yoshihira at the Nunobiki waterfall. *c.*1825. T10.
39. *Triptych:* Sadayo striking Kintsura before Masakado. *c.*1833–4. T23.
40. *Triptych:* Ushiwaka and Benkei fighting on Gojō bridge. *c.*1839. T47.
41. *Triptych:* Kiyomori arresting the sunset by incantations. *c.*1842–3. T83.
42. *Triptych:* The battle of Fujiidera in driving rain. *c.*1836. T34.
43. *Triptych:* Inudzuka Shino at bay on the Hōryūkaku roof. *c.*1836–7. T41.
44. *Triptych:* The Ashikaga fleet sailing in to attack Nitta. *c.*1839–41. T78.
45. *Triptych:* Ushiwaka visiting Jōruri-hime. *c.*1842–3. T108.
46. *Triptych:* Tadatsune and the giant boar. *c.*1839–41. T72.
47. *Triptych:* Tametomo's master-shot. *c.*1844. T140.
48. *Triptych:* Bridge of boats at the battle of the Nagaragawa. *c.*1842–3. T105.
49. *Triptych:* Death of Tomomori at Dan-no-ura. *c.*1844. T144.
50. *Triptych:* Yoshitsune, his wife Kita-no-kata, and Benkei in the snow. *c.*1844. T133.
51. *Triptych:* Takiyasha and her brother Yoshikado learning toad-magic. *c.*1845. T166.
52. *Triptych:* Takiyasha the witch and the skeleton-spectre. *c.*1844. T138.
53. *Triptych:* Tadatsune and the goddess of Mount Fuji. *c.*1844. T143.
54. *Triptych:* Oniwaka Maru about to slay the giant carp. *c.*1845. T171.
55. *Triptych:* Japanese troops attacking a Korean city. *c.*1845. T145.
56. *Triptych:* Asahina Saburō and the crocodiles. 1849. T218.
57. *Triptych:* Kamei Rokurō and the black bear in the snow. 1849. T215.
58. *Triptych:* Katō Kiyomasa and the tiger in the snow. *c.*1846. T183.

59. *Triptych:* Last stand of the Kusunoki clan at Shijō-nawate. 1851–2. T271.
60. *Triptych:* The rival generals fording the Ujigawa. 1849. T217.
61. *Triptych:* Gentoku leaping his horse into the gorge of Tan. 1853. T296.
62. *Triptych:* Asahina Saburō breaking down the gate. 1852. T281.
63. *Triptych:* Yamamoto Kansuke preparing for his last stand. 1854. T313.
64. *Vertical triptych:* Mongaku Shōnin under the waterfall. 1851–2. T253.

BLACK-AND-WHITE ILLUSTRATIONS IN PART I OF THE CATALOGUE

These illustrations are included in order to show the characteristics of the prints in each series, thereby helping with identification. Full details can be found in their respective Catalogue entries.

INDEX of Characters Portrayed

This Index cannot, of course, be exhaustive; in many triptychs of crowded scenes of battle or court thirty or more figures may well be named, and to include all of them would be out of place in a book of this kind, and would in any case be vetoed by considerations of space. In such cases, therefore, only the main protagonists have been listed. It would be similarly impracticable to include here full biographical entries for such well-known characters as Yoshitsune, when all the necessary information is to be found in the standard works of reference listed in the Bibliographical References; entries are therefore confined to the barest essentials, with selected references. For those characters mentioned in the Introduction, page references are included following the Catalogue numbers at the end of each entry.

The whole subject of Japanese names and titles, their varieties and construction, is admirably dealt with by *Koop* (pp.67–88). For the purposes of this Index we are mainly concerned with the family name (*myōji*), the personal name (*zokumyō*), and the official name (*nanori*), e.g. Hōjō Shirō Tokimasa, or Yamamoto Kansuke Haruyuki. But in general the Japanese had what seems to us a somewhat cavalier attitude to names, which makes an Index such as this difficult to compile. While many heroes are almost invariably known by their *nanori*—Yoshitsune, Kiyomori, Masashige—others are more commonly referred to by their family and personal names—Kamei Rokurō, Ōboshi Yuranosuke—or by their family names and titles—Shinodzuka Iga no Kami, Hara Hayato-no-shō. Rigid consistency is therefore not necessarily the best principle, and I have tried to index the names under the form most commonly encountered, with cross-referencing in doubtful cases. The matter is further complicated by the frequent use of child-names (usually ending in Maru), and Buddhist names which were assumed on becoming a 'retired layman' (*nyūdō*), and, even more so, by the convention of altering the names of characters dead for less than three centuries (this is particularly evident in S62). In addition, the names of, for example, the Forty-Seven *Rōnin* and the heroes of the *Suikoden* appear in differing versions. The reader is therefore requested to exercise patience and indulgence.

ADACHI-GA-HARA, Hag of, see HITOTSUYA.

ADZUMA, FUJIYA: female dramatic character (*Iro no dekiaki*). S46.80.

AKABORI MIDZUYEMON: dramatic villain (*Kameyama-zome*). S45.51.

AKAGARI DAIDŌ: son of Hana-no-moto. S36.61.

AKAHITO, YAMABE NO: (eighth century) one of the Hundred Poets. S19.4; S27.4; S44.18.

AKAZAWA JŪNAI: dramatic character in the Soga cycle. S46.83.

AKISUKE, SAKYŌ-NO-DAYŪ: one of the Hundred Poets; of the Fujiwara clan. S19.79.

AKITSUSHIMA: a wrestler in the play *Shōbudzuke*. S45.52.

AKIYAMA CHŌBEI: servant to Iyemon in *O-Iwa kwaidan*. S45.25.

AKIYUKI, SUGIMOTO: (fourteenth century) follower of Kusunoki Masashige. T352.

AKOGI HEIJI: filial character in *Samezaya*. S46.71.

AKOYA: mistress of Kagekiyo (*Edmunds*, p.282). S36.9; S46.18.

AMA ('diving-girl'): associated with Fujiwara no Kamatari (*Edmunds*, p.424). S1f.2; S35.15; S45.22; S46.11; T189; T299.

AMAGAWAYA GIHEI: *Chūshingura* character (*Dickins*, pp.142ff.). S56.6; S74.53; S86.10.

AMAKASU ŌMI NO KAMI KAGETOKI: Uyesugi warrior at Kawanakajima (1550–60). S34.9; T324.

AMAMIUCHI-NO-SUKUNE: (third century) brother of Takeshiuchi-no-sukune. S74.35.

ANJU-HIME: tragic heroine of romance (*Edmunds*, p.284). S20.1; S23.1; S36.37.

ANTOKU TENNŌ: boy-Emperor, drowned at Dan-no-ura (*Papinot*, p.17; *Edmunds*, p.285). S46.22; T96. pp.17, 22f.

ARAI MARU: servant of the witch Takiyasha (late tenth century). S74.28; T138.

ARAKAWA IDZU NO KAMI: Uyesugi warrior at Kawanakajima (1550–60). S34.10.

ARAKI MATAYEMON (or KARAKI MASAYEMON): celebrated swordsman in the Igagoye revenge story (*Mitford*, 'Kazuma's Revenge'). S36.6; S37.1; T29; T106; T250; T290.

ARIKUNI, MUSASHI SABUROZAYEMON: Taira warrior slain by Tomoye-gozen. S1e.8.

ARIMASA, SADA MUTSU NO KAMI: retainer of Nobunaga, and then of Shibata Katsuiye (late sixteenth century). S62.29.

ARIŌ MARU: servant of Shunkwan (late twelfth century). S1c.13; S15.9.

ASAHINA SABURŌ YOSHIHIDE: early thirteenth-century warrior and strong man (*Papinot*, p.22; *Edmunds*, p.286). S1a.12; S1c.14; S22.3; S31.27; S32.1; S43.4; S45.34; S73.16; S89.1; T31; T102; T119; T218; T281; T342. pp.13, 15, 26.

ASAKA: wife of Yokoyama Tarō in the dramatized story of Oguri Hangwan. S46.58.

ASATADA, CHŪNAGON: one of the Hundred Poets; son of Fujiwara no Sadakata. S19.44.

ATSUMORI, MUKWAN-NO-TAYŪ TAIRA NO: young Taira warrior slain at Ichi-no-tani (*Papinot*, p.625; *Edmunds*, p.289; *Heike*, pp.561–3). S31.1; S46.73; S88.6; T226; T228; T229. p.22.

ATSUTADA, GON-CHŪNAGON: one of the Hundred Poets, 906–43 (*Papinot*, p.94). S19.43.

AYAME-NO-MAYE: wife of Yorimasa (*Edmunds*, p.660). T107. p.21.

BABA MINO NO KAMI, see NOBUFUSA.

BACHŌ: Chinese warrior in the Wars of the Three Kingdoms (early third century). S10.3; T306; T348.

BANZUI CHŌBEI: (seventeenth century) leader of the *otokodate* of Yedo (*Mitford*, 'The Loves of Gompachi and Komurasaki' and 'A Story of the Otokodate of Yedo'). S36.16; S37.2; S40.1; T130.

BENKEI, MUSASHI-BŌ: warrior-monk and henchman of Yoshitsune (*Edmunds*, p.293; *Heike* and *Gikeiki*, *passim*). S1a.9; S1b.1; S1f.3; S1f.10; S4a.13; S7.5; S8.4; S28.2; S31.2; S32.2; S43.3; S45.58; S46.13, 86; S49.1; S61.8; S65.9, 10, 12, 15; S68 *passim*; S74.33; S84.5; S88.37; S89.9; S95d.2; S95e.2; T1; T16; T47; T54; T68; T97; T117; T124; T126; T133–T135; T147; T150; T164; T171; T178; T179; T194; T230; T242; T267; T282; T319; T327; T338. pp.16, 20f., 22, 24f.

BINGO SABURŌ, see TAKANORI.

BINSHIKEN (Min-tzu-ch'ien): Chinese Paragon of Filial Piety. S13.3; S60.5.

BIZENKŌ SHUDŌ: Chinese hero of the *Suikoden*. S2.1; S3.5.

BOKUTENŌ RIŌ: Chinese hero of the *Suikoden*. S2.2; S3.6.

BOTAICHŪ KODAISŌ: Chinese heroine of the *Suikoden*. S2.3; S3.12; S47.1.

BOTSUMEMMOKU SHUTEI: Chinese hero of the *Suikoden*. S3.7.

BOTSUSHARAN BOKKŌ: Chinese hero of the *Suikoden*. S2.2; S3.8.

BOTSU-USEN CHŌSEI: Chinese hero of the *Suikoden*. S2.4; S3.1.

BOYASHA SONJIRŌ: Chinese heroine of the *Suikoden*. S2.5; S3.12.

(GYŌJA) BUSHŌ: Chinese hero of the *Suikoden*. S2.6; S2a.1; S3.8; S47.6; S88.48.

BYŌKWANSAKU YŌYŪ: Chinese hero of the *Suikoden*. S2.7; S3.8; S47.2, 3.

BYŌTAICHŪ SETSUYEI: Chinese hero of the *Suikoden*. S2.8.

BYŌ-UTSUSHI SONRYŪ: Chinese hero of the *Suikoden*. S2.9; S3.3.

CHIDORI: a servant-girl in *Sembonzakura*. S43.1; S45.45; S46.64.

CHIDORI-NO-MAYE: mistress of Katō Shigeuji (Karukaya Dōshin). S46.51.

CHIKAFUSA, YAMAYOSHI GEMBA-NO-JŌ: Takeda warrior at Kawanakajima. S63.11.

CHIKAHIRA, IDZUMI SABURŌ (or KOJIRŌ): d.1213; warrior in the Wada rebellion (*Edmunds*, p.309). S73.14; T75. p.26.

CHIKARA, see RIKIYA.

CHIKATADA, TATE ROKURŌ: retainer of Kiso Yoshinaka. S94.2.

CHIKATSUNE, HONDA JIRŌ: wrestler and retainer of Yoritomo. T74.

CHIKUDŌ MARU: young companion of Kusunoki Masatsura. S1c.7.

CHIMATSU: young son of Masaoka in *Koi sumo hana no Yedo kata*. S45.48.

CHINKYŪ: Chinese warrior in the Wars of the Three Kingdoms (early third century). T301.

CHINSANZAN KŌSHIN: Chinese hero of the *Suikoden*. S2.10; S3.4.

CHITASEI GOYŌ: Chinese hero of the *Suikoden*. S2.11; S3.1.

CHIYO, KAGA NO: eighteenth-century poetess (*Edmunds*, p.309). S20.2; S21.8; S29.1; S33.1; S46.3; S95c.3.

CHIYONŌ-HIME: daughter of Yūki Kageuji, who rebelled against Yoritomo. S23.2.

CHŌHAN, KUMASAKA: twelfth-century warrior-monk and robber chief (*Edmunds*, p.458). S28.18; S65.5; S89.4; T5; T40; T53; T224; T238. p.20.

CHŌHI: Chinese hero in the Wars of the Three Kingdoms (early third century) (*Edmunds*, p.101). S10.7; T277; T291; T294; T307; T348.

CHŌKANKO CHINTATSU: Chinese hero of the *Suikoden*. S2.12; S3.2.

CHŌKI: Chinese warrior in the Wars of the Three Kingdoms (early third century). T310.

CHŌKICHI: youthful character in *Megumi no Kagekiyo*. S46.79.

CHŌKŌ: Chinese warrior in the Wars of the Three Kingdoms (early third century). S10.4.

CHŌKŌ (Chang Hsiao): Chinese Paragon of Filial Piety. S60.21.

CHŌREI (Chang Li): Chinese Paragon of Filial Piety. S60.21.

CHŌRYŌ (Chang Liang): Chinese hero of the Han dynasty (*Edmunds*, p.104). S74.21.

CHŌSEN, Lady: character in the Wars of the Three Kingdoms (early third century). T302.

CHŌ-UN: Chinese warrior in the Wars of the Three Kingdoms (early third century). S10.4.

CHŪJŌ-HIME: daughter of Udaijin Toyonari (eighth century) (*Papinot*, p.89; *Edmunds*, p.300). S23.3; S29.2; S45.59.

CHŪSENKO TEITOKUSON: Chinese hero of the *Suikoden*. S2.13; S2a.2; S3.7; S47.4.

CHŪTŌDA NO TSUBONE: lady of Yenya's household in the *Chūshingura*. S56.5.

CHŪYŪ (Chung Yu): Chinese Paragon of Filial Piety. S60.20.

DAIKOKU: one of the Seven Gods of Good Luck. S43.1.

DAITŌ KWANSHŌ: Chinese hero of the *Suikoden* (sometimes Taitō). S2.14; S3.1; S47.23.

DAKKI (T'a Ki): Chinese manifestation of the Nine-tailed Fox (*Edmunds*, p.184). S66.1.

DAKOSHŌ RICHŪ: Chinese hero of the *Suikoden*. S2.15; S3.2.

DANSHICHI KUROBEI: a flamboyant fishmonger in *Natsu matsuri*. S40.2; S42.1; S45.26; S46.98; S74.5.

DARUMA (Bodhidharma): Buddhist saint, often appearing as a popular toy (*Edmunds*, p.235). S74.70; T235.

DEMBEI: character in *Hanakawado*. S45.33.

DOI JIRŌ: retainer of Yoritomo. S73.9.

DŌIN-HŌSHI: one of the Hundred Poets, originally Fujiwara no Atsuyori. S19.82.

DOKKAKURYŪ (-RYŌ) SŪJUN: Chinese hero of the *Suikoden*. S2.16; S3.4.

DOKKWASEI KŌRYŌ: Chinese hero of the *Suikoden*. S2.73; S3.3.

DŌKWAN, ŌTA: 1432–86; originally Sukenaga (*Papinot*, p.496; *Edmunds*, p.540). S1a.1; S67.4.

DŌSEI: foster-father of Tamamo-no-maye (twelfth century). S66.5.

FUCHIBE IGA NO KAMI, see YOSHIHIRO.

FUDŌ MYŌ-Ō: Buddhist divinity, 'the immovable' (*Edmunds*, p.243). T253. p.26.

FUJIKAGE, NAGAO TŌTŌMI NO KAMI: Uyesugi warrior at Kawanakajima. S63.16.

FUJIKAWA MIDZUYEMON: villainous dramatic character in *Gojūsan tsugi*. S44.39.

FUJI NO TSUBONE: heroine of a ghost-story (*Mitford*, 'The Vampire Cat of Nabeshima'). S44.43.

FUJINOYE: wife of Tadahira and sister of Satō Tadanobu. S4a.1; S20.30; T167; T196.

FUJITSUNA, AOTO: a thirteenth-century upright judge (*Papinot*, p.18; *Edmunds*, p.353), and later a dramatic character. S45.54.

FUJIYA IZAYEMON: character in *Kuruwa bunsho*. S46.53.

FUKUOKA MITSUGI: hero of a melodrama, *Ise ondo*. S36.7; S45.38; S51.2.

FUKUROKUJU: one of the Seven Gods of Good Luck. S43.1.

FUNADA NYŪDŌ: warrior-monk and follower of Nitta Yoshisada. T76.

FUSE-HIME: heroine of Bakin's *Hakkenden* (*Edmunds*, p.355). S4c.3; S36.17; T233. p.30.

FŪTEN: the Wind-God. S11.2.

FUWA BANZAYEMON: villain in several plays (*Mitford*, 'A Story of the Otokodate of Yedo'). S37.3; S45.20; S46.96; T287.

GANRYŪ, SASAKI: enemy of Miyamoto Musashi (see *Dening*). S37.18; S51.7; T335. p.29.

GAPPŌ, TAKAHASHI: hero of a revenge story, *Gappō gatsuji*. S53.7; T9.

GEMBA: character in the play *Sugawara*. S45.53.

GEMBA, TAKUMA (Sakuma Morimasa): enemy of Hideyoshi (*Hawley*, 472ff.). T336.

GEMBEIBORI GEMBEI: character in *Megumi no Kagekiyo*. S46.79.

GENŌ: Buddhist priest-exorcist (*Edmunds*, p.613). S66.6.

GENSHŪ, WADA: cousin and retainer of Kusunoki Masatsura (*Papinot*, p.731). T271; T346.

GENTOKU (Liu Pei): chief character in the Wars of the Three Kingdoms, later became the Emperor Chao Lieh Ti (*Edmunds*, p.152). S10.5; T291; T294; T296; T301; T307.

GINYO: sister of Giō and mistress of Kiyomori (*Heike*, ch.VI). S20.3; S30.1. p.19.

GIŌ: *shirabyōshi* dancer and mistress of Kiyomori (*Heike*, ch.VI). S20.3; S30.1; S46.23. p.19.

GION-NYŌGO: favourite of the Emperor Go-Shirakawa and later of Kiyomori. S30.2; S46.26.

GOKUMON SHŌHEI: character in *Kurofune de-iri no minato*, a play with a homosexual theme. S74.13.

GOMŌ (Wu Mêng): Chinese Paragon of Filial Piety. S13.13; S60.23.

GONTA: character in *Sembonzakura*. S45.46.

GO-Ō-HIME: daughter of Kamada Masakiyo and beloved of Yoshitsune. S20.4.

GORŌ MARU SHIGEMUNE: wrestler and retainer of Yoritomo. S7.3; T159. p.25.

GOSHAKU SOMEGORŌ: character in *Shōchikubai* and other plays. S40.3; S70.1.

GŌTENRAI RYŪSHIN, see HŌTENRAI RYŪSHIN.

GO-TOBA-NO-IN: 1180–1239; eighty-second Emperor; an amateur swordsmith, and one of the Hundred Poets. S19.99.

GO-TOKUDAIJI-SADAIJIN: i.e. Fujiwara no Sanesada, one of the Hundred Poets. S19.81.

GYŌJA BUSHŌ, see BUSHŌ.

GYOKKIRIN ROSHUNGI: Chinese hero of the *Suikoden*. S2.17; S3.8.

GYOKUBANKAN MŌKŌ: Chinese hero of the *Suikoden*. S3.12.

GYOKUHISHŌ KINDAIKEN: Chinese hero of the *Suikoden*. S3.11.

HACHIMAN SABURŌ: retainer of Kudō Suketsune. S74.26.

HACHIMAN TARŌ, see YOSHI-IYE.

HAIJŌKAI: villainous monk in the *Suikoden*. S2.62.

HAKKWAJA YŌSHUN: Chinese hero of the *Suikoden*. S2.18; S3.2; S47.7.

HAKO-Ō MARU, child-name of Soga Gorō Tokimune, q.v.

HAKUJISSO HAKUSHŌ: Chinese hero of the *Suikoden*. S2.19; S2a.3; S3.10.

HAKUMENRŌKUN TEITENJU: Chinese hero of the *Suikoden*. S2.20; S3.2.

HAKUSHŪYEI, Lady: erring wife in the *Suikoden*. S2.67.

HAMANO TADANOSHIN: retainer of Moronao in the *Chūshingura*. S57.37.

HANA-JO: daughter of Oribe Kanamaru in the *Chūshingura*. S56.3.

HANA-NO-MOTO, son of, see AKAGARI DAIDŌ.

HANAREGOMA CHŌKICHI: wrestler in the play *Futatsu chōchō*. S74.60; T172.

HANGAKU-JO: amazon; daughter of Jō Shirō Sukekuni (*Edmunds*, p.372). S20.5; T25; T61.

HANGAMI DANJŌ-NO-JŌ ARAKAGE: monster-fighter of Idzumo. S1c.12.

HANJO-GOZEN: mother of Umewaka Maru (*Edmunds*, p.647). S29.3.

HANSOKU: King of Southern India in the Nine-tailed Fox story.

S66.2, 3, 4; S88.21. p.11.

HANZAWA ROKURŌ: retainer of Yoritomo. S8.7.

HARA HAYATO-NO-SHŌ: Takeda warrior at Kawanakajima. S34.5.

HARUHIRA, HITSU-NO-SAISHŌ: son of envoy to China (*Joly*, s.v. Karu no Daijin). S23.7.

HARUKATA, SUYE: treacherous retainer of Ōuchi Yoshitaka, 1507–51 (*Papinot*, p.505). S36.50; S74.37.

HARUNAGA, ŌTA (Oda Nobunaga): war-lord, 1534–82 (*Papinot*, p.465; *Edmunds*, p.521; *Hawley*, 16–348). S62.28; T204. pp.14, 28.

HARUNORI, KATAYAMA KATARŌ: retainer of Oguri Hangwan. S26.12.

HARUTAKA, KATAYAMA KAJIRŌ: retainer of Oguri Hangwan. S26.11.

HARUTAKA, TAIRA NO (Kambe Nobutaka): third son of Nobunaga, 1558–83 (*Papinot*, p.469). S62.43.

HARUYOSHI, AMARI SAYEMON-NO-JŌ: Takeda warrior at Kawanakajima. S63.6.

HARUYUKI, see YAMAMOTO KANSUKE.

HATA ROKUROZAYEMON: retainer of Nitta Yoshisada. S17.11; S84.11; S94.3; T6.

HATSUBINADA KŌJŌ, see NYŪBINATA KŌJŪ.

HATSU-HANA: self-sacrificing wife of Iinuma Katsugorō (*Edmunds*, p.377). S20.7; T8. p.13.

HATSU-JO, see O-HATSU.

HAYAKAWA AYUNOSUKE: resourceful fisherman. S4a.2.

HAYANO KAMPEI TSUNEYO: supernumerary to the Forty-Seven *Rōnin* (*Dickins*, pp.60–88; *Edmunds*, p.313). S54.47; S59.3; S72.8; S86.5; S90.47.

HAYASE SAYEMON: warrior under Kusunoki Masashige. T350.

HEIDAICHŪ SETSUYEI: Chinese hero of the *Suikoden*. S3.4.

HEKIREKKWA SHIMMEI: Chinese hero of the *Suikoden*. S3.1.

HIDEHIRA, FUJIWARA NO, MUTSU NO KAMI: Yoshitsune's northern protector (*Papinot*, p.101; *Gikeiki*, chs.2, 7, 8). S65.8; T93; T255. pp.20, 25.

HIDEKAZU, ONODERA, see HIDETOMO.

HIDEMOTO, AKASHI RIDAYŪ: retainer of the Toki family (late sixteenth century). S62.2.

HIDENAO, URAMATSU (RYŪYEN): one of the Forty-Seven *Rōnin*. S54.42; S71.4; S90.42.

HIDESATO, TAWARA TŌDA FUJIWARA NO: warrior and loyalist of the tenth century (*Papinot*, p.95; *Edmunds*, p.380). S44.54; T354. pp.18, 21.

HIDETAKE, KUROGANE KŌDZUKE NO SUKE: Uyesugi warrior at Kawanakajima. S63.12.

HIDETATSU, SAITŌ YAMASHIRO NO KAMI (Saitō Yoshitatsu): 1527–61; prominent warrior in the civil wars (*Papinot*, p.529). S62.33.

HIDETOME (-TOMI), ONODERA TŌYEMON: one of the Forty-Seven *Rōnin*. S54.30; S80.9; S90.30.

HIDETOMO (-KAZU), ONODERA JŪNAI: one of the Forty-Seven *Rōnin*. S54.9; S90.9.

HIDETOMO, ONODERA, wife of. S56.4.

HIDEYOSHI, KINOSHITA (Toyotomi Hideyoshi): war-lord and dictator, 1536–98 (*Papinot*, p.693; *Edmunds*, p.381; *Hawley*, *passim*). S62.20; T204; T355. pp.14, 28.

HIGUCHI JIRŌ, see KANEMITSU.

HINADORI: heroine of *Imoseyama* (*Edmunds*, p.457). S45.8.

HIRAGAWARA JIROZŌ: character in *Samezaya*. S46.71.

HIROARI, OKI JIRŌ: early fourteenth-century courtier and archer (*Taiheiki*, p.371). S1a.2.

HIRONAO (or TADAZUMI), II (or I) NO HAYATA: squire to Yorimasa (*Edmunds*, p.660). S4a.6; S89.2; S95d.3; T7; T107; T112. p.21.

HIROTSUNA, see YEDA GENZŌ.

HIROTSUNE, KADZUSA NO SUKE TAIRA NO: twelfth-century warrior (*Papinot*, p.622). S4a.7; S7.1; T24.

HIROYUKI, OGATA, see JIRAIYA.

HISAHIDE, MATSUNAGA DAIZEN: war-lord, 1510–77 (*Papinot*, p.363; *Edmunds*, p.382; *Hawley*, 274). S62.22.

HISAMATSU: lover of O-Some in *O-Some Hisamatsu*. S45.15; S46.89.

HISAMITSU, AIGŌ KOZAYEMON: served under Shibata Katsuiye (possibly Saigō Masakatsu, d.1561; *Papinot*, p.525). S62.1.

HISAYOSHI, NAKA-URA SARUKICHIRŌ, pseudonym for Hide-yoshi, q.v. S62.25; T204.

HITENTAISEI RIKON: Chinese hero of the *Suikoden*. S2.21; S3.10.

HITOMARO, KAKINOMOTO NO: d.729; one of the Hundred Poets. S19.3; S27.3.

HITO MARU: daughter of Kagekiyo. S36.64; S46.97.

HITOTSUYA ('Lonely House'), Hag of: villainess of popular mythology (*Edmunds*, p.281). S23.6; S74.49; T82; T318; T330. p.30.

HŌKAI-BŌ: villainous character in *Sumidagawa* and other plays. S46.68.

HOKKE CHŌBEI: *otokodate* dramatic character. S42.2.

HOMMA SABURŌ: murderer of Hino Suketomo, father of Kumawaka Maru, in 1332, and subsequently slain by the latter. S61.3.

HŌNAN SHŌNIN: priest involved in a ghost-story. S44.28.

HONKŌSHIN DŌMŌ: Chinese hero of the *Suikoden*. S3.3.

HORIBE YASUBEI, wife and daughter of. S74.47 (cf. T148 and T213).

HORIKOSHI DAIREI (stage name for Hotta Kōdzuke no Suke): tyrannical land-owner (*Mitford*, 'The Ghost of Sakura'). S74.50.

HŌTARŌ: child dramatic character. S74.55.

HOTEI ICHIYEMON: strong man of Osaka. S70.2.

HŌTENRAI RYŌSHIN: Chinese hero of the *Suikoden*. S2.22; S3.3; S47.5.

HŌTENTEI: enemy general in the *Suikoden*. S2.61.

HOTOKE-GOZEN: *shirabyōshi* dancer and mistress of Kiyomori (*Sadler*, pp.29, 30; *Edmunds*, p.395; *Heike*, pp.22ff.). S15.2; S20.8; S33.2; S46.12. p.19.

HŌTOKU: Chinese warrior in the Wars of the Three Kingdoms. S10.8.

HYAKUMAN: left by her husband, she went mad and could not recognize her own child. S20.9.

HYAKUSHŌSHŌ KANTŌ: Chinese hero of the *Suikoden*. S3.9.

HYŌSHITŌ RINCHŪ: Chinese hero of the *Suikoden*. S2.23; S2a.4; S3.1; S47.8; S88.29.

IBARAKI: female demon encountered by Watanabe no Tsuna. S28.45; S46.6.

ICHIJŌSEI KOSANRYŌ, see KOSANRYŌ ICHIJŌSEI.

ICHIRAI-HŌSHI: warrior-monk, late twelfth century (*Heike*, p.266). S8.3; S73.10. p.21.

ICHIYEMON: dramatic character; an inferior retainer (*ashigaru*). S46.88.

IDZUMI SHIKIBU: eleventh-century poetess (*Papinot*, p.224). S19.56; S20.10.

IDZUTSU-HIME: daughter of Ki no Aritsune and wife of the poet Narihira. S20.11.

IGA NO JUTARŌ: elderly retainer of Yoshikado (tenth century). S17.4; S61.10; S87.1; S88.17; T89; T111; T219. p.18.

IGA NO TSUBONE: daughter of Shinodzuka Iga no Kami and wife of Kusunoki Masanori. S46.40.

IHEI: a servant (dramatic character). S43.2.

II (or I) NO HAYATA, see HIRONAO.

IINUMA KATSUGORŌ: a cripple cured by his wife's devotion. S53.2; T8.

IKKYŪ: 1394–1481; an eminent but eccentric priest (*Papinot*, p.201; *Edmunds*, p.404). S44.49.

IMA-JO: a poor but filial girl of Takenouchi in Yamato. S23.9.

IMAKUNI, KANAWA GORŌ: loyal retainer of Fujiwara no Kamatari. S46.28.

IMARO, IDZUMO NO: seventh-century slayer of sea-monsters. S1c.9.

INAGAWA JIROKICHI: a wrestler (dramatic character). S46.54.

INUDA KOBUNGO YASUYORI: hero of Bakin's *Hakkenden*. S4c.1; S5.3; S37.4; S38.11; T36; T233.

INUDZUKA SHINO MORITAKA: hero of Bakin's *Hakkenden*. S4a.3; S5.1; S37.5; S74.3; S95f.3; T41; T42; T233. p.30.

INUKAI KEMPACHI NOBUMICHI: hero of Bakin's *Hakkenden*. S4a.4; S5.2; S37.6; S95f.3; T41; T42; T233. p.30.

INUKAWA SŌ- (SHŌ)SUKE YOSHITŌ: hero of Bakin's *Hakkenden*. S5.5; S37.7; T36; T233.

INUMURA DAIKAKU (KAKUTARŌ) MASANORI: hero of Bakin's *Hakkenden*. S4b.2; S5.8; S37.8; T42; T233.

INUYAMA DŌSETSU TADATOMO: hero of Bakin's *Hakkenden*. S4c.2; S5.6; S37.9; S74.4; T42; T233. p.30.

INUYE SHIMBYŌYE MASASHI: hero of Bakin's *Hakkenden*. S4c.3; S5.4; S37.10; T233.

INUZAKA KENO TANETOMO: hero of Bakin's *Hakkenden*. S4a.5; S5.7; S37.11; T36; T233.

ISAMI TOMOKICHIRŌ: character in the dramatized story of Jiraiya. S46.57.

ISE: poetess of the Fujiwara family. S27.19.

ISHIDŌ MARU: son of Karukaya Dōshin (*Edmunds*, p.429). S46.35.

ISHIDOME BUSUKE: retainer of Araki Matayemon (*Mitford*, 'Kazuma's Revenge'). S46.70; T29.

ISHII HANZŌ: hero of a revenge story; he killed Akabori Midzuyemon, the murderer of several of his relatives. S53.3.

ISHI-JO: wife of Ōboshi Yuranosuke in the *Chūshingura*. S56.1.

ISHIKAWA GOYEMON: late sixteenth-century robber (*Papinot*, p.212; *Edmunds*, p.411). S36.52.

ISOGAI HYŌDAYŪ: dramatic character in a story of a stolen sword. S44.39.

ISSUN TOKUBEI: character in *Natsu matsuri*. S46.98.

ITSUSHIKWA SAIKEI: Chinese hero of the *Suikoden*. S3.10.

IWADZU TETSUYEMON SHIGENOBU: retainer of Odai Matarokurō (sixteenth century). S4a.11; T201.

IWAFUJI, TSUBONE: villainess in *Kagamiyama*. S45.30.

IYETERU, MENJU SŌSUKE: retainer of Shibata Katsuiye (*Hawley*, 29, 505, 508). S62.23.

JAKUREN-HŌSHI: priest-poet of the Fujiwara family. S19.87.

JIGOKU: courtesan patronized by the priest Ikkyū, q.v. S35.3; S44.49. p.13.

JIJŪ, MATSUYOI NO: twelfth-century poetess, also known as Kojijū. S15.3.

JINGŌ KŌGŌ: Empress (170–269), conqueror of Korea (*Papinot*, p.229; *Edmunds*, p.414). S21.5; S31.3; S77.4; T51. pp.17, 28, 29.

JINGORŌ, HIDARI: 1594–1634; celebrated sculptor in wood (*Papinot*, p.152; *Edmunds*, p.378). S35.2.

JINKIGUNSHI SHUBU: Chinese hero of the *Suikoden*. S2.24; S3.2.

JINKYŌTAIHŌ TAISŌ: Chinese hero of the *Suikoden*. S2.25.

JINSABURŌ: servant to Shikamatsu Kanroku, one of the Forty-Seven *Rōnin*. S54.51.

JIRAIYA: robber chief, formerly Ogata Hiroyuki (*Edmunds*, p.415). S4a.12; S24.3; S74.14; S87.2; T356.

JITŌ TENNŌ: Empress (687–96) and poetess (*Papinot*, p.232). S19.2; S27.2.

JŌMYŌ, TSUTSUI: late twelfth-century warrior-monk (*Edmunds*, p.416). S8.3; S73.10. p.21.

JŌRURI-HIME: daughter of the headman of Yahagi in Mikawa;

loved and deserted by Yoshitsune (*Edmunds*, p.417; *Gikeiki*, pp.47–50). S20.12; S36.10; S44.40; S65.6; T85; T108. p.20.

JUNTEI, TSUCHII YAMATO NO KAMI (Tsutsui Junkei): 1549–84; allied with Nobunaga, Akechi Mitsuhide, and Hideyoshi successively (*Papinot*, p.706; *Hawley*, 275). S62.48.

JUROBEI, AWA NO: chief character in *Awa no naruto*; killed his own daughter in ignorance. S36.54; S51.1.

JU-UNRYŪ KŌSONSHŌ: Chinese hero of the *Suikoden*. S2.26; S3.8; S47.10.

KAGECHIKA, ŌBA: defeated Yoritomo at Ishibashiyama, 1180 (*Papinot*, p.463). T340.

KAGEHISA, MATANO GORŌ: d.1182; warrior and wrestler on the Taira side (*Edmunds*, p.419). S1a.13; S1c.8; S1f.6; S8.1; S16.6; S46.85; S95b.1; T28; T39; T94; T141; T197; T227; T340; T353. p.21.

KAGE-IYE, KAKIZAKI IDZUMI NO KAMI: Uyesugi warrior at Kawanakajima. S63.11.

KAGEKADO, KATŌJI: twelfth-century warrior (*Edmunds*, p.618). S15.4; T312.

KAGEKIYO, AKUSHICHIBYŌYE TAIRA NO: Taira champion (*Papinot*, p.623; *Edmunds*, p.420). S22.6; S31.4; S46.56, 97; S52.4; S74.51; S76.4; S88.52; T60; T98; T109; T146; T157; T300.

KAGESUYE, KAJIWARA GENDA: d.1200; Minamoto warrior (*Edmunds*, p.421). S22.7; S28.32; S31.5; S67.3; S73.5; T18; T62; T153; T191; T193; T217; T225; T334. p.22.

KAGESUYE, KAJIWARA, wife of. S20.28.

KAGETOKI, KAJIWARA HEIZŌ: father of Kagesuye (*Papinot*, p.246; *Edmunds*, p.422). S36.55; T67; T153; T241; T320. pp.21, 22, 24.

KAGUYA-HIME: daughter of the old bamboo-gatherer (*taketori*) (*Edmunds*, p.611). S44.14.

KAJI(-JO) of Gion: waitress in a Kyoto tea-house and talented poetess; niece of the artist Kōrin. S20.13; S25.1; S29.4; S35.4.

KAKOGAWA HONZŌ: chief retainer of Wakasa no Suke in the *Chūshingura*. S45.56; S86.2, 9.

KAKUGAWA MONZŌ, see KAKOGAWA HONZŌ.

KAKUHAN, YOKOGAWA: warrior-monk of Yoshino (*Gikeiki*, pp.183–6). S8.2; S65.16; S89.8; T2; T257.

KAKUJU: old lady in the play *Sugawara*. S46.30.

KAKUMEI, TAYŪ-BŌ: warrior-monk and secretary to Yoshinaka (*Heike*, p.405). T25.

KAKUREGA NO MOHEI: dramatic character, involved with a *kappa*. S42.3.

KAKUTEI, KAWACHI: one of Chōhan's robber-gang. S65.4.

KAKUYA-HIME, see KAGUYA-HIME.

KAKUZEN, HŌZŌ-IN. S89.3.

KAMADA MATAHACHI: strong man of Matsuzaka, Ise, and monster-slayer. S1e.3; S23.10; S43.3; S74.20.

KAMEGIKU: *shirabyōshi* dancer under the Emperor Go-Toba; mistress of Suketsune. S36.46; T304.

KAMEI ROKURŌ, see SHIGEKIYO.

KAMEYA CHŪBEI: dramatic character; lover of Umegawa. S46.75.

KAMIGASHI-HIME: heroine under the Emperor Keikō (71–130) (*Edmunds*, p.425, s.v. Kaminatsugi-hime; cf. *Nihongi* I, pp.192–4). S1a.8; S87.3.

KAMIYA IYEMON (or NIYEMON), see TAMIYA IYEMON.

KAMIYA JIHEI: hero of a double-suicide play, *Ten no Amijima*. S51.3.

KANAI TANEGORŌ: monster-slayer. S74.63.

KANAMARU, ORIBE YAHEI: one of the Forty-Seven *Rōnin*; a septuagenarian. S54.21; S78.8; S80.6; S90.21.

KANCHIKOTSURITSU SHUKI: Chinese hero of the *Suikoden*. S2.27; S3.12.

KANEFUSA, YOSHIOKA: dyer by profession, but an expert swordsman. S37.22.

KANEHIDE, OKANO GINYEMON: one of the Forty-Seven *Rōnin*. S54.11; S90.11.

KANEHIDE, OKANO, wife of. S56.14.

KANEHIRA, IMAI SHIRŌ: d.1184; retainer of Yoshinaka and brother of Higuchi Kanemitsu (*Papinot*, p.204; *Edmunds*, p.427). S94.4; T63; T265.

KANE-JO (or O-KANE): strong woman of Ōmi province (*Edmunds*, p.427). S1a.5; S20.14; S24.5; S29.5; S35.5; S48.4; S95a.2.

KANEMASA, MINAMOTO NO: one of the Hundred Poets. S19.78.

KANEMITSU, HIGUCHI JIRŌ: retainer of Yoshinaka; later said to have become a sailor named Matsuyemon (*Papinot*, p.154; *Edmunds*, p.427). S1a.14; S46.34; S73.8; S94.2; T181.

KANEMORI, TAIRA NO: one of the Hundred Poets. S19.40.

KANESADA, YOSHIDA SADAYEMON: one of the Forty-Seven *Rōnin*. S54.6; S71.3; S78.3; S90.6.

KANESUKE, YOSHIDA CHŪZAYEMON: one of the Forty-Seven *Rōnin*. S54.50; S80.16; S90.50.

KANETAKA, YAMAKI HANGWAN: Taira ally, slain by Yoritomo (*Heike*, p.303). S92.4; T88; T123; T239; T312. pp.15, 21.

KANETSUGU, see NAOYE YAMASHIRO NO KAMI.

KANETSUNE, MIURA JIROYEMON: one of the Forty-Seven *Rōnin*. S54.49; S72.4; S80.5; S90.49.

KANEYOSHI, KOBAYASHI HEIHACHI(RŌ): retainer of Moronao in the *Chūshingura*. S57.8; T184.

KANKAI, see TANKAI.

KANKE: i.e. Sugawara no Michizane, q.v.; one of the Hundred Poets. S19.24.

KAN NO BUNTEI (Wên Ti of Han): Chinese Paragon of Filial Piety; son of the founder of the Han dynasty (*Edmunds*, p.204). S60.3.

KANSHIN (Han Sin): late third-century BC Chinese warrior (*Edmunds*, p.124). T27.

KAOYO-GOZEN: wife of Yenya in the *Chūshingura* (*Dickins*, pp.15ff.). S46.90; S86.1; T248.

KARAKI MASAYEMON, see ARAKI MATAYEMON.

KARIYA-HIME: heroine of the play *Sugawara*. S45.49; S46.30.

KARUKAYA DŌSHIN, see SHIGEUJI, KATŌ.

KARUMO: filial girl of Matsuyama (*Edmunds*, p.475). S23.16.

KARUMO: courtesan, associated with Hayano Kampei. S72.8.

KASANE: wife of Yoyemon; heroine of a ghost-story (*Edmunds*, p.530). S30.3; S74.54.

KASHIWADE NO OMI HADESU (HANOSHI, HATEBE, or HASUHI): envoy to Korea under the Emperor Kimmei (545) (*Nihongi* II, p.60; *Edmunds*, p.370). S1e.7; S4a.8; S17.3.

KASHIWAGI-DAYŪ: courtesan of Shimabara in the *Chūshingura*. S56.12.

KATSUCHIYO MARU, child-name of Takeda Shingen, q.v.

KATSUIYE, SHIBATA, see TATSUIYE, CHIBATA.

KATSUMA GENGOBEI, see SATSUMA GENGOBEI.

KATSUMASA, TAKAGAWA: victor over the Hōjō at Shinagawa. S61.11.

KATSUMASA, TATSUGAWA SAKON (Takigawa Kazumasu): skilled strategist in the service of Nobunaga (*Papinot*, p.640). S62.45.

KATSUOKI, SAITŌ UHYŌYE-NO-TAYŪ (Saitō Tatsuoki): defeated by Nobunaga, 1564 (*Papinot*, p.529; *Hawley*, 236, 255, 256). S62.32.

KATSUTOYO, SHIMURA MASAZŌ: a prominent retainer of Katō Kiyomasa. S62.38.

KATSUYORI, TAKEDA INASHIRŌ: son of Takeda Shingen (*Papinot*, p.637; *Edmunds*, p.597). S34.2.

KAWABE NO OMI: shipbuilder under Shōtoku Taishi (618) (*Nihongi* II, p.147). S14.2.

KAWADAMURA KŌJO: Japanese Paragon of Filial Piety. S30.4.

KAWADZU SABURŌ, see SUKEYASU.

KAWARA NO SADAIJIN: i.e. Minamoto no Toru (822–95), one of the Hundred Poets (*Papinot*, p.374). S19.14; S27.14.

KAZUTADA, ONIKOJIMA YATARŌ, probably identical with To-rahide, q.v. S81.5.

KAZU-UJI, HOSOKAWA: Ashikaga general against Kusunoki Masatsura. T34; T333.

KENDŌJIN IKUHŌSHI: Chinese hero of the *Suikoden*. S3.4.

KENGYŪ (K'ien Niu): the Divine Herdsman of the Milky Way legend (*Edmunds*, p.620). S19.6.

KENREI-MONIN: daughter of Kiyomori and consort of the Emperor Takakura (*Edmunds*, p.447). S46.43; T48; T96.

KENSHIN, UYESUGI: 1530–78; war-lord of Echigo (*Papinot*, p.716; *Edmunds*, p.625, s.v. Terutora). S24.1; S31.6; S32.3; S34.8; S73.2; S95c.5; S95f.1; T136; T160; T162; T165; T175; T231; T292; T314; T325; T332; T345. pp.13, 28.

KESA-GOZEN: twelfth-century tragic heroine (*Edmunds*, p.335, s.v. Endō). S20.15; S33.3; T129. p.26.

KEYAMURA ROKUSUKE: late sixteenth-century strong man and expert swordsman. S1e.4; S23.11; S37.12; S45.43; S53.4; S88.23; T131; T137; T170.

KEZORI KUYEMON: pirate captain (dramatic character). S36.51; S45.18; S52.5.

KICHIJI: gold-merchant; companion of Yoshitsune (*Gikeiki*, pp.43–8, 76–88). T149.

KICHIYEMON: dramatic character; an inferior retainer (*ashigaru*). S45.50.

KICHIZO: dramatic character; lover of O-Shichi. S43.5; S74.29.

KIDŌ MARU (see also YASUSUKE, HAKAMADARE): robber and wizard in the late tenth century (*Edmunds*, p.432). S1f.1; S8.6; S17.2; S88.28; T3; T169; T262. p.18.

KIHEIJI, HATCHŌ-TSUBOTE: retainer of Tametomo; husband of Yatsushiro. S35.1; S64.4; S76.5.

KII, YŪSHI-NAISHINNŌ-KE: poetess (one of the Hundred Poets). S19.72.

KIKAKU: poetess of the Tokugawa period. S35.6.

KIKENJI TOKYŌ: Chinese hero of the *Suikoden*. S2.28; S3.12; S47.11.

KIKU-NO-MAYE: beloved of Satsuma no Kami Tadanori (*Edmunds*, p.602). S28.38.

KIKUŌ MARU: page to Noritsune (*Heike*, p.656). T49; T230.

KIKYŌ-NO-MAYE: lady of the court of Masakado. T177.

KIMMŌKEN DANKEIJŪ: Chinese hero of the *Suikoden*. S2.29; S3.9.

KIMMŌKO YENJUN: Chinese hero of the *Suikoden*. S3.2.

KIMPYŌSHI YŌRIN: Chinese hero of the *Suikoden*. S2.30; S3.9.

KINGAMPYŌ SHION: Chinese hero of the *Suikoden*. S3.4.

KINSEMPYŌSHI TŌRYŪ: Chinese hero of the *Suikoden*. S2.31; S3.11.

KINSŌSHU JONEI: Chinese hero of the *Suikoden*. S2.32; S3.6.

KINSUKE, TAKENORI: Japanese Paragon of Filial Piety. S23.12.

KINTARŌ: inferior retainer (*ashigaru*). S48.2.

KINTARŌ, see KINTOKI.

KINTŌ, DAINAGON: 966–1041; of the Fujiwara family and one of the Hundred Poets (*Papinot*, p.95). S19.57.

KINTOKI, SAKATA NO (started life as KWAIDŌ MARU): strong man and retainer of Raikō (*Mitford*, 'The History of Sakata Kintoki'; *Edmunds*, p.435). S1d.1; S1e.11; S7.2; S12 *passim*; S17.10; S31.7; S46.25; S74.27; S87.6; S88.12; S93.3; S94.1; T3; T4; T21; T44; T46; T90; T128; T169; T261; T262; T298; T305; T357. pp.9, 18f.

KINTSURA, ROKURŌ: brother of Masakado (mid tenth century). S61.5; T23; T252. p.18.

KINUGAWA TANIZŌ: wrestler; character in *Date kurabe*. S45.39.

KIRI-ISHI TANGE: dramatic character. S43.1.

KISANDA: servant to Yoshitsune (*Gikeiki*, esp. pp.145ff.). S65.3; T20; T47; T108; T185; T264.

KISEN-HŌSHI: priest; one of the Hundred Poets. S19.8; S27.8.

KITA-NO-KATA: wife of Yoshitsune. T133; T164.

KIYOHIDE, WAKAGAWA (Nakagawa): 1542–83; follower of Nobunaga (*Papinot*, p.427; *Hawley*, 502). T336.

KIYO-HIME: dragon-demon heroine of the story of the bell of Dōjōji (*Edmunds*, p.437). S49.2; S87.4.

KIYOKAZU, SAKURAI TAKICHI: one of the Three Swordsmen of Shidzu-ga-mine (1583) (*Hawley*, 494). S62.34.

KIYOMASA, KATŌ: 1562–1611; leading general of Hideyoshi (*Papinot*, p.262; *Edmunds*, p.438; *Hawley*, 190ff.). S1e.1; S62.8; S76.8; S84.3; S88.30; S95b.2; T183; T203; T205; T317. pp.28f.

KIYOMORI, TAIRA NO: war-lord and dictator, 1118–81 (*Papinot*, p.620; *Edmunds*, p.440; *Heike*, pp.4–370 *passim*). S15.5; S31.8; S36.49; S46.47; S52.3; T10; T83; T139; T155. pp.19, 20, 21, 23.

KIYOSHIGE, SURUGA JIRŌ: retainer of Yoshitsune (*Gikeiki*, p.340 etc.). S31.9.

KŌCHŪ: Chinese warrior in the Wars of the Three Kingdoms. T309.

KOGA SABURŌ. S16.4.

KŌGO NO TSUBONE: beloved of the Emperor Takakura (1169–81) (*Heike*, ch.IV). S21.1.

KŌHŌGI SŌKŌ: Chinese hero of the *Suikoden*. S3.1; S95f.2.

KOJORŌ: female character in the play *Shōbu katabira*. S74.8.

KOJŌSŌ JISEN: Chinese hero of the *Suikoden*. S2.33; S3.3.

KŌJU MARU: sacrificed himself in place of his father Fujiwara no Nakamitsu. S23.13.

KŌJUN: Chinese warrior in the Wars of the Three Kingdoms. T301.

KŌKAKU (Chiang Ko): Chinese Paragon of Filial Piety. S79.5.

KOKONOHE-TAYŪ: courtesan in *Gosan no kiri*. S46.61.

KŌKŌ TENNŌ: Emperor (885–7); one of the Hundred Poets. S19.15; S27.15.

KOKUSEMPŪ RIKI: Chinese hero of the *Suikoden*. S1f.9; S2.34; S2a.5; S3.1; S36.28.

KŌKYŌ (Huang Hsiang): Chinese Paragon of Filial Piety. S60.13.

KOMACHI, ONO NO: 834–900; court beauty and poetess (*Papinot*, p.490; *Edmunds*, p.449). S1d.2; S19.9; S27.9; S29.8; S36.1; S46.95.

KOMAN: heroine who saved the Minamoto banner from capture by the Taira (*Edmunds*, p.451). S36.23; S74.71; T180.

KOMAN: *geisha* in the play *Godairiki*. S46.63.

KŌMEI: Chinese sage and strategist in the Wars of the Three Kingdoms (*Edmunds*, p.113). S10.1; T278; T294.

KOMIDZUCHA, NEGORO NO: warrior-priest of the Negoro temple, Konraiji; follower of the Saitō (cf. *Hawley*, 533, 534). S62.26.

KŌMYŌ KŌGŌ: 701–60; Imperial consort (*Papinot*, p.305; *Edmunds*, p.453). S74.58.

KONAMI: daughter of Honzō; betrothed to Rikiya in the *Chūshingura*. S68.8.

KONGARA-DŌJI: acolyte of Fudō Myō-ō. S93.4; T253. p.26.

KONJIN CHŌGORŌ: wrestler who encountered demons, in *Futatsu chōchō*. S42.4.

KONKŌRYŪ RISHUN: Chinese hero of the *Suikoden*. S2.35; S3.6.

KON-Ō MARU: fisherman who introduced the *tai* as a New Year speciality. S45.9.

KONOMURA ŌINOSUKE: elderly character of Chinese origin in *Gosan no kiri*. S74.15.

KONSEIMAŌ HANZUI: Chinese hero of the *Suikoden*. S2.36; S3.10; S47.12. p.10.

KOREMOCHI, TAIRA NO: eleventh-century hero of the play

Momiji-gari (*Papinot*, p.619; *Edmunds*, p.454). Sometimes confused with Koreshige (S87.5). S1c.15; S28.7.

KOREMORI, SAMMI CHŪJŌ TAIRA NO: son of Shigemori (*Papinot*, p.625; *Edmunds*, p.454; *Heike, passim*). S46.99.

KORESHIGE, TAIRA NO, see KOREMOCHI.

KOSANRYŌ ICHIJŌSEI: Chinese heroine of the *Suikoden*. S2.37; S3.2; S47.9.

KŌSEKIKŌ (Huang-shih-kung): the 'yellow stone elder'; Chinese worthy (*Edmunds*, p.105). S74.21.

KOSHIKIBU-NO-NAISHI: eleventh-century poetess; daughter of the poetess Idzumi-shikibu (*Papinot*, p.312; *Edmunds*, p.455). S35.7.

KOSHIO DENSHIRŌ: retainer of Moronao in the *Chūshingura*. S57.43.

KOSHIRŌ HYŌGO: Kusunoki warrior killed at Shijō-nawate (1348). T347.

KOTARŌ: son of Matsuō Maru in the play *Sugawara*. S46.16.

KŌTEIKEN (Huang T'ing-chien): Chinese Paragon of Filial Piety. S60.24.

KOTŌDA, ŌMI NO: retainer of Kudō Suketsune in the *Soga monogatari*. S74.26.

KŌTŌ-NO-NAISHI: wife of Nitta Yoshisada (*Edmunds*, p.456). T244.

KUDAYŪ: spy for Moronao in the *Chūshingura* (*Dickins*, pp.88–110). S86.7.

KUGANOSUKE: hero of the play *Imoseyama* (*Edmunds*, p.457). S46.66.

KUMAWAKA MARU, HINO: son of Hino Suketomo (d.1332), later named Hino Kunimitsu (*Papinot*, p.157; *Edmunds*, p.458). S23.5; S36.35; S61.3; T120.

KUME SENNIN: indiscreet magician of Yamato (*Edmunds*, p.459). S74.46.

KUNIHARU, OBATA MATABEI: Takeda warrior at Kawanakajima. S63.10.

KUNIHIRA, SAIJŌ TOTARŌ: son of Hidehira of Mutsu. T326.

KUNITOMO, YASUDA TAKUBYŌYE: retainer of the Toki family (sixteenth century). S62.49.

KUNITOSHI: Minamoto warrior at Yashima (1184). T109.

KURIU SAYEMON: leading retainer of Nitta Yoshisada. T6.

KUROFUNE CHŪYEMON: character in the play *Kurofune de-iri no minato*. S74.13.

KUROTSUKA HACHIRŌ: Taira warrior slain by Tomoye-gozen. T25.

KUZUNOHA: fox-wife of Abe no Yasuna (tenth century); mother of Seimei. S36.4; S45.2; S46.27; S74.44.

KWACHŌKO KYŌ-Ō: Chinese hero of the *Suikoden*. S3.7.

KWAGANSHUNKEI TŌHI: Chinese hero of the *Suikoden*. S3.9.

KWAIDŌ MARU, child-name of Kintoki, q.v.

KWAKKYO (Kuo Chü): Chinese Paragon of Filial Piety. S13.11; S60.14; S79.4.

KWAKUBIMBA ŌTEIROKU: Chinese hero of the *Suikoden*. S2.38; S3.12.

KWANNON: Buddhist divinity of mercy. S44.51; S74.49; T82; T318; T330. p.30.

KWANSHŌJŌ, see MICHIZANE.

KWANU: Chinese warrior *par excellence* in the Wars of the Three Kingdoms (*Edmunds*, p.141). S10.2; S17.8; S46.50; S88.16; T291; T293–T295; T297; T307; T309; T311.

KWAOSHŌ ROCHISHIN: Chinese hero of the *Suikoden*. S2.39; S2a.6; S3.5; S46.17; S47.13.

KWATSUYENRA GENSHŌSHICHI: Chinese hero of the *Suikoden*. S2.40; S2a.7; S3.6; S47.14.

KWAYŌ-FUJIN: incarnation of the Nine-tailed Fox in India. S66.2, 3, 4.

KYŌGOKU TAKUMI: villain of the Ichimisai revenge story. S46.65; T131; T137; T170. p.30.

KYŌ-NO-KIMI, see KITA-NO-KATA.

KYŌSHI (Chiang Shih): Chinese Paragon of Filial Piety. S13.7; S60.9.

KYUBIKI TŌSŌ-Ō: Chinese hero of the *Suikoden*. S3.7.

KYUMONRYŌ SHISHIN: Chinese wrestler-hero of the *Suikoden*. S2.41, 42, 43; S3.4; S47.15; S88.38.

KYŪSAKU, YAMAZAKI NO: character in the play *O-Some Hisamatsu*. S45.15.

KYŪSEMPŌ SAKUCHŌ: Chinese hero of the *Suikoden*. S2.44; S3.8.

MACHŪ: Chinese warrior in the Wars of the Three Kingdoms. T310.

MAGOYEMON: elderly dramatic character; father of Umegawa, q.v. S46.75.

MAMA, faithful wife of: of lowly origin, but a beauty and married to a man of quality. S21.6.

MASA-AKI, MASE CHŪDAYŪ: one of the Forty-Seven *Rōnin*. S54.44; S72.2 (Yase Chindayū); S90.44.

MASAFUSA, ŌYE NO: eleventh-century courtier. S1f.5; S17.1.

MASAHARU, TAI NO JURŌ: retainer of Minamoto no Mitsunaka. S4b.6.

MASAHISA, ISOAI JUROYEMON: one of the Forty-Seven *Rōnin*. S54.10; S80.17 (Isogaya Jirozayemon); S90.10.

MASAKADO, TAIRA NO: 901–40; arch-rebel and usurper (*Papinot*, p.618; *Edmunds*, p.464). S61.5; T23; T177; T252. p.18.

MASAKAGE, NAGAO ECHIZEN NO KAMI: Uyesugi warrior at Kawanakajima. S34.11.

MASAKAGE, YAMAGATA SABUROHEI: Takeda warrior at Kawanakajima. S63.5; S82.4; T331.

MASAKATA, SAKAGAKI GENZŌ: one of the Forty-Seven *Rōnin*. S54.7; S90.7.

MASAKATA, TOMIMORI SUKEYEMON: one of the Forty-Seven *Rōnin*. S54.27; S78.9 (Tominomori); S80.2; S90.27.

MASAKATA, TOMI(NO)MORI, mother of. S56.9.

MASAKIYO, FUJIWARA NO, see KIYOMASA, KATŌ.

MASAKIYO, MOROZUMI BUNGO NO KAMI: Takeda warrior at Kawanakajima. S63.9.

MASAKO: daughter of Hōjō Tokimasa and wife of Yoritomo (*Edmunds*, p.465). S44.10.

MASAKUNI, KAZAMA: retainer of Oguri Hangwan. S26.8.

MASAMORI, FUKISHIMA (Fukushima Masanori, 1561–1624): follower, successively, of Hideyoshi and Iyeyasu (*Papinot*, p.108; *Hawley*, 238). S62.9.

MASANAO, SASAI UKON: follower of Nobunaga (*Hawley*, 221). S62.37.

MASANORI, KUSUNOKI: d.1390; youngest son of Masashige (*Papinot*, p.334). S61.4.

MASAOKA: nurse to the Ashikaga family; also appears in *Sendai hagi*. S20.16; S45.48.

MASASADA, KAZAMA: retainer of Oguri Hangwan. S26.10.

MASASHIGE, KUSUNOKI: 1294–1336; loyalist leader against the Ashikaga (*Papinot*, p.333; *Edmunds*, p.467; *Taiheiki, passim*). S16.3; S31.10; S73.33; T121; T341; T344; T350; T352. p.27.

MASASHIGE, KUSUNOKI, wife of. S20.29.

MASATADA, INA-UYE DAIKURŌ: retainer of Katō Kiyomasa; fought in Korea. S62.16.

MASATADA, YENDŌ GIYEMON: retainer of the Asai family (*Hawley*, 214). S62.50.

MASATAKA, SHIŌREN SAJIMA-NO-KAMI: retainer of the Toki family. S62.40.

MASATANE, FUWA KATSUYEMON: one of the Forty-Seven *Rōnin*. S54.4; S57.9; S59.2; S80.15; S90.4.

MASATATSU, MASE MAGOYEMON: one of the Forty-Seven *Rōnin*. S54.41; S90.41 (Magokurō Masatoki).

MASATATSU, NAKAMURA KANSUKE, see TADATOKI.

MASATATSU, OYAMADA BITCHŪ NO KAMI: Takeda warrior at

Kawanakajima. S63.7.

MASATOKI, MASE MAGOKURŌ, see MASATATSU.

MASATOKI, NAKAMURA KANSUKE, see TADATOKI.

MASATOMO, WADA: cousin of Kusunoki Masatsura (*Papinot*, p.731). T271; T346.

MASATOSHI, HIDA MAGOBEI: follower of Katō Kiyomasa; fought in Korea. S62.12.

MASATOSHI, SUGENOYA SANNOJŌ: one of the Forty-Seven *Rōnin*. S54.33; S90.33 (Sugatani Inojō).

MASATOYO, NAITŌ SHURI: Takeda warrior at Kawanakajima. S34.6; S82.5.

MASATSURA, KUSUNOKI: 1326–48; eldest son of Masashige (*Bertin*, pp.311–18; *Papinot*, p.334; *Edmunds*, p.472). S1c.7; S23.15; S73.33; S81.2; T79; T105; T271; T346. p.27.

MASAYASU, SASAI KYŪZŌ (Sakai): son of Masanao (*Hawley*, 136, 170, 211). S62.36. pp.9, 15.

MASAYOSHI, OGATA SABURŌ: umpire at wrestling under Yoritomo. T74.

MASAYUKI, SANADA KIHEI: Takeda warrior at Kawanakajima. S34.7.

MASUHARA, SACHŪ: retainer of Moronao in the *Chūshingura*. S57.41.

MATABEI, IWASA, TOSA, UKIYO or DOMO NO: 1578–1650; traditionally the founder of the Ukiyoye school of painting (*Papinot*, p.221; *Edmunds*, p.472). S36.57; S44.55, 56; S74.64.

MATABEI, wife of. S36.57; S44.56.

MATAGORŌ, KAWAI (or SAWAI): villain of the Igagoye revenge story (*Mitford*, 'Kazuma's Revenge'). T106; T250; T290.

MATANO GORŌ, see KAGEHISA.

MATSUGAYE SEKINOSUKE: dramatic character; son of Masaoka, q.v. S45.55.

MATSUI MINJIRŌ. S74.18.

MATSUŌ MARU: faithful and self-sacrificing supporter of Michizane in the play *Sugawara*. S45.53.

MATSUŌ MARU, wife of. S46.16.

MATSUSHIMA NO TSUBONE: daughter of Sado no Kami Yasuchika and wife of Asahina Saburō Yoshihide. S22.10; S29.6.

MATSUWAKA MARU: character in the play *Onna Seigen*. S46.91.

MATSUYAMA KARUMO, see KARUMO.

MATSUYEMON, see KANEMITSU, HIGUCHI JIRŌ.

MA-UNKINSHI ŌBŌ: Chinese hero of the *Suikoden*. S2.45; S3.9.

MEGA MAGOSABURŌ, see NAGAMUNE.

MICHI-IYE, NAGAMURA BUNKASAI: veteran counsellor of Shibata Katsuiye. S62.24.

MICHITSUNA, mother of: poetess of the Fujiwara family. S19.53.

MICHIZANE, SUGAWARA NO (also called KWANSHŌJŌ and KANKE): 845–903; statesman, poet, and hero of the play *Sugawara* (*Papinot*, p.604; *Edmunds*, p.475). S1f.13; S45.49; S46.30, 62.

MIIDERA, madwoman of: her child had been stolen by a merchant, but they were eventually reunited. S46.33.

MIMYŌ: *shirabyōshi* dancer; daughter of the poet and historian Fujiwara no Tamenari (late twelfth century). S22.17.

MINADZURU-HIME: daughter of Ki-ichi Hōgen; beloved of Yoshitsune. S22.11; S45.42.

MINATO: wife of Yura Hyōgo, a retainer of the Nitta family. S44.5.

MINO (province), dutiful youth of: Japanese Paragon of Filial Piety. S23.17.

MITONO KOTARŌ. S74.43.

MITSUCHIKA, TOKI JUROZAYEMON: relative of Akechi Mitsuhide; killed at the battle of Yododzutsumi. S62.46.

MITSUHARU, AKECHI SAMA-NO-SUKE: cousin of Mitsuhide; killed himself, 1582 (*Papinot*, p.8; *Edmunds*, p.480). S62.51; T206. p.28.

MITSUKAZE, YAZAMA SHINROKU: one of the Forty-Seven *Rōnin*. S54.40; S90.40 (Shunroku).

MITSUKAZU, ONCHI SAKON: retainer of Kusunoki Masashige. S81.4; T350.

MITSUKUNI, ŌYAKE TARŌ: retainer of Masakado (tenth century). T138.

MITSUKUNI, HAMAJI SHŌGEN: retainer of Shibata Katsuiye. S62.10.

MITSUMORI, TEDZUKA TARŌ: retainer of Kiso Yoshinaka. T95.

MITSUNOBU, YAZAMA KIHEI: one of the Forty-Seven *Rōnin*. S54.43; S57.6; S90.43.

MITSUTADA, CHIBA SABUROHEI: one of the Forty-Seven *Rōnin*. S54.31; S57.22; S80.21; S90.31.

MITSUTAKA, HAYAMI SŌZAYEMON: one of the Forty-Seven *Rōnin*. S54.29; S57.17 (Tōzayemon); S90.29.

MITSUTOKI, ASHIODA, see TAKANORI, USHIODA.

MITSUTOKI, SAGA GORŌ: Taira warrior at the battle of Dan-no-ura (1185). T96.

MITSUYORI, FUJIWARA NO: statesman of the late eleventh century. S74.6; T52.

MIURA SHIROYEMON, see KANETSUNE.

MIYAGI ASOJIRŌ: hero of the play *Asagao monogatari*; lover of Miyuki. S46.77.

MIYAGINO: together with her younger sister Shinobu she was revenged on her father's murderer, Shiga Danshichi. S53.5.

MIYA-ISHI SHŌZAYEMON: retainer of Moronao in the *Chūshingura*. S57.38.

MIYAMOTO MUSASHI: 1583–1647; swordsman, poet, painter, and craftsman (*Edmunds*, p.483). S1f.4; S4b.3; S35.8; S37.16; S43.6; S48.3; S52.2; S53.6; S61.6; S74.68; S89.5; T33; T176; T208; T232; T335; T358. p.29.

MIYUKI: lover of Asojirō in the play *Asagao monogatari*. S46.77.

MOCHAKUTEN TOSEN: Chinese hero of the *Suikoden*. S2.46; S3.7.

MOCHISUKE, see DŌKWAN.

MOKUSUKE, MATSUMOTO: Uyesugi warrior at Kawanakajima. S63.15.

MOMOTARŌ: fairy-tale hero (*Mitford*, 'The Adventures of Little Peachling'; *Edmunds*, p.484). S1e.12; S9.3; S88.15.

MONGAKU SHŌNIN, see MORITŌ.

MORIMASU, TAKUMA GEMBA-NO-JŌ (Sakuma Morimasa): 1554–83; retainer of Shibata Katsuiye (*Papinot*, p.533; *Hawley*, 432–520). S62.42.

MORINAGA SHINNŌ, see ŌTO-NO-MIYA.

MORITŌ, YENDŌ MUSHA (later MONGAKU SHŌNIN): twelfth-century lover of the ill-fated Kesa-gozen (*Papinot*, p.400; *Edmunds*, p.335). S1e.6, 13; S15.6; S24.2; S45.7; S46.44; S52.1; S93.4; T129; T253. p.26.

MORITSUGU, ETCHŪ ZENJI: Taira warrior (*Edmunds*, p.502; *Heike*, pp.397–682). T38; T69.

MORITSUNA, SASAKI: Minamoto warrior (*Papinot*, p.545; *Edmunds*, p.503). S1a.6; S84.10; S89.7; S93.6; T220.

MORIYA NO OMURAJI, MONONOBE NO: d.587; an early enemy of Buddhism (*Papinot*, p.402; *Edmunds*, pp.578, 645). S14.4, 5; T279. p.17.

MORONAGA, FUJIWARA NO: 1137–92; character in a ghost-story. S44.38.

MORONAO, MUSASHI NO KAMI KŌ NO: d.1351; general under the Ashikaga; later adopted as the villain of the *Chūshingura* (*Papinot*, p.291; *Dickins, passim*). S22.9; S46.90; S54.38; S55.1; S74.9; S86.1, 3, 11; S90.38; T34; T248; T260; T272; T285. pp.27, 29f.

MOROYASU, TAKANO: retainer of Moronao in the *Chūshingura*. S57.2.

MŌSŌ (Mêng Tsung): Chinese Paragon of Filial Piety. S13.2; S60.2.

MOTO-OKI, YAZAMA JŪJIRŌ: one of the Forty-Seven *Rōnin*. S46.92 (Jūtarō); S54.13; S72.9 (Jūtarō); S90.13.

MOTOSADA, DOKI TAISHIRŌ: retainer of Gamō Sadahide (sixteenth century). S4b.1.

MŌTŌSEI KŌMEI: Chinese hero of the *Suikoden*. S2.47; S3.3.

MOTOSUKE, KIYOWARA NO: one of the Hundred Poets. S19.42.

MOTOTOKI, HARA GŌYEMON: one of the Forty-Seven *Rōnin*. S54.46; S72.2; S80.1; S90.46.

MOTOTSUGU, KUDŌ SHŌHEI. S92.1.

MOTOYOSHI-SHINNŌ: prince-poet, son of the Emperor Yōzei (877–85). S27.20.

MUNEFUSA, AIHARA YESUKE: one of the Forty-Seven *Rōnin*. S54.26; S59.1 (Aibara); S90.26 (Aibara).

MUNEFUSA, AIHARA, sister of. S56.11.

MUNEMORI, TAIRA NO: 1147–85; son and heir of Kiyomori (*Papinot*, p.623; *Heike, passim*). T68. p.23.

MUNENORI, YUKUGAWA SAMPEI: one of the Forty-Seven *Rōnin*. S54.8; S78.4 (Yokogawa Kampei); S90.8 (Yodogawa Kampei).

MUNESADA, see YOSHITADA, SANADA.

MUNETŌ, ABE NO: eleventh-century rebel (*Papinot*, p.1; *Edmunds*, pp.552, 664). S22.1; S74.6; T52; T111a.

MURAKAMI SHŌYEMON: villain in the story of Yasubei's revenge. T148; T213. p.18.

MURASAKI-SHIKIBU: d.992; court lady and authoress (*Papinot*, p.413; *Edmunds*, p.506). S95e.3.

MURASHIGE, ARAGI SETTSU NO KAMI (Araki): ally of Nobunaga (*Papinot*, p.19; *Edmunds*, p.507; *Hawley*, 242, 292). S62.4.

NAGACHIKA, KIDŌ TAKUZAYEMON: vassal of Konishi Yukinaga; fought in Korea. S62.19.

NAGAHIDE, TANABE: retainer of Oguri Hangwan. S26.5.

NAGAMOCHI, JŌ SHIRŌ: d.1201; fought Yoshinaka, but later joined Yoritomo (*Papinot*, p.232). T25; T61; T240. p.21.

NAGAMUNE, MEGA MAGOSABURŌ: warrior prominent in the attack on the Hōjō at Rokuhara, Kyoto (1333) (*Taiheiki*, pp.227–8, 256–7). S88.42; T270.

NAGASAKA GENGORŌ: Takeda warrior at Kawanakajima. T292.

NAGASAKI, KANGAYŪ SAYEMON. S1c.16.

NAGASE HANGWAN: retainer of Kiso Yoshinaka. T95.

NAGATAME, TANABE: retainer of Oguri Hangwan. S26.6.

NAGAYASU, see RAN MARU.

NAGOYA SANZA(BURŌ): dramatic character in several plays (*Mitford*, 'A Story of the Otokodate of Yedo'). S36.41; S37.17; S46.7; T287. p.14.

NAKAMARO, ABE NO: 701–70; poet and expatriate in China (*Papinot*, p.2; *Edmunds*, p.511). S19.7; S27.7; S95e.4.

NAKAMASA, ASAI BIZEN NO KAMI (Nagamasa): 1545–73; fought Nobunaga, but married his sister (*Papinot*, p.23; *Edmunds*, p.430). S62.5.

NAKAMATSU KUROBEI: retainer of Moronao in the *Chūshingura*. S57.22.

NAKANARI, FUJIWARA NO: d.810; conspirator (*Papinot*, p.91). (ghost of) S46.40.

NAKANISHI DAIROKURŌ: Uyesugi warrior at Kawanakajima. T316.

NAKASAINA SONJA: one of the Sixteen *Rakan* (*Edmunds*, p.229). S1d.3.

NAMBA JIRŌ: d.1160; retainer of Kiyomori (*Edmunds*, pp.546, 667). S1c.4; T10.

NAMIKO: disguised name of Konami, daughter of Honzō in the *Chūshingura*. S45.56.

NAOIYE, KOJIRŌ: son of Naozane. S74.10.

NAONORI, see NIKKI DANJŌ.

NAOSADA, KUMAGAYE: father of Naozane (mid twelfth century). S1a.11.

NAOYE YAMASHIRO NO KAMI KANETSUGU: Uyesugi warrior at Kawanakajima. S34.12; S36.34; S83.2.

NAOYOSHI, ASHIKAGA, see TADAYOSHI.

NAOZANE, KUMAGAYE JIRŌ (later RENSHŌ-BŌ): d.1208; Minamoto warrior who killed Atsumori (*Papinot*, p.322; *Edmunds*, p.514; *Heike*, pp.511–652). S32.4; S44.23; S45.6; S46.78; S50.1; S88.6; T38; T48; T66; T226; T228; T229. p.22.

NAREGINU: daughter of Mikawa Zenji and beloved of Yoshi-iye. T111a.

NARIHIRA, ARIWARA NO: 825–80; courtier, poet, and Don Juan (*Papinot*, p.22; *Edmunds*, p.516). S19.17; S27.17; S44.41; S45.28; S74.41.

NARUKAMI SHŌNIN: eponymous hero of the play *Narukami*. S46.74.

NASU NO YOICHI MUNETAKA: b.1167; Minamoto warrior celebrated as an archer (*Edmunds*, p.505; *Heike*, pp.659, 660). T256. p.22.

NICHIREN: 1222–82; priest and founder of the Hokke-shū sect (*Papinot*, p.438; *Edmunds*, p.517). S6 *passim*. p.10.

NII NO AMA: d.1185; wife of Kiyomori and grandmother of the boy-Emperor Antoku (*Papinot*, p.445; *Edmunds*, p.286; *Heike*, esp. pp.676–7). T96. p.23.

NIJŌ NO TSUBONE: beloved of the poet Narihira. S74.41.

NIKKI DANJŌ NAONORI: villain and magician in the play *Sendai hagi* (*Edmunds*, p.519). S45.41.

NIKKI GENNOSUKE. S1e.2.

NIKKYŌ: disciple of Nichiren. S6.2.

NOBU: a filial girl, who looked after her mother and eventually became a nun. S23.18.

NOBUFUSA, BABA MINO NO KAMI: Takeda warrior at Kawanakajima. S81.1; S88.13.

NOBUKIYO, ŌBOSHI SEIZAYEMON: one of the Forty-Seven *Rōnin*. S54.32; S71.6; S72.3; S80.19 (Ōishi); S90.32.

NOBUNAGA, ODA, see HARUNAGA, ŌTA.

NOBUSHIGE, TAKEDA SAMA-NO-SUKE: younger brother of Shingen; fought at Kawanakajima. S34.3; S63.9; S82.2.

NOBUTOMO, ŌBOSHI SAMPEI. S56.17.

NOBUTSUNA, SASAKI: d.1242; fought for the Hōjō (*Papinot*, p.545). T198.

NOBUTSURA, HASEBE CHŌHYŌYE-NO-JŌ: d.1217; Minamoto warrior who distinguished himself at the defence of the Takakura palace (*Papinot*, p.142; *Edmunds*, p.524; *Heike*, esp. pp.241–5). S1c.11; S15.7; S46.41.

NOBUYOSHI, ANAYAMA IDZU NO KAMI: Takeda warrior at Kawanakajima. S63.3.

NOBUYUKI, TERAOKA HEIYEMON: one of the Forty-Seven *Rōnin*. S54.18; S58.1; S90.18.

NODA SHIRŌ: Kusunoki warrior slain at Shijō-nawate (1348). T347.

NORIHISA, KURIU SAYEMON: retainer of Nitta Yoshisada. S94.3; T6.

NORIKANE, YATŌ YOMOSHICHI: one of the Forty-Seven *Rōnin*. S54.3; S57.41; S59.8; S71.1; S72.4 (Satō); S78.2; S80.11; S90.3.

NORIMORI, TAIRA NO: d.1185; younger brother of Kiyomori (*Heike*, p.678 etc.). T229.

NORITAKA: retainer of Yoshinaka at the Uji river battle (1184). T191.

NORITSUNE, NOTO NO KAMI: 1160–85; Taira champion and giant; son of Norimori (*Papinot*, p.625; *Edmunds*, p.526; *Heike*, esp. pp.678–81). S36.32; S65.13; T68; T69; T109; T222; T230; T256; T337. pp.22, 23.

NORIYASU, SENZAKI YAGORŌ: one of the Forty-Seven *Rōnin*. S54.12; S57.7; S58.2; S72.7; S78.5 (Kanzaki); S80.12 (Kanzaki); S90.12.

NORIYORI, MINAMOTO NO: 1156–93; brother of Yoritomo and Yoshitsune (*Papinot*, p.383; *Edmunds*, p.526; *Gikeiki*, esp.

pp. 15–19). S44.46; T45. p.22.

NOZARASHI GOSUKE: a chivalrous dramatic character (*kyōkaku*). S40.4; S42.5.

NUREGAMI CHŌGORŌ: wrestler in the play *Futatsu chōchō*. S40.5; S46.10; S74.60; T172.

NUREGAMI KATSUNOSUKE: wrestler; perhaps identical with the preceding. S74.2.

NUYE: a composite monster that afflicted the Emperor Konoye (1153) (*Edmunds*, p.660). S74.72; S95d.3; T112. p.21.

NYOGETSU-NI: witch; perhaps an alternative name for Taki-yasha-hime, q.v. S74.28.

NYŪBINATA KŌJŪ: Chinese hero of the *Suikoden*. S2.48; S3.10.

ŌANAMUCHI-NO-MIKOTO: resident divinity at the Kita shrine of Hagui, Noto. S4a.10.

ŌBOSHI RIKIYA, see RIKIYA.

ŌBOSHI YURANOSUKE, see YURANOSUKE.

ODAI MATAROKURŌ YORISADA: opponent of Takeda Shingen (mid sixteenth century). S4a.11; S61.7; T201.

O-FUNE: daughter of Tombei the ferryman in *Yaguchi no watashi*. S45.37; S46.93.

OGATA SHUMA, see JIRAIYA.

OGURI HANGWAN SUKESHIGE: 1398–1464; semi-historical hero of romance (*Papinot*, p.475; *Edmunds*, p.533). S26.1; S35.9; S36.20; S44.7.

O-HANA: sister of Ishidome Busuke in the Igagoye revenge story. S46.70.

O-HATSU (or HATSU-JO): maid to Onoye, and heroine of *Kagamiyama*; killed Tsubone Iwafuji. S20.6; S45.13; S46.60; S53.1.

ŌHŌ (Wang P'ou): Chinese Paragon of Filial Piety. S13.14; S60.22.

ŌIKO: strong woman of Takashima in the province of Ōmi. S20.17; S29.7; S44.52; S74.24.

OIMATSU: *ama* who attempted to recover the Sword of the regalia (1185). T134.

O-IRI: daughter of Uramatsu Rihei (Kihei) in the *Chūshingura*. S72.1.

O-IWA: wronged and murdered wife, then a ghost in *Yotsuya kwaidan* (*Edmunds*, p.529; J. S. de Benneville, *Yotsuya Kwaidan*, Philadelphia, 1917). S45.25; S74.22.

ŌJIN TENNŌ: Emperor, 270–313; son of the Empress Jingō (*Papinot*, p.478). S28.1.

O-KANE, see KANE-JO.

O-KARU: daughter of Yoichibei and maid to Kaoyo in the *Chūshingura*. S86.6, 7.

ŌKAWA KUMOYEMON: an expert archer who saved a famous painting of Daruma in a fire, and was a homosexual. S52.8.

OKIKAZE, FUJIWARA NO: one of the Hundred Poets. S19.34.

O-KIKU: heroine of a ghost-story and play (*Mitford*, tailpiece to 'The Ghost of Sakura'; *Edmunds*, p.530). S36.44; S46.48.

O-KOMA: daughter of Shirokiya, a timber-merchant, in *Koi musume mukashi hachijō*; involved in a murder plot. S38.8.

O-KON: mistress of Fukuoka Mitsugi, q.v. S36.8.

ŌKUMO TESSAN (Aoyama Shūzen): chief of police; master and murderer of the maid O-Kiku, q.v. S36.44; S51.5.

O-KUNI: d.c.1640; traditional founder of the Kabuki theatre (*Papinot*, p.324; *Edmunds*, p.530); she herself was a character in several plays. S36.41.

O-MATSU: female dramatic character. S44.48; S45.51.

O-MIWA: female dramatic character in *Imoseyama*. S38.7; S45.10.

ŌMORI HIKOSHICHI: vassal of the Ashikaga; fought at the Minatogawa (1336) (*Edmunds*, p.539). S24.4; S93.5.

ONCHI SAKON-TARŌ, see MITSUKAZU.

ONIKOJIMA YATARŌ, see TORAHIDE.

ONIWAKA MARU, child-name of Benkei, q.v.

ONIYASHA: henchman of Tametomo in his exile. T92; T113; T140; T214.

ONO NO TŌFŪ (MICHIKAZE): 896–966; celebrated calligrapher (*Papinot*, p.490; *Edmunds*, p.628). S35.10.

ONO SADAKURŌ: robber and murderer of Yoichibei in the *Chūshingura*. S74.48.

ORI-HIME (Shokujo): the Weaving Princess (the Heavenly Weaver) in the Milky Way legend (*Edmunds*, p.619, s.v. Tanabata). S13.10; S19.6; S60.12; S79.3.

O-RIYE: wife of Yazama Jūtarō (Jūjirō), one of the Forty-Seven *Rōnin*. S45.4; S46.92; S72.9.

O-ROKU: dramatic character; a tough lady and a heavy drinker. S38.6; S74.36.

O-SADA: widow of Yoshioka Ichimisai, who avenged his murder. T131; T170.

O-SATO: beloved of Taira no Koremori in *Goban Tadanobu*. S46.99.

O-SEKI: female character in the play *Futatsu chōchō*. T172.

O-SHICHI: daughter of a greengrocer (*yaoya*), and incendiary; dramatic character in *Furisode meoto* (*Edmunds*, p.532). S45.21; S46.45; S74.29.

ŌSHŌ (Wang Hsiang): Chinese Paragon of Filial Piety. S13.5; S60.7; S79.2.

O-SHUN: a *geisha*; character in several plays. S43.7.

O-SOME: heroine of *O-Some Hisamatsu*. S46.89.

O-SONO: daughter of Yoshioka Ichimisai, who avenged his murder on Kyōgoku Takumi. S23.19; S37.20; S45.43; T131; T137; T170.

O-SONO: wife of Amagawaya Gihei in the *Chūshingura*. S72.6; S86.10.

O-TAKE, see TAKE-JO.

O-TANI: heroine of a local legend of Kōriyama, and wife of Araki Matayemon. S46.19.

ŌTANI FURUINOSUKE: boy-prodigy; killed a boar with his bare hands. S4a.14; S85.1.

ŌTOMO NO KURONUSHI: ninth century; one of the Six Poets (*Papinot*, p.502). S46.95.

ŌTŌNAI: dramatic character in the *Soga monogatari* cycle. S46.83.

ŌTO-NO-MIYA (MORINAGA SHINNŌ): 1308–35; son of the Emperor Go-Daigō, whose cause he championed (*Papinot*, p.408; *Edmunds*, p.501; *Taiheiki*, *passim*). S1c.5; S16.5; S73.13; S74.38. p.27.

O-TOWA: wife of the wrestler Inagawa Jirokichi. S46.54.

O-TSŪ: the madwoman of Fumi-hiroge, daughter of Chiyo, frustrated in her literary studies; character in *Adzuma kagami*. S45.36; S46.14.

O-TSUJI: dramatic character; nurse to Hōtarō. S74.55.

O-TSURU: daughter of Awa no Jurobei. S43.8.

ŌWASHI BUNGO: subsidiary character in the *Chūshingura*. S72.3.

O-YASU: female character in *Hime komatsu*. S45.29.

O-YUMI: wife of Awa no Jurobei. S43.8.

RAIGEN, NOGI NYŪDŌ. S88.51.

RAIGŌ AJARI: priest of Onjōji (Miidera) in the late eleventh century; a disappointed man, he later haunted the temple in rat form (*Edmunds*, p.544). S1f.5; S17.1.

RAIJIN: the Thunder-God. S11.1; S87.6; T240. p.21.

RAIKŌ, see YORIMITSU.

RAN MARU, HORI (Mori), NAGAYASU: squire to Nobunaga (*Hawley*, 338). S62.13; S93.1; T204.

RENSHŌ-BŌ (-HŌSHI), see NAOZANE.

RIJU: Chinese warrior in the Wars of the Three Kingdoms. T302.

RIKIYA, ŌBOSHI: young son of Yuranosuke in the *Chūshingura* (also called Chikara). S46.82; S54.2; S57.2; S58.4; S59.4; S72.1; S80.14; S86.9; S90.2.

RIKUSEKI (Lu Chi): Chinese Paragon of Filial Piety. S13.12; S60.19.

ROKUDAI-GOZEN: d.1199; young son of Taira no Koremori, beheaded by Yoritomo; character in *Sembonzakura* (*Sadler*, pp.225–38; *Heike*, pp.735–60). S45.46.

ROKUYA ONGUNDAYŪ: a villain in *Jiraiya*. S46.57.

RŌNIN, the Forty-Seven (see also under individual names). S54–S59; S71; S72; S78; S80; S90; T11–T15; T80; T81; T186–T188; T209–T211; T249; T260; T272; T273; T276; T285. pp.14, 29f.

RŌRAISHI (Lao-lai-tzu): Chinese Paragon of Filial Piety. S13.6; S60.8.

RŌRIHAKUCHŌ CHŌJUN: Chinese hero of the *Suikoden*. S2.49; S3.6; S47.16.

RŌSHI YENSEI: Chinese wrestler-hero of the *Suikoden*. S2.50; S2.51; S3.8.

RYOFU: general under Gentoku in the Wars of the Three Kingdoms. S10.6; T301; T302.

RYŌTŌJA KAICHIN: Chinese hero of the *Suikoden*. S2.52; S2a.8; S3.5.

RYŌZEN-HŌSHI: priest; one of the Hundred Poets. S19.70.

RYŪCHITAISAI GENSHŌJI: Chinese hero of the *Suikoden*. S2.53; S2a.9; S3.6; S47.17.

SADA-IYE, GONCHŪNAGON FUJIWARA NO: 1162–1241; one of the Hundred Poets (*Papinot*, p.104). S19.97.

SADA-IYE, KUMAGAYE: Minamoto warrior at Ichi-no-tani (1184). T38.

SADAKAGE, NAGAO SHINROKU: Taira warrior at Ishibashiyama (1180). S8.1.

SADAMASA, ISONO TAMBA NO KAMI: fought Nobunaga at the Anegawa (1570) (*Hawley*, 227, 234). S62.18.

SADAMASA, see SHINODZUKA IGA NO KAMI.

SADAMITSU, USUI NO: retainer of Raikō (*Edmunds*, p.551). S1e.9; S61.2; S94.1; T3; T4; T21; T44; T46; T128; T169; T261; T262; T298; T305; T357. p.18.

SADATŌ, ABE NO: 1019–62; rebel (*Papinot*, p.1; *Edmunds*, p.551). S88.34.

SADATOMO, ISHIKAWA SŌSUKE (Hyōsuke): one of the Three Swordsmen of Shidzu-ga-mine (1583) (*Hawley*, 480, 490, 491, 494). S62.17.

SADATSUNA, see SHINODZUKA IGA NO KAMI.

SADA-UJI, see KAZU-UJI.

SADAYO, MUSASHI GORŌ: squire to Masakado (mid tenth century). S52.6; S61.5; T23; T252.

SADAYUKI, KIURA OKAYEMON: one of the Forty-Seven *Rōnin*. S54.22; S90.22 (Kimura Okuyemon).

SADAYUKI, USAMI SURUGA NO KAMI: Uyesugi warrior at Kawanakajima. S63.17.

SADAZUMI SHINNŌ: 874–916; son of the Emperor Seiwa; ancestor of the Minamoto (Seiwa branch) (*Papinot*, p.523). T122.

SAGAMI: eleventh-century poetess; daughter of Raikō (*Papinot*, p.524). S19.62.

SAGAMI-BŌ, KODERA: retainer of Ōto-no-miya (early fourteenth century). S73.13.

SAGAMI GORŌ: retainer of Taira no Tomomori (late twelfth century). T144.

SAGI-NO-IKE HEIKURŌ: strong man; retainer of the Kusunoki. S4b.4; S74.67; S88.31; T322; T323; T350.

SAIGYŌ-HŌSHI: 1118–90; warrior, monk, and poet (*Papinot*, p.526; *Edmunds*, p.552). S19.86.

SAIJINKI KWAKUSEI: Chinese hero of the *Suikoden*. S2.54; S3.10.

SAIJUN (Ts'ai Shun): Chinese Paragon of Filial Piety. S60.17.

SAIKI: Indian victim of Kwayō-fujin (the Nine-tailed Fox). S66.3.

SAIMEIHANGWAN RIRYŪ: Chinese hero of the *Suikoden*. S3.12.

SAIYENSHI CHŌSEI: Chinese hero of the *Suikoden*. S2.55; S3.12.

SAKURA-HIME: beloved of the tragic monk Seigen in *Kiyomidzu Seigen* and other plays (*Edmunds*, p.554). S45.57; S74.17.

SAKURAI RINZAYEMON: one of the villains in the Igagoye revenge story (*Mitford*, 'Kazuma's Revenge'). T250.

SAKURA MARU: loyal supporter of Michizane in the *Sugawara* play. S38.2; S46.84.

SANADA YOICHI, see YOSHITADA.

SANEMORI, SAITŌ: 1118–83; Taira warrior killed fighting Yoshinaka (*Papinot*, p.529; *Edmunds*, p.554; *Heike*, p.414). T180.

SANETOMO, UDAIJIN MINAMOTO NO: 1192–1219; son of Yoritomo; Shōgun, 1204 (*Papinot*, p.386; *Edmunds*, p.555). T48.

SANKATSU: a *geisha*; character in the play *Aoto-zōshi*. S45.36; S74.62.

SANO JIROZAYEMON: character in *Iro no Yedo-zome* who killed his mistress Yatsuhashi of Manji-ya, and several other people. S51.6.

SANSUKE: retainer of Moronao in the *Chūshingura*. S57.42.

SANUGI NO MIYAKKO: the old bamboo-gatherer in *Taketori monogatari* (*Edmunds*, p.611). S44.14.

SARASHINA-HIME: daughter of Rakuganji Umanosuke, wife of Aiki Morinosuke, and mother of Shikanosuke; she revenged herself on her seducer Daikurō. S22.14.

SARUNOSUKE. S74.59.

SASARAYE: mistress of Tametomo in his exile. T113; T140.

SATSUKI: wife of Takahashi Yajurō, q.v. S46.81.

SATSUMA (or KATSUMA) GENGOBEI: character in *Godairiki*, in which, in pursuit of a stolen sword, he kills the *geisha* Koman and Sangobei the thief. S36.66; S51.4.

SAYO-HIME: d.536; wife of Ōtomo no Sadehiko; died of grief when he went to Korea (*Edmunds*, p.558). S20.18.

SEIBOKKAN KAKUSHIBUN: Chinese hero of the *Suikoden*. S2.56; S3.3.

SEIGANKO RIUN: Chinese hero of the *Suikoden*. S3.11.

SEIGEN: a monk whose hopeless passion for Sakura-hime forms the subject of the play *Kiyomidzu Seigen* (*Edmunds*, p.554). S45.57; S74.17.

SEIGEN-NI: feminine counterpart of the preceding in the play *Onna Seigen*. S43.9; S45.27; S46.91.

SEIJURŌ: lover of O-Natsu in *O-Natsu Seijurō*. S36.38.

SEIMENJŪ YŌSHI: Chinese hero of the *Suikoden*. S2.57; S3.5.

SEISHUSHOSEI SHŌJŌ: Chinese hero of the *Suikoden*. S2.58; S3.11.

SEISUISHŌ TANTEIKEI: Chinese hero of the *Suikoden*. S3.9.

SEITAKA-DŌJI: acolyte of Fudō Myō-ō. S93.4; T253. p.26.

SEKIBAKKI RYŪTŌ: Chinese hero of the *Suikoden*. S2.59; S2a.10; S3.8; S47.18.

SEKIGUCHI YATARŌ: companion of Miyamoto Musashi. T358.

SEKISHŌGUN SEKIYŪ: Chinese hero of the *Suikoden*. S2.60; S3.4; S47.19.

SEMIMARU: tenth-century courtier, poet, and musician; but blind (*Papinot*, p.554). S19.10; S27.10.

SENJŪ-NO-MAYE: beloved of Taira no Shigehira. S44.21.

SENKWAJI CHŌ-Ō: Chinese hero of the *Suikoden*. S2.61; S3.6; S47.20.

SHAMEISANRŌ (-SABURŌ) SEKISHŪ: Chinese hero of the *Suikoden*. S2.62; S3.8; S47.21.

SHANAŌ, boy-name of Yoshitsune, q.v.

SHIBORI NO SOMEGORŌ: *otokodate* dramatic character. S42.6.

SHIDZUKA-GOZEN: 1168–87; *shirabyōshi* dancer and courageous mistress of Yoshitsune (*Papinot*, p.583; *Edmunds*, p.573; *Gikeiki*, esp. pp.145f., 166ff., 220ff.). S20.19; S21.2; S25.2; S33.4; S35.12; S46.86, 94; S65.14; S95c.2; T16; T86; T97; T127; T135; T267; T282. pp.16, 24f.

SHIDZUMA, WATANABE: hero of the Igagoye revenge story (*Mitford*, 'Kazuma's Revenge'). S53.8; T106; T250; T290.

SHIGEHARU, TATENAKA KWAMBYŌYE (Takenaka Hambei): soldier-scholar; retainer of the Saitō family of Mino (*Hawley*, 235, 305). S62.44.

SHIGEHIRA, TAIRA NO: 1158–85; son of Kiyomori (*Papinot*, p.625). S44.21.

SHIGEKIYO (or NARIKIYO), KAMEI ROKURŌ: retainer of Yoshitsune. S31.11; T215. p.13.

SHIGEMORI, TAIRA NO: 1138–79; eldest son of Kiyomori and most admirable of the Taira family (*Papinot*, p.623; *Edmunds*, p.565; *Heike*, passim). S15.8; S22.8; S23.14; S31.12; S32.5; S44.31; T55; T195. p.19.

SHIGEMORI, TOKUDA MAGODAYŪ: one of the Forty-Seven *Rōnin*. S54.37; S90.37 (Okada Toyonari).

SHIGENAKA, MATSUI TOMIJIRŌ: avenger of his brother's murder; helped by a female *sennin* to cope with snakes at a river-crossing. S37.13.

SHIGENOBU, see IWADZU TETSUYEMON.

SHIGETADA, HATAKEYAMA: 1164–1205; Minamoto warrior, though of Taira descent (*Papinot*, p.144; *Edmunds*, p.566; *Gikeiki*, pp.136–294; *Heike*, pp.511–17). S31.13; S45.1; S73.5; S88.1; T18; T115; T191; T217; T225; T268; T334. p.25.

SHIGEUJI, KATŌ (later KARUKAYA DŌSHIN): *daimyō* of the Ashikaga period who forsook the world and his family (*Edmunds*, p.429). S36.65; S43.4; S45.11; S46.35.

SHIGEUJI, KATŌ, wife of. S45.11; S46.51.

SHIGEYUKI, MINAMOTO NO: one of the Hundred Poets. S19.48.

SHIGEYUKI, SUZUCHI (Suzuki) HIDA NO KAMI: a marksman who attempted to shoot Nobunaga from ambush (cf. *Hawley*, 192, 232). S62.41; S76.2; S88.40.

SHIMMI YASHICHIRŌ: retainer of Moronao in the *Chūshingura*. S57.7.

SHIMOSAKA (YASUTSUGU): swordsmith to Tokugawa Iyeyasu. S44.27.

SHIMOSE KAGA: early sixteenth-century retainer of Yoshimi Mikawa no Kami. S4a.16.

SHINGEN, TAKEDA (HARUNOBU): 1521–73; war-lord of Kai province (*Papinot*, p.636; *Edmunds*, p.375). S1a.4; S24.6; S31.14; S32.6; S34.1; S44.37; S50.2; S63.1; S73.2; S82.1; S88.33; S95c.4; S95f.1; T136; T154; T160; T162; T165; T175; T246; T258; T289; T325; T332; T345. pp.13, 28.

SHINGYŌTAIHŌ TAISŌ: Chinese hero of the *Suikoden*. S3.5.

SHINI ANDŌZEN: Chinese physician-hero of the *Suikoden*. S2.3; S3.11.

SHINKIGUNSHI SHUBU, see JINKIGUNSHI SHUBU.

SHINKWASHŌ GITEIKOKU: Chinese hero of the *Suikoden*. S3.9.

SHINOBU SŌDA: slave-dealer who kidnapped Umewaka Maru (*Edmunds*, p.647). S46.21.

SHINODZUKA HACHIRŌ: retainer of the Nitta family. S44.5.

SHINODZUKA IGA NO KAMI SADAMASA (or SADATSUNA): d.1348; strong man and retainer of Nitta Yoshisada (*Papinot*, p.576; *Edmunds*, p.569). S36.30; S84.4; S88.25; S94.3; T6; T37.

SHINODZUKA IGA NO KAMI, wife of. T120.

SHINSANSHI SHŌKEI: Chinese hero of the *Suikoden*. S3.7.

SHIRADAYŪ: loyal farmer in the Sugawara tragedy. S41.1.

SHIRAFUJI GENDA: wrestler in *Kusa no irotoki* and other plays. S36.18.

SHIRAFUJI HIKOSHICHIRŌ: retainer of the Nitta family and strong man. S9.4; S73.36; S84.7; T243.

SHIRAGIKU MARU: son of Chūnagon Fujiwara no Muneyuki; involved with the priest Jikyū. S36.15; S46.29.

SHIRAI GOMPACHI: lover of Komurasaki; robber and murderer (late seventeenth century) (*Mitford*, 'The Loves of Gompachi and Komurasaki'; *Edmunds*, p.362). S36.39; S37.19; S40.6;

S44.2; S45.16; S46.67; S51.8; S74.12; T130.

SHIRAKURA GENGOYEMON (or DENGOYEMON): treacherous foe of Miyamoto Musashi. T33; T176.

SHIRANUI-HIME: daughter of Aso Tadakuni and wife of Tametomo (*Edmunds*, p.618). S22.18; S64.8; S87.7; T30; T223; T263. p.19.

SHIRATAYE: daughter of Sano Tsuneyo, who helped to entertain Hōjō Tokiyori (*Edmunds*, p.368, s.v. Hachinoki). S28.46; S46.2; T110.

SHISEMPAKU KŌHOTAN: Chinese hero of the *Suikoden*. S3.11.

SHŌBUTSU MARU, alternative boy-name of Benkei, q.v. S48.5.

SHŌHAŌ SHŪTSŪ: Chinese hero of the *Suikoden*. S3.2.

SHOKATSURYŌ, nickname of Kōmei, q.v.

SHOKUJO, see ORI-HIME.

SHŌMENKO SHUBU: Chinese hero of the *Suikoden*. S3.7.

SHŌ-ONKŌ RYOHŌ: Chinese hero of the *Suikoden*. S2.63; S3.10.

SHŌRIKŌ KWAYEI: Chinese hero of the *Suikoden*. S2.64; S3.6.

SHŌSEMPŪ SAISHIN: Chinese hero of the *Suikoden*. S3.5.

SHŌSHARAN BOKUSHUN: Chinese hero of the *Suikoden*. S2.8; S3.4.

SHŌSHŌ, TEGOSHI NO: mistress of Soga Gorō; assisted the brothers in their revenge. S21.7; S45.5; T125; T132; T193; T304. pp.25, 26.

SHŌSHUN, TOSA-BŌ: d.1185; renegade warrior-monk; attacked Yoshitsune at Horikawa (*Papinot*, p.689; *Edmunds*, p.639; *Gikeiki*, pp.139–48, 151–3). S68.6; S74.33; T282. p.24.

SHŌTOKU TAISHI: 572–621; son of the Emperor Yōmei; champion of Buddhism (*Papinot*, p.591; *Edmunds*, p.577). S14 *passim*; T279. p.17.

SHŌ-UTSUCHI SONSHIN: Chinese hero of the *Suikoden*. S3.12.

SHŪGUMBA SENSAN: Chinese hero of the *Suikoden*. S2.65; S3.3; S47.22.

SHUJUSHŌ (Chu Shou-ch'ang): Chinese Paragon of Filial Piety. S60.15.

SHUKUYŪ-FUJIN: woman-warrior, wife of Mōkwaku, in the Wars of the Three Kingdoms. T310.

SHUNDŌ JIROYEMON: avenger of his father's murder disguised as a *hinin*; character in the play *Tsudzure no nishiki*. S51.9.

SHUNKWAN: 1142–78; priest and conspirator; exiled to Kikai-ga-shima (*Papinot*, p.595; *Edmunds*, p.580; *Heike*, esp. pp.162ff., 189ff.). S15.9; S46.38.

SHŪSHIKI: poetess; daughter of a confectioner of Yedo (Tokugawa period). S21.4; S35.13; S95e.5.

SHŪSO: Chinese warrior in the Wars of the Three Kingdoms. S10.8.

SHUTEN-DŌJI: drunken demon monster slain by Raikō (*Edmunds*, p.581). S1a.3; S19.60; T21; T261; T280; T298; T305. p.18.

SHUTSUDŌKŌ DŌI: Chinese hero of the *Suikoden*. S3.5.

SHUTSURINRYŌ SŪYEN: Chinese hero of the *Suikoden*. S2.66; S3.4.

SŌBIKATSU GAIHŌ, see SŌKOKATSU KAIHŌ.

SOGA GORŌ TOKIMUNE (1174–93) and SOGA JURŌ SUKENARI (1172–93): sons of Kawadzu Sukeyasu (q.v.) who devoted their short lives to avenging his murder on Kudō Suketsune (*Papinot*, p.599; *Edmunds*, p.583). S1c.14; S1e.8; S7.3; S8.7; S17.7; S22.19; S23.4; S31.20; S38.3; S44.9, 11; S45.3, 34; S46.5; S48.1; S61.9; S74.61; T35; T100–T104; T125; T132; T158; T159; T193; T269; T304; T328; T349. pp.14, 15, 16, 25, 26.

SŌGEN (cf. SEIGEN): priest, infatuated with Orikoto-hime of the Ōtomo family (variation on the Seigen story). S46.39.

SŌJŌ-BŌ: king of the *tengu* wood-sprites (*Edmunds*, p.624). S1f.11; S65.2; S88.8; T20; T194; T264; T351.

SŌJŌ HENJŌ: 816–90; priest-poet; formerly Yoshimine Munesada (*Papinot*, p.757; *Edmunds*, p.587). S19.12.

SŌKOKATSU KAIHŌ: Chinese hero of the *Suikoden*. S2.16; S3.5.

SŌMONJIN HŌKYOKU: Chinese hero of the *Suikoden*. S3.4.

SONGOKU (Sun Wu K'ung): monkey-king in Bakin's romance *Seiyuki* (*Edmunds*, p.216, s.v. Yüan Chwang; Pearl Buck's *Monkey* provides an English version). S17.9.

SONO, see O-SONO.

SONOBE SAYEMON: lover of Usuyuki-hime in a romance of the Ashikaga period dramatized in the play *Usuyuki monogatari*. S46.9.

SŌSEI-HŌSHI: ninth-century priest-poet; probably a son of Sōjō Henjō, q.v. S19.21.

SŌSHIKO RAIŌ: Chinese hero of the *Suikoden*. S2.67; S2a.11; S3.5.

SŌSHIN (Ts'êng Shen): Chinese Paragon of Filial Piety. S13.4; S60.6.

SŌSŌ (Ts'ao-ts'ao): Chinese soldier of fortune in the Wars of the Three Kingdoms (*Edmunds*, p.192). T277; T293; T297; T301; T306.

SŌSŌSHŌ TŌHEI: Chinese hero of the *Suikoden*. S3.1.

SŌTŌKI SŌSEI: Chinese hero of the *Suikoden*. S2.68; S3.11.

SUGARU, KOSHIBE NO: fifth-century hero under the Emperor Yūryaku; perhaps identifiable with Sukaru (*Nihongi* I, p.347). S1c.2. p.12.

SUGIMOTO SAKUBEI: retainer of Kusunoki Masashige, probably identical with Akiyuki, q.v. S35.14.

SUIKODEN (Shui-ho-ch'uan): semi-historical romance of twelfth-century China, translated by Bakin (*Edmunds*, p.590; *Riccar 1979, passim*). S2; S2a; S3; S47. pp.10, 12, 13.

SUKECHIKA, see SUKEYASU.

SUKEMORI, JŌ KURŌ: d.1202; son of Nagamochi (*Papinot*, p.232). T61.

SUKENAGA, IKE-NO-SHŌJI: retainer of Oguri Hangwan. S26.9.

SUKENARI, see SOGA JURŌ.

SUKEROKU, HANAKAWADO: populist hero of the play *Sukeroku*. S45.47.

SUKESHIGE, see OGURI HANGWAN.

SUKETADA, HOMMA: fourteenth-century loyalist. S23.8.

SUKETAKA, GOTŌ: retainer of Oguri Hangwan. S26.3.

SUKETAKE, YATA GOROYEMON: one of the Forty-Seven *Rōnin*. S54.36; S57.42; S59.7 (Jiroyemon); S72.7 (Yada); S78.11 (Yada Gorozayemon); S80.8 (Yada Gorozayemon); S90.36 (Gorozayemon).

SUKETOKI, YAMATO NO: filial son whose dead parents appeared to him as butterflies. S23.20.

SUKETSUNE, KUDŌ: d.1193; villain of the *Soga monogatari* (*Papinot*, p.319). T100; T132; T158; T198; T304. p.25.

SUKEYASU, KAWADZU SABURŌ: d.1177; famous wrestler; father of the Soga brothers (*Edmunds*, p.595). S16.6; T141; T340; T353. p.25.

SUKUNE TARŌ: lover of Tatsuta-no-maye in the play *Ume-matsu-sakura*. S46.69.

SUMIMOTO, GON-NO-SUKE: Crown Prince, late tenth century. S4b.6.

SUMINO CHŪHEIJI, see TSUGIFUSA.

SUŌ-NO-NAISHI: court lady and poetess; daughter of Taira no Tsuginaka. S19.67; S23.21.

SUSA-NO-O-NO-MIKOTO: the 'impetuous male', brother of the Sun-Goddess (*Nihongi* I, esp. pp.34–59; *Papinot*, p.609; *Edmunds*, p.597). S17.5.

SUTOKU(-IN): Emperor, 1124–42, and poet; defeated in the war of Hōgen (1156) and banished to Sanuki (*Papinot*, p.611). S19.77; S64.9. p.19.

SUYESHIGE, HIRAYAMA: Taira warrior (*Heike*, pp.534–46). T38; T228.

SUYETAKE, URABE NO: retainer of Raikō, 950–1022 (*Papinot*, p.724; *Edmunds*, p.589). S46.25; S94.1; T3; T4; T21; T46;

T128; T169; T261; T262; T298; T305; T357. p.18.

TACHIBANA-HIME (or OTO-TACHIBANA-HIME): wife of Prince Yamato-take (second century) (*Papinot*, p.502; *Edmunds*, p.657). S87.8.

TADABUMI, FUJIWARA NO: 873–947; suppressor of Masakado's rebellion (*Papinot*, p.93). S61.1.

TADAHIRA, IDZUMI SABURŌ: Minamoto warrior. T167.

TADAHIRA, wife of, see FUJINOYE.

TADAKUNI, ASO HIGO NO KAMI: Tametomo's father-in-law. T223.

TADAMORI, TAIRA NO: 1096–1153; reputed father of Kiyomori (*Papinot*, p.620; *Edmunds*, p.598). S1e.11; S15.10; S74.65; T182.

TADANOBU, SATŌ SHIRŌ: 1160–87; retainer of Yoshitsune; brother of Tsuginobu and Fujinoye (*Edmunds*, p.599; *Gikeiki, passim*). S1e.5; S4a.15; S8.2; S16.2; S22.15; S31.15; S36.2; S45.23; S46.31, 94; S65.16; S89.8; T2; T16; T168; T257; T321. pp.11, 25.

TADANORI, SATSUMA NO KAMI TAIRA NO: 1144–84; brother of Kiyomori; warrior and poet (*Papinot*, p.622; *Edmunds*, p.601; *Heike*, pp.264–568 *passim*). S22.16; S28.38; S67.5; S73.11; S91.1; S92.3; T48; T173; T228.

TADAO, ŌTAKA GENGO: one of the Forty-Seven *Rōnin*. S54.14; S80.13; S90.14 (Dengo).

TADATOKI, NAKAMURA KANSUKE: one of the Forty-Seven *Rōnin*. S54.16; S78.6 (Masatatsu); S90.16 (Masatoki).

TADATSUNE, NITTA SHIRŌ: retainer of Yoritomo (*Edmunds*, p.604). S17.6; S89.6; T72; T73; T99; T104; T143; T159; T200; T269. p.25.

TADAYOSHI, ASHIKAGA: 1307–52; younger brother of Taka-uji (*Papinot*, p.29). S22.4. p.27.

TADAZUMI, OKABE ROKUYATA: Minamoto warrior (*Heike*, pp.557, 558). S91.1; T228.

TADAZUMI, see HIRONAO.

TAHEIJI: character in the play *Igagoye* (revenge story). S46.52.

TAIRA ghosts. S65.15; T1; T70; T147; T242; T266. pp.14f., 16, 24, 25.

TAISHUN (T'a Shun): Chinese Paragon of Filial Piety. S13.1; S60.1.

TAITŌ KWANSHŌ, see DAITŌ KWANSHŌ.

TAKAFUSA, KATAOKA DENGOYEMON: one of the Forty-Seven *Rōnin*. S54.15; S57.10; S80.4; S90.15.

TAKAGI ORIYEMON: dramatic character who destroyed a robber-gang; hero of the play *Takagi Oriyemon*. S24.7; S37.21.

TAKAGI TORANOSUKE: a native of Hyūga, expert in the martial arts. S1c.6; S74.32.

TAKAGI UMANOSUKE: young man whose father was killed by Nagoya Sanzaburō (*Mitford*, 'A Story of the Otokodate of Yedo'). S36.48; T287.

TAKAHASHI KAMBŌ: perhaps identical with Takahashi Gappō (see GAPPŌ). T9.

TAKAHASHI YAJURŌ, identical with Gappō, q.v. S46.81.

TAKAKAGE, HAYAKAWA. S45.32.

TAKAKANE, KO-AYAKAWA SAYEMON-NO-SUKE (Kobayakawa Takakage): 1532–96; fought Nobunaga and Hideyoshi, but later served in Korea (*Papinot*, p.291; *Hawley*, 310). S62.21.

TAKAKO-HIME: beloved of the poet Narihira. S45.28.

TAKAMASA, UNO SAMA-NO-SUKE: Uyesugi warrior at Kawanaka-jima. S63.13.

TAKANAO, URAMATSU HANDAYŪ: one of the Forty-Seven *Rōnin*. S54.19; S57.43; S78.7 (Muramatsu Sandayū); S90.19.

TAKANAO, URAMATSU, wife of. S56.13.

TAKANORI, KOJIMA NO (BINGO SABURŌ): d.1358; loyalist (*Papinot*, p.298; *Edmunds*, p.605). S16.1; S36.43.

TAKANORI, SHIMAMURA: d.1509; fought with the Hosokawa against Ashikaga Yoshitane (*Edmunds*, p.606). S1f.12.

TAKANORI, USHIODA MASANOJŌ: one of the Forty-Seven Rōnin. S54.28; S78.10; S90.28 (Ashioda Matanojō Mitsutoki).

TAKAO, MIURA NO: courtesan in the Sendai cycle of plays. S46.24; S74.7.

TAKASADA, YENYA HANGWAN: former lord of the Forty-Seven Rōnin in the Chūshingura. S54.39; S86.1, 3; S90.39; T248. p.29.

TAKASHIGE, TAKEBAYASHI SADASHICHI: one of the Forty-Seven Rōnin. S54.24; S59.6; S74.45; S80.3; S90.24; T184.

TAKASHIGE, SADASHICHI, mother of. S56.10.

TAKATOSHI, HORIMOTO GIDAYŪ: retainer of Katō Kiyomasa; fought in Korea. S62.14.

TAKATSUGU, GOTŌ: retainer of Oguri Hangwan. S26.4.

TAKATSUNA, SASAKI SHIRŌ: Minamoto warrior (Papinot, p.545; Edmunds, p.608; Heike, pp.508–34). S15.11; S31.16; S44.47; S50.3; S73.5; S92.2; T18; T62; T94; T191; T197; T217; T225; T334. p.22.

TAKA-UJI, ASHIKAGA: 1305–58; the first Ashikaga Shōgun (Papinot, p.28; Edmunds, p.609; Taiheiki, pp.237–381 passim). T275; T323. p.27.

TAKEDA SAMA-NO-SUKE, see NOBUSHIGE.

TAKE-JO (or O-TAKE): the saintly servant-girl. S20.20.

TAKE-JO: wife of Yamaoka Kakubei in the Chūshingura. S56.2.

TAKESHIUCHI-NO-SUKUNE: 85–367(?); commander-in-chief and minister to the Empress Jingō (Papinot, p.639; Edmunds, p.612 (Take-uchi)). S8.5; S28.1; S31.17; S74.35; S88.22; T51; T145; T234. pp.17, 28.

TAKETAKA, KATSUTA SHINYEMON: one of the Forty-Seven Rōnin. S54.23; S57.29 (Shinzayemon); S80.7; S90.23 (Kazuta).

TAKETOSHI, HAYASHI TANSHIRŌ: d.1582; retainer of Akechi Mitsuharu, killed at Uchide-no-hama (Hawley, 411). S62.11.

TAKETSUNE, ORIBE YASUBEI: one of the Forty-Seven Rōnin. S54.34; S57.8 (Horiye); S58.3; S72.6 (Yasahei); S80.18 (Orinabe); S90.34 (Horibe); T148 (Horiguchi); T184; T213. p.30.

TAKEUCHI-NO-SUKUNE, see TAKESHIUCHI-NO-SUKUNE.

TAKEYUKI, KURAHASHI ZENSUKE: one of the Forty-Seven Rōnin. S54.25; S90.25 (Karahashi).

TAKIGUCHI-NO-SUKE (or KŌDZUKE): villain in the Hakone revenge story (Hatsu-hana and Katsugorō). T274.

TAKIYASHA-HIME: tenth-century witch; daughter of Masakado (Edmunds, p.482). See also NYOGETSU-NI. S36.33; S38.5 (Tatsuyasha); S87.1; T89; T111; T138; T166; T219. p.18.

TAMAMO-NO-MAYE: early twelfth-century court lady and Japanese incarnation of the Nine-tailed Fox (Edmunds, p.613). S1c.1; S36.25; S46.37; S66.5, 6.

TAMAMUSHI-NO-MAYE: Taira court lady and beauty. S21.3; T179. p.22.

TAMAORI- (or TAMAYORI-)HIME: wife of Taira no Atsumori. S20.21; S45.12; S46.73.

TAMATORI, see AMA.

TAMATSUKURI, see KOMACHI.

TAMAYA SHIMBEI: character in the play Tsukinode-mura. S74.8.

TAMEHARU (or TSUNEHARU), KATAOKA HACHIRŌ: retainer of Yoshitsune (Gikeiki, pp.145–320 passim). S31.18.

TAMEHISA, MITONO: retainer of Oguri Hangwan. S26.7.

TAMEMITSU, ARAKAWA IDZU NO KAMI: Uyesugi warrior at Kawanakajima. S83.1.

TAMETOMO, CHINZEI HACHIRŌ MINAMOTO NO: 1139–70; formidable archer and colonist (Papinot, p.380; Edmunds, p.615). S9.1; S22.5; S31.19; S32.15; S36.63; S49.3; S64 passim; S76.5; S77.1; T30; T91; T92; T140; T214; T223; T235–T237; T254; T263. pp.15, 19.

TAMIYA (or KAMIYA) IYEMON: villain of Yotsuya kwaidan; husband of O-Iwa (Edmunds, p.529). S45.25; S46.49; S74.66.

TAMMEIJIRŌ GENSHŌGO: Chinese hero of the Suikoden. S2.69, 70; S2a.12; S3.6; S47.24.

TAMON MARU, child-name of Masatsura, q.v.

TAMURA SHŌGUN (Sakanoye Tamura-maro): 758–811; distinguished suppressor of the aborigines (Papinot, p.532; Edmunds, p.619). S44.51.

TANENAGA, YEGARA (WADA) HEITA: early thirteenth century; son of Wada Yoshinaga; serpent-slayer (Edmunds, pp.331, 671). S1c.10; S1f.8; S84.6; T75.

TANKAI, KITASHIRAKAWA: apprentice to Ki-ichi Hōgen (Gikeiki, pp.102–6). S4a.9; S65.7.

TATSU-HIME: daughter of Itō Sukechika; married Yoritomo (Edmunds, p.465). S36.14; S46.36.

TATSUIYE, CHIBATA SHURI-NO-SHIN (Shibata Katsuiye): 1530–83; overthrown by Hideyoshi at Shidzu-ga-mine (Papinot, p.563; Edmunds, p.430). S62.7; T329.

TATSUTA-NO-MAYE: female character in the play Ume-matsu-sakura. S46.69.

TATSUYASHA-HIME, see TAKIYASHA-HIME.

TAYEMA, KUMO NO: female character in the play Narukami. S46.74.

TEIJO ('faithful wife'), MAMA NO: a girl of lowly origin at Mama in the province of Shimosa, who married a person of quality. S21.6.

TEIRAN (Ting Lan): Chinese Paragon of Filial Piety. S60.4; S79.1.

TEKKYŌSHI RAKKWA: Chinese hero of the Suikoden. S3.9.

TEMMOKUSHŌ HŌKI: Chinese hero of the Suikoden. S2.71; S3.9.

TENCHI (or TENJI) TENNŌ: Emperor (662–71) and poet (Papinot, p.648; Edmunds, p.622). S19.1; S27.1.

TENGAN ISOBEI: wrestler. S4a.17.

TENJIKU TOKUBEI: 1619–86; adventurer and traveller (Edmunds, p.633). S1a.7.

TENJI NO TSUBONE: mistress of Taira no Tomomori. S46.22; T96; T144.

TERANISHI KANSHIN: rōnin appearing in several otokodate plays. S40.7; S45.60; S74.23.

TERUKUNI, HANGWANDAI: retainer of Michizane in Sugawara. S46.62.

TERUTA-HIME: daughter of Abe no Mashika of Asazawa, Settsu; a dutiful girl mistreated by her stepmother. S23.22.

TERUTE-HIME: faithful wife of Oguri Hangwan (Papinot, p.475, where the name is wrongly given as Teruta-hime; Edmunds, pp.534ff.). S20.22; S26.2; S35.9; S44.7.

TESSENSHI SŌSEI: Chinese hero of the Suikoden. S3.7.

TETSUBIHAKU SAIFUKU: Chinese hero of the Suikoden. S3.10.

TETSUMENKŌMOKU HAISEN: Chinese hero of the Suikoden. S3.11.

TETTEKISEN BARIN: Chinese hero of the Suikoden. S2.72; S3.10.

TŌDAYŪ: fisherman who showed Moritsuna the ford over the Inland Sea (Edmunds, p.503). S1a.6; S89.7; S93.6.

TŌFUJIN (T'ang Fu-jên): Chinese female Paragon of Filial Piety. S13.8; S60.10.

TOGASHI SAYEMON IYENAO: officer-in-charge at the Ataka Barrier when Yoshitsune and his men passed through (1186). S95d.2; T126; T164.

TOGISHI TOZAYEMON: sword-polisher in the Chūshingura. S56.15.

TŌJŌ NO SAYEMON: attacked Nichiren on Komatsu moor (1264). S6.2.

TŌKEN GOMBEI: an apprentice of Banzui Chōbei (Mitford, 'A Story of the Otokodate of Yedo'). S40.8.

TOKIMASA, HŌJŌ SHIRŌ: 1138–1215; powerful ally and father-in-law of Yoritomo (Papinot, p.163; Edmunds, p.629; Heike, pp.730–47). T115.

TOKIMUNE, see SOGA GORŌ.

TOKIUJI: a native of Mino who travelled in early life and later served Nobunaga. S62.47.

TOKIWA-GOZEN: mistress of Minamoto no Yoshitomo and mother of Yoshitsune (*Papinot*, p.659; *Edmunds*, p.631; *Gikeiki*, pp.12, 13, 70–2). S20.23; S29.9; S65.1; S74.52; S95c.1; T155; T308. pp.19, 20.

TOKIYORI, HŌJŌ (SAIMYŌJI): 1226–63; regent (*shikken*) (*Papinot*, p.165; *Edmunds*, p.632). S28.46; S46.2; T110.

TOKIYOSHI, see HATA ROKUROZAYEMON.

TOKUZŌ: ship's pilot who encountered the 'Sea Monk'. S44.44.

TOMBEI: ferryman and father of O-Fune in *Yaguchi no watashi*. S45.37.

TOMOMORI, SHINCHŪNAGON TAIRA NO: 1152–85; son of Kiyomori; Taira military leader (*Papinot*, p.624; *Edmunds*, p.635; *Heike, passim*). S1f.7; S31.21; S32.8; S36.53, 68; S45.40; S49.4; S77.5; T1; T96; T144; T152; T266. pp.14, 16, 23.

TOMONOBU, KAIDA YADAYEMON: one of the Forty-Seven *Rōnin*. S54.48; S90.48 (Kaiga Yazayemon).

TOMONOBU, SAITŌ SHIMOTSUKE NO KAMI: Uyesugi gunnery expert at Kawanakajima. S63.18.

TOMONORI, KI NO: tenth-century poet. S19.33.

TOMONORI, MIKAWA NO KAMI: Taira commander against Yoshinaka. S9.2; T43; T146; T300; T303. p.21.

TOMOYE-GOZEN (-JO): warrior-mistress of Yoshinaka; daughter of Gon-no-kami Kanetō, and reputed mother of Asahina Saburō (*Papinot*, p.687; *Edmunds*, p.635; *Heike*, pp.519, 521). S7.4; S20.24; S22.20; S29.10; S30.5; S31.22; S32.9; S46.15; S69.1; S76.3; T25; T43; T60; T95; T116; T146; T265; T315. pp.22, 26.

TOMOYUKI, SHINANO SAKON: retainer of Tsutsui Junkei. S62.39.

TONASE: wife of Honzō in the *Chūshingura* (*Dickins*, pp.111–41). S86.8, 9.

TORA(-GOZEN) of Ōiso: mistress of Soga Jurō and assisted the brothers in their revenge. S20.25; S25.2; S44.9; T328. p.25.

TORAHIDE, ONIKOJIMA YATARŌ: Uyesugi warrior at Kawanakajima. S63.16; T316.

TORAMASA, Ō HYŌBU-SHŌYŪ: Takeda warrior at Kawanakajima. S63.8.

TORAZŌ, see YOSHITSUNE (name he used in the Ki-ichi Hōgen episode).

TORII MATASUKE: character in the *Kagamiyama* cycle of plays. S74.25.

TORIYE RIYEMON: retainer of Moronao in the *Chūshingura*. S57.9.

TOSHIKAZU, SAITŌ KURANOSHIN: veteran counsellor of the Toki family. S62.30.

TOSHIMOTO, SAITŌ NYŪDŌ RYŪHON: retainer of Katō Kiyomasa; fought in Korea. S62.31.

TOSHINARI, KŌTAIKŌGŪ-NO-TAYŪ FUJIWARA NO: 1114–1204; statesman and poet (*Papinot*, p.104). S19.83.

TOSHIYUKI, FUJIWARA NO: one of the Hundred Poets. S19.18; S27.18.

TŌTAKU: Chinese war-lord in the Wars of the Three Kingdoms. T302.

TŌYEI (Tung Yung): Chinese Paragon of Filial Piety. S13.10; S60.12; S79.3.

TOYONARI, OKADA, see SHIGEMORI, TOKUDA.

TOYONARI, UDAIJIN FUJIWARA NO: 704–65; statesman (*Papinot*, p.89; *Edmunds*, pp.300, 506). S45.59.

TSŪBIYEN KŌKEN: Chinese hero of the *Suikoden*. S3.11.

TSUGICHIYO MARU, child-name of Ashikaga Taka-uji(?), q.v. S20.16.

TSUGIFUSA, SUMINO CHŪHEIJI: one of the Forty-Seven *Rōnin*. S54.45; S59.5; S71.5 (Sugino Jūheiji); S78.12 (Sugino Jūheiji); S90.45 (Kadono Jūheiji).

TSUGINOBU, SATŌ: retainer of Yoshitsune, 1158–85 (*Edmunds*, p.642). T109; T256. p.22.

TSUNA, WATANABE NO: retainer of Raikō (*Edmunds*, p.642). S1a.16; S28.45; S31.23; S46.6; S61.2; S94.1; T3; T4; T21; T44; T46; T128; T169; T261; T262; T298; T305; T357. pp.18f.

TSUNEKI, TOSHIMA, see TSUNETATSU, OKAJIMA.

TSUNEMASA, TAJIMA NO KAMI: Taira warrior at Ichi-no-tani (*Edmunds*, p.643). T229.

TSUNENARI, HAYANO WASUKE: one of the Forty-Seven *Rōnin*. S54.35; S57.37; S90.35.

TSUNENOBU, DAINAGON MINAMOTO NO: one of the Hundred Poets. S19.71.

TSUNETANE, MIURA-NO-SUKE: warrior who slew the Nine-tailed Fox (*Edmunds*, p.614, 'Miura Kuranosuke'). T24.

TSUNETATSU, OKAJIMA YASŌYEMON: one of the Forty-Seven *Rōnin*. S54.17; S80.10 (Yasuyemon); S90.17 (Toshima Tsuneki).

TSUNEYO, SANO: entertainer of Hōjō Tokiyori (*Edmunds*, p.368). T110.

TSUNEYO, see HAYANO KAMPEI.

TSUSHIŌ MARU: younger brother of Anju-hime, q.v. S23.1; S36.37.

UCHIDA SABURŌ: Taira warrior slain by Tomoye-gozen. S7.4.

UDE NO KISABURŌ: *otokodate* dramatic character. S40.9; S42.7.

UKAREME, MURO NO: 'courtesan of Muro' (now Murotsu); said to have been an incarnation of Fugen Bosatsu (*Edmunds*, p.260). S33.5.

UKIYO WATABEI: dramatic character (perhaps Matabei). S74.2.

UKON: poetess; mother of Suō-no-naishi. S19.38.

UMEGAWA: beloved of Chūbei in *Meido no hikyaku*. S46.75.

UME NO YOSHIBEI: dramatic character; husband of Ko-ume. S40.10; S46.79.

UMEWAKA MARU: child carried off by a slave-dealer (*Edmunds*, p.647). S46.21.

UMI BŌZU (the 'Sea Monk'): monstrous marine apparition. S44.44.

UNEME: heroic girl who saved her village from a monstrous serpent. S20.26 (a different Uneme?); S23.23.

UNNO KOTARŌ: protagonist at the battle of Kurikaradani (2 June 1183). T303.

UNRIKONGŌ SŌMAN: Chinese hero of the *Suikoden*. S2.73; S3.7.

URASHIMA TARŌ: Japanese Rip Van Winkle (*Edmunds*, p.648). S74.39.

USAMI SURUGA NO KAMI: Uyesugi warrior at Kawanakajima. T331.

USHIWAKA MARU, child-name of Yoshitsune, q.v.

USUI MATAGORŌ: monster-slayer of Hida province. S1c.3.

USUYUKI-HIME: heroine of *Usuyuki monogatari*; beloved of Sonobe Sayemon. S46.46.

UYESHIMA MONYA: youthful retainer of Yenya in the *Chūshingura*. S56.7.

WADA HYŌYE: character in the play *Ōmi Genji*. S74.30.

WADA IDZUMI NO KAMI: Kusunoki warrior in the war against the Ashikaga. T350.

WAIKYAKKO ŌYEI: Chinese hero of the *Suikoden*. S2.74; S3.2.

WAKABA-NO-NAISHI: mother of Rokudai, q.v. S45.46.

WAKAMATSU: *ama* who tried to recover the Sword of the regalia after the battle of Dan-no-ura. T134.

WAKASA NO SUKE (Kamei Sama): under instruction, with Yenya, by Moronao in the *Chūshingura*. S86.1, 2; T248.

WAKATSUKI HEIDAYŪ: Takeda warrior at Kawanakajima. T292.

WANKYŪ (Wanya Kyūyemon): late seventeenth-century poet distracted by love. S46.42.

WASHI(-NO-)O SABURŌ TSUNEHISA (or YOSHIHISA): young hunter who showed Yoshitsune the Hiyodori-goye path at Ichi-no-tani (*Edmunds*, pp.296, 682). S1a.10; S65.11; T64. p.22.

WATANABE WATARU: mid twelfth century; husband of Kesa-gozen (*Edmunds*, p.335). T129. p.26.

WATARI (sometimes wrongly read as TADA) SHINZAYEMON: retainer of Nitta Yoshisada. S94.3; T6.

WATŌNAI: 1623–62; pirate offspring of a Chinese father and Japanese mother (*Edmunds*, p.447); often used as a substitute name for Katō Kiyomasa, q.v.

YADAHEI: son of Konomura Ōinosuke (q.v.) in *Gosan no kiri*. S46.61.

YAKAMOCHI, CHŪNAGON ŌTOMO NO: d.785; one of the Hundred Poets. S27.6.

YAMABUKI-GOZEN: formerly Sarashina-hime (q.v.); wife of Yoshinaka, and fought beside him (*Heike*, p.519). S20.27; T60; T95.

YAMAMOTO KANSUKE NYŪDŌ HARUYUKI DŌKISAI: d.1561; leading Takeda general at Kawanakajima; one-eyed, and in early life a considerable scholar. S34.4; S35.16; S38.12; S44.37; S63.2; S81.6; S82.3; S84.2; S92.5; T154; T161; T190; T247; T259; T313. pp.14, 16, 28.

YAMANAKA DANKURŌ. S1f.16; T212.

YAMATO-TAKE-NO-MIKOTO (or YAMATOTAKERU-NO-MIKOTO): 81–113; son of the Emperor Keikō and active against the aborigines (*Nihongi* I, esp. p.205; *Papinot*, p.747; *Edmunds*, p.656). S4b.5; S88.27. pp.15, 17.

YAMA-UBA: mother of Kintoki, formerly called Yayegiri (*Edmunds*, p.435). S38.4; S74.18, 34; S88.12; T44. p.19.

YAMAZAKI YOGORŌ: character in several plays, e.g. *Michiyuki koi no Yamazaki*. S46.80.

YAOYA ('greengrocer') HAMBEI: character in the play *Yoigoshin*. S46.59.

YASHA ARASHI: wrestler. S4a.17.

YASUAKIRA, SAMA-NO-SUKE FUJIWARA NO (Katō Yoshiaki): 1563–1631; fought in Korea (*Papinot*, p.263; *Hawley*, 285, 286). S62.35.

YASUBEI, HORIBE, see TAKETSUNE, ORIBE.

YASUCHIKA, ABE NO: court astrologer who unmasked Tamamo-no-maye as the Nine-tailed Fox (cf. *Edmunds*, pp.560, 613, 658). S1c.1.

YASUHARU, ORIO MOSUKE (Horio Yoshiharu): youthful retainer of Hideyoshi (*Papinot*, p.178; *Hawley*, 105, 106, 155). S62.27; T202.

YASUHIDE, FUMIYA (BUNYA): eminent ninth-century poet (*Papinot*, p.110). S19.22.

YASUKATA, UTOU: character in the play *Sōma dairi*. S45.19.

YASUMASA, HIRAI (or FUJIWARA) NO: retainer of Raikō (*Papinot*, p.104; *Edmunds*, p.432). S35.11; S74.42; T3; T4; T21; T128; T169; T261; T262; T298; T305; T357. p.18.

YASUMASA, see WATARI (TADA) SHINZAYEMON.

YASUNA, ABE NO: husband of the fox-woman Kuzunoha (*Edmunds*, p.658). S45.24; S74.44.

YASUSUKE, HAKAMADARE: robber, sometimes identified with Kidō Maru, q.v. S24.8; S35.11; S46.76; S74.42. p.18.

YATA JIROYEMON, see SUKETAKE.

YATSUSHIRO: wife of Tametomo's retainer Kiheiji. S35.1; S64.5.

YAWATA SABURŌ: retainer of Kudō Suketsune; perhaps identical with Hachiman Saburō, q.v. T102.

YAYE: wife of Sakura Maru in the play *Sugawara*. S45.35; S46.84.

YAYEGAKI-HIME: betrothed to Takeda Katsuyori, and faithful to his memory. S36.13; S45.17; S46.72; S74.31.

YAYEGIRI (see also YAMA-UBA): wife of Sakata Kurando (*Ed-munds*, p.435). S46.87. p.19.

YAZAMA JŪTARŌ, see MOTO-OKI.

YEBINA GEMPACHI: wrestling umpire before Yoritomo. T353.

YEDA GENZŌ HIROTSUNA (or HIROTSUGU): retainer of Yoshi-tsune killed at Horikawa (*Gikeiki*, pp.141–50). S4a.18; S74.40; S76.6; T185. p.24.

YEGARA HEITA, see TANENAGA.

YENDŌ MUSHA, see MORITŌ.

YENSHI (Yen Tzu): Chinese Paragon of Filial Piety. S60.16.

YENYA HANGWAN, see TAKASADA.

YODOHEI, SHIMOBE: character in *Go-nin otoko*. S45.14.

YODOYA SHINSHICHI: loyal servant in *Yodo no koi*. S51.10.

YOICHIBEI: farmer, father of O-Karu in the *Chūshingura*. S74.48.

YOJI: Japanese Paragon of Filial Piety. S23.24.

YOJIBEI: a ship's captain who attempted to assassinate Hide-yoshi. T251.

YOJIRŌ: brother of the courtesan Otoshi in *Sarumawashi*, a play on the lovers' double-suicide theme. S38.9.

YOJŌ (Yü Jang): Chinese would-be avenger of his lord's death in the third century BC (*Edmunds*, p.217). S46.20.

YŌKŌ (or YŌKYŌ) (Yang Hsiang): Chinese Paragon of Filial Piety. S13.9; S60.11.

YOKOYAMA TARŌ: character in the dramatized story of Oguri Hangwan. S46.58.

YORI-IYE, MINAMOTO NO: 1182–1204; eldest son of Yoritomo (*Papinot*, p.385). T119; T218. p.26.

YORIKANE, ASHIKAGA SAKINGO: murderer of Takao in *Date kurabe*. S45.44; S74.2.

YORIMASA, GEN (MINAMOTO) SAMMI: 1106–80; warrior and poet (*Papinot*, p.379; *Edmunds*, p.660; *Heike*, pp.234–82 *passim*). S15.12; S31.24; S46.8; S48.6; S67.1; S74.72; S77.2; S89.2; S95d.3; T7; T48; T107; T112. pp.16, 21.

YORIMITSU (RAIKŌ), MINAMOTO NO: 944–1021; hero of a number of bold feats with his Four Retainers (*Shitennō*) (*Papinot*, p.377; *Edmunds*, p.546). S1a.3; S8.6; S31.25; S88.19; T3; T4; T21; T128; T169; T261; T262; T280; T298; T305. pp.15, 18–19, 21.

YORITOMO, UDAISHŌ MINAMOTO NO: 1147–99; destroyer of the Taira and first Minamoto Shōgun (*Papinot*, p.381; *Edmunds*, p.661; *Heike* and *Gikeiki*, *passim*). S22.12; S31.26; S32.10; S44.10; S44.30; S46.36; S67.6; S73.9; T39; T45; T48; T56; T57; T71–T74; T87; T94; T99; T103; T114; T115; T118; T141; T200; T216; T283; T320; T326; T340; T353. pp.20, 21ff.

YOSHIHARU, DŌJI, see YASUHARU, ORIO.

YOSHIHIDE, see ASAHINA SABURŌ.

YOSHIHIRA, AKUGENDA MINAMOTO NO: 1140–60; eldest son of Yoshitomo (*Papinot*, p.381; *Edmunds*, p.666; *Heike*, p.617). S1c.4; S22.2; S31.28; T10; T195. pp.11, 19.

YOSHIHIRO, FUCHIBE: murderer of Prince Morinaga (Ōto-no-miya) (*Papinot*, p.409; *Edmunds*, p.502). S1c.5; S16.5; S74.38. p.27.

YOSHIHISA, SANADA, see YOSHITADA.

YOSHI-IYE, HACHIMAN-TARŌ MINAMOTO NO: 1041–1108; war-rior and suppressor of rebels (*Papinot*, p.377; *Edmunds*, p.667). S8.8; S28.16; S31.29; S67.2; S77.3; S88.34; T52; T111a. p.12.

YOSHIKADO, SŌMA TARŌ: son of Masakado; wizard and brigand. S45.19; S61.10; T89; T111; T166; T219. p.18.

YOSHIKANE, ASAKURA SAYEMON-NO-TAYŪ (Yoshikage): 1533–73; fought Nobunaga (*Papinot*, p.24). S62.6.

YOSHIKANE, ŌBOSHI, see RIKIYA.

YOSHIMINE: character in the play *Yaguchi no watashi*. S46.93.

YOSHIMORI, ISE SABURŌ: retainer of Yoshitsune (*Papinot*, p.210; *Gikeiki*, esp. pp.251–98). S9.5; S31.30.

YOSHIMORI, WADA: 1147–1213; Minamoto warrior, said to have married Tomoye-gozen (*Papinot*, p.730; *Edmunds*, p.670). S61.9; T101; T134; T315. p.26.

YOSHIMOTO, INAGAWA JIBU-NO-TAYŪ MINAMOTO NO (Imagawa): 1519–60; fought Nobunaga (*Papinot*, p.203; *Hawley*, 51–71). S62.15; S76.7; S93.2. p.28.

YOSHINAKA, KISO MINAMOTO NO: 1154–84; rebel cousin of Yoritomo (*Papinot*, p.385; *Edmunds*, p.671; *Heike*, *passim*). S9.2; S31.31; S37.15; S73.8; S94.2; T43; T95; T116; T146; T192; T265; T300; T303; T315. pp.21–2, 26.

YOSHININ-NI: name taken by Kaoyo-gozen (q.v.) after Yenya's death. S56.8.

YOSHIO, ŌBOSHI, see YURANOSUKE.

YOSHIOKI, NITTA: d.1358; second son of Yoshisada; killed at the Yaguchi crossing (*Papinot*, p.456; *Edmunds*, p.674). S28.51; S44.3. p.27.

YOSHIOTO, see YOSHIMOTO.

YOSHISADA, NITTA: 1301–38; loyalist leader against the Ashikaga (*Papinot*, p.455; *Edmunds*, p.675; *Taiheiki*, pp.188–319). S31.32; S73.4; S81.3; S94.3; T22; T76; T78; T142; T244; T343. pp.27, 29.

YOSHISADA, SANADA, see YOSHITADA.

YOSHISHIGE, WADA KOJIRŌ: took part in the Wada rebellion against the Hōjō (1213). T75.

YOSHISUKE, WAKIYA: d.1340; younger brother of Nitta Yoshisada (*Papinot*, p.734). T244.

YOSHITADA, SANADA YOICHI: retainer of Yoritomo, killed at Ishibashiyama (1180) (*Edmunds*, p.677). S1a.13; S1c.8; S1f.6; S8.1; S31.33; T28; T39; T94; T139; T197; T227. p.21.

YOSHITAKA, FUJIWARA NO: one of the Hundred Poets. S19.50.

YOSHITAKA, ŌUCHI: 1507–51; warrior and debauchee (*Papinot*, p.505). S36.50.

YOSHITAKA, SHIMIDZU KWANJA: son of Yoshinaka (*Edmunds*, p.677). S36.21; S43.10; S74.69.

YOSHITOMO, MINAMOTO NO: 1123–60; defeated and murdered in the war of Heiji (*Papinot*, p.380; *Edmunds*, p.678). S31.34. pp.19, 20.

YOSHITSUNE, KURŌ HANGWAN MINAMOTO NO: 1159–89; ninth son of Yoshitomo, by Tokiwa-gozen; the Japanese hero-paragon (*Papinot*, p.383; *Edmunds*, p.679; *Gikeiki*, *passim*; *Heike*, esp. pp.501–709). In early life he used the names Ushiwaka Maru and Shanaō. S1b.2; S1f.3; S1f.11; S7.5; S8.4; S9.5; S22.13; S28.2; S31.35; S32.11; S36.22; S37.14; S45.3, 42; S46.1, 11; S52.7; S65 *passim*; S74.16; S76.1; S84.9; S88.8, 37; S89.9; T1; T5; T16; T17; T20; T32; T40; T45; T47; T53; T54; T56; T59; T63; T64–T70; T84; T93; T97; T108; T109; T117; T122; T124; T126; T127; T133–T135; T147; T149–T151; T163; T164; T167; T185; T194; T215; T221; T222; T224; T227; T230; T241; T242; T264; T267; T282; T319; T327; T337; T339; T351. pp.14, 15, 16, 19, 20ff.

YOSHIYASU: Minamoto warrior at Yashima. T229.

YOYEMON, KINUGAWA: farmer who murdered his wife Kasane (*Edmunds*, p.530). S46.32; S74.54.

YŌZEI(-IN): Emperor, 877–84; eccentric and poet (*Papinot*, p.758). S19.13; S27.13.

YUKICHIKA, NENOI: retainer of Yoshinaka (*Edmunds*, p.673). S94.2.

YUKI-HIME: dramatic character in the story of the sword *Kurikara Maru*. S38.1; S46.55.

YUKIHIRA, CHŪNAGON ARIWARA NO: 818–93; poet and statesman; brother of Narihira (*Papinot*, p.22; *Edmunds*, p.688). S19.16; S27.16.

YUKIMORI, AMANAKA SHIKANOSUKE: vassal of Amako Yoshihisa (sixteenth century). S62.3.

YUKINARI, DAINAGON (brother of the Empress Sadako, *c*.1000), daughter of. S20.31.

YUKINRŌ (Yü Ch'ien-lou): Chinese Paragon of Filial Piety. S60.18.

YUKISHIGE, SHIKAMATSU KANROKU: one of the Forty-Seven *Rōnin*. S54.5; S71.2 (Hanroku); S90.5 (Hanroku).

YUKITAKA, TOKUDA SADAYEMON: one of the Forty-Seven *Rōnin*. S54.20; S57.38 (Tadayemon); S80.20 (Okuta); S90.20 (Tadayemon).

YUKIUJI: Minamoto warrior. S7.1.

YUME NO ICHIROBEI: character in the *Go-nin otoko* cycle of plays. S42.8.

YURA HYŌGO: retainer of the Nitta family. S44.5.

YURANOSUKE, ŌBOSHI, YOSHIO: leader of the Forty-Seven *Rōnin*. S46.82; S54.1; S78.1; S86.4, 7, 9, 12; S90.1; T11; T272. pp.29f.

YURIWAKA DAIJIN: giant archer in the reign of the Emperor Saga (810–24). S74.11.

YŪRYAKU TENNŌ: Emperor (457–80); a mighty man of valour and promoter of prosperity (*Nihongi* I, pp.333–72; *Papinot*, p.762; *Edmunds*, p.690). S17.12.

YUYA: daughter of the headman of Ikeda, Tōtōmi, and favourite of Taira no Munemori; cared for her old mother. S23.25.

ZENKICHI: lover of O-Roku. S74.36.

ZENNOJŌ: devotee of Jizō Bosatsu, who accorded him a vision of hell. S23.26.

DATE DUE

-18 10 pm

DEMCO 38-297